<u>SCOTTISH FAL</u>

VISION W

C000000862

Tom McArthur was fc
reporter and feature writer with the Scottish
Daily Express and the Sunday Express. For
the past fourteen years he has worked as a
freelance journalist, writing general features
and series which have been syndicated
through Europe, America, Japan, Australia
and New Zealand.

Dr Peter Waddell is a Senior Lecturer in
Mechanical Engineering at the University of
Strathclyde, Glasgow. He is the inventor of
the image derotator, which is now sold
worldwide. His most recent invention is the
vacuum-deformable plastic mirror, which has
been described as the biggest break-through
in optics since Galileo's telescope.

SCOTTISH
FALCON

Scottish Falcon Books are a new series featuring in particular books on science and technology, general biography, history, enterprise and adventure.

VISION
WARRIOR

The hidden achievement of
John Logie Baird

Tom McArthur
and Peter Waddell

A Scottish Falcon Book

THE ORKNEY PRESS

To Margaret Baird

Published by The Orkney Press Ltd.
12 Craigiefield Park, St Ola
Kirkwall, Orkney.

First published by Century Hutchinson 1986
under the title
THE SECRET LIFE OF JOHN LOGIE BAIRD

Published in Scottish Falcon Books 1990
ISBN 0 907618 04 9

Book design by Iain Ashman

Typeset by Image & Print, Glasgow

Printed and bound by
Nørhaven Rotation, Viborg, Denmark

Contents

Acknowledgements

Sincere thanks to Mrs Margaret Baird and her family, Professor Malcolm Baird and Mrs Diana Richardson both for providing important material and their full co-operation.

Thanks also to Sir Samuel Curran, ex-Principal of Strathclyde University; Sir Graham Hills, Principal of Strathclyde University; Professor Hugh Simpson, Department of Mechanical Engineering, Strathclyde University; Professor Colin MacCabe, British Film Institute; Ben Clapp, C.L. Richards, Philip Hobson and Ray Herbert, all former members of the Baird Company; British Telecom; Neil Rimington; Norman Loxdale; Laura Hamilton, Curator, the Collins Gallery, Strathclyde University; Jim Forson, Strathclyde University; Brian Fair; Florence Donaldson; Renata Vinken, the Netherlands; Isabel Mungall; Kerron A. Harvey; Sheena Nelson; Richard Smith, Clydesdale Bank, Glasgow; Angela and Marina McLaughlin of Image & Print, Glasgow, Doreen Barclay; Morag Mitchell; Audrey Calder and Donald McLean.

Finally, our thanks to Jimmy Bain, former chairman of Trinidad and Tobago Television, Vivian Ventour and all other friends in the West Indies.

Foreword

By Professor Sir Graham Hills,
Principal and Vice-Chancellor, University of Strathclyde.

I am delighted that this new edition of *The Secret Life of John Logie Baird* has been published, and that a wider audience will therefore have the opportunity of learning more about John Logie Baird and his remarkable life. The University of Strathclyde is proud of its association with Baird, and has recently taken steps to preserve further this connection by helping with the establishment of the John Logie Baird Foundation. If one thing is certain in these uncertain times, it is that the medium of television will continue to develop technologically and be an enduring (and hopefully beneficial) influence on all our lives. John Logie Baird played a vital part in the development of television - as well as being involved in many other areas of broadcasting technology - and this book helps to remind us of his contribution and his place in the great tradition of Scottish engineering genius.

Preface

It is now more than 40 years since the death of John Logie Baird, the man who gave the world its first true television pictures and launched a crucial new technology that would affect the world both in peace and war.

During that time he has remained an enigmatic figure, and historians have been puzzled by the seeming contradictions in his life and character. Most opted for the legend of the inventor with broken dreams whose work was superseded.

The first edition of this book, *The Secret Life of John Logie Baird*, argued otherwise and presented facts that revealed Baird not only as a prime shaper of all modern television, but as a man whose undercover work on radar and secret signalling contributed greatly to the Allied victory in World War II.

This account received a welcome reception from critics, but some historians opposed it. Few of these addressed themselves to the copious evidence in the footnotes, and seemed to work on the assumption that the facts could not be true or they would have encountered such information themselves.

It seems to the authors that this is a case of the Emperor's New Clothes. Earlier historians worked on official stories and propaganda releases which eventually took root as the established version.,

Some of these critics noticed anomalies in their own arguments and politely withdrew. A few paid a backhanded compliment by selecting details from the book and publishing them unattributed, as if they were well-known facts.

The controversy sparked by the book continues to this day in the pages of *Television: Journal of the Royal Television Society*, though not one of the major claims has been refuted.

Meanwhile Baird's reputation has grown. Business

awards are now named after him. British Telecom has sponsored an exhibition on his life and work to tour Britain.

Even his old adversary, the BBC, made a conciliatory gesture during his centenary year, producing a dramatised documentary with the curious title "I Preferred Madness", a quote isolated from his own writings.

This was daring enough to dent the halo of Sir John Reith, the BBC's first Director General, but, not surprisingly they stuck to the old story, almost totally ignoring Baird's secret life which had been confirmed by their own researchers following the lead of this book.

The time has now come to put the record straight and, in the course of this story, many other accepted facts about television, radar, secret signalling and the lead up to and conduct of the Second World War, will bite the dust.

Re-learning can be a painful process, but the truth is necessary if future generations are to make proper judgements for their own welfare. There can be little place in the complexities of the modern world for convenient legends and over-simplifications.

Tom McArthur

Prologue

It was R.A. Watson-Watt who, early in 1935, produced the first practical and detailed proposals for locating aircraft by radio. From this moment started the development of Radar as we have come to know it.

Sir Stafford Cripps, 1945

If you believe that, you will believe anything.
Duke of Wellington to a gentleman who had accosted him in the street, saying 'Mr Jones, I believe?'

'Yes, I have a pair of eyes,' replied Sam, 'and that's just it. If they wos a pair o' patent double million magnifying gas microscopes of hextra power, p 'raps I might be able to see through a flight o' stairs, and a deal door; but bein' only eyes, you see, my wision's limited.'

Charles Dickens, The Pickwick Papers.

On 8 June 1946, the victorious forces of the British Empire and Allies staged a triumphal march through the streets of London. It was a day of jubilation and celebration for a nation still facing the austerities resulting from the struggle against the Axis powers, and the B B C found it a symbolic and opportune moment to launch its first television service since the outbreak of war. But despite a monopoly of the airwaves, its cameras were not alone. Also focusing on the scene were the lenses of an independent and almost forgotten figure whom many believed had vanished into history.

John Logie Baird, the pioneer inventor, had presented the first genuine live television pictures to a wondering but sceptical world just twenty years before, fulfilling mankind's long-cherished dream of a crystal ball that conjured up far-flung images. He had lived and breathed the concept of television since youth and it was his resoluteness that had pressurized the still fledgling BBC to extend its preoccupation with sound radio to include television. Now the presence of his camera at this revival of television, after the long years of war, had more than a hint of the ghost at the wedding for the national broadcasting corporation. The BBC after all, had subtly assumed his mantle. The apprentice had taken over from the master.

Baird had taught the B B C the rudiments of the new medium as early as 1929, using his own technicians, but had been jettisoned by the Corporation when it opted for his rivals Marconi-EMI in 1937, following a controversial contest between the two systems. Since then his name had scarcely, if ever, been mentioned publicly by the Corporation in their broadcasts and eventually they adopted an attitude, gradually accepted by the public, that television was their own dreamchild and special province.

Baird, however, in his dogged fashion had never left the scene. Despite his rejection he had worked for the future, concentrating on colour and stereoscopics with startlingly successful results, which were beginning to show by 1939. But television had ceased that year; it was now regarded as a luxury that a nation fighting for survival could ill afford, not just in terms of money, but because of the dangers of supplying an enemy with unintentional intelligence and of interfering with vital navigational and other communications. The service signed off with a cartoon of Mickey Mouse and Baird found himself the great specialist in a technique which, on the surface, had no value at that time. Undeterred, he prepared for peace, working in London through a welter of bombs which blew out his windows like tiddly-winks. Many believed - wrongly, as it will be seen - that he was ignored and played no part in the war effort.

His friends and family noticed that he emerged from those years looking haggard and unwell. He had never been physically strong, but something had demanded from him a grievous toll. However, after the war he started to reassert his continuing challenge. If transmissions to people's homes were denied him, he would revive his prewar dream of reaching audiences by televising to cinemas. That was accomplished the day after the victory parade, when the Baird Television Company showed the march on giant television screens in the Classic Cinema, Baker Street, the News Theatre, Agar Street, and the Savoy Hotel. It seemed to be a promising start and a clear indication that Baird had not lost his ambitions for an independent television service.

Five days later that dream ended. Fate, in Baird's case

Baird of Television

3

always a capricious ally, dealt him the final blow. He had endured an illness of four months involving a stroke and his childhood scourge of bronchitis. He worked on relentlessly, apparently unaware that it was the end, even conducting the victory proceedings from his sickbed. He slipped quietly away in his sleep on 14 June at his home in Bexhill, Sussex, just a-few miles from Hastings, the scene of his first public breakthrough in television in 1924 and the start of his fame.

His death secured for him a brief prominence. Newspapers headlined his obituary and stressed the theme of the inventor with broken dreams. They described a disappointed man who had known fame without fortune, whose invention was changing the world and making millions for others, but had done little for him. The legend of the disillusioned inventor was already taking shape. It was, in some ways, inevitable that such should be the view of his life at that point. Only a very select few, and these not even in his own family, had access to facts that could establish that Baird's life had been a triumph.

As it was, the very universality of television had paradoxically helped to eclipse his reputation. He was eventually bracketed as just one among an international clutch of television pioneers;

Mihaly in Hungary, Rosing in Russia and Zworykin the U S A. After a time people would be extremely surprised to hear that he had been alive and operating in 1946. The reason for this was simple. Those cohorts returning from desert, mountain and plain after the war were to be assimilated into a society transformed by six years of armed struggle. The thirties as a decade was already a completely distinct era with an outdated flavour, and in the public imagination Baird was firmly planted in it, one with the air pioneers, the transatlantic liners, Chamberlain and Munich. He had indeed worked on and survived the war, but had done so virtually unnoticed. He had died at a crucial time, before he could assert a modern identity, just as the world was picking itself up, dusting itself down and taking in the new view.

And so one of the busiest and most vital sections of his life remained a closed book. His name was dutifully mentioned at the beginning of postwar television. It became fashionable to refer to him in a patronizing manner. He was frequently dismissed with faint praise as the eccentric inventor of an outmoded form of mechanical television, whose basic form owed more to others than to himself. His system was said to be not quite practical and he was described as submerging before the onslaught of the brilliant electronics inventors. The publicity stunts which he had used to advance television were remembered and he was branded a showman. Emphasis was placed on his early commercial ventures, which in fact had financed his experiments, and it was forgotten that he had had a thorough and, for the time, progressive scientific training in electrical engineering at one of the first and most advanced technical colleges in Europe, and at the University of Glasgow.

Poor Baird: he was stuck like a fly in amber, his image forever frozen at one point. It was as if his career had stopped abruptly with the development of the first mechanically scanned equipment, so beloved by illustrators of textbooks and encyclopedias. These pictures showed, and still do, the intense, bespectacled young inventor, a shock of fair hair spilling across his brow, sleeves rolled up, standing beside the familiar Nipkow discs, large and primitive and with their spirals of holes and lenses for breaking up and reconstituting light in those first successful television images.

Those who knew anything about him tended to belong to one of two categories. One group knew that he had developed the first pictures using a form of mechanical television which proved unsatisfactory. They assumed he had been beaten in the battle for BBC television by a far superior electronic system which had ended his career. The second group, slightly better informed, saw him as an important figure who could not be ignored and knew vaguely that he had ventured further into electronics, but believed that he had been outclassed by many others.

However, nagging doubts arose about such appraisals among those who chanced upon isolated but remarkable fragments of information concerning Baird. The most obvious was the striking fact that Baird, the loner, who apparently had no backing from any large financial, academic, scientific or military organization, had beaten with the first pictures so many famous and talented figures throughout the world who did enjoy these resources. It seemed unlikely that such a man would go no further. A quick glance through record books and contemporary reports reinforced such misgivings. They revealed that he had pioneered almost every early television technique including the first outside broadcast, the first pictures between Britain and Europe and the first pictures across the Atlantic. A little-noted invention by Baird was a patented hollow tube or solid glass rod for channelling light to help in his television, a development better known today as fibre optics, the basis of a whole modern industry involving communications and medicine. As early as 1926 he produced the forerunner of a modern video recorder, making his own television recordings on wax and metal magnetic discs.

By the 1970s there was a growing recognition of the breadth of his imagination and the importance of his work. Belatedly he was growing in stature, and as he did so controversy stirred in such diverse areas as the New York Times and the columns of the journal of the Royal Television Society in London. The shade of Baird seemed to rise and challenge the supremacy of some figures still alive, notably Zworykin in America. In tune with all this, in his Scottish birthplace, Helensburgh, the headmaster of a school named after Baird demanded that the education authorities remove a plaque erected by the BBC which grudgingly termed Baird as 'a pioneer' of television. He wanted this changed to 'the inventor' of television. In 1984 British Caledonian Airlines named their brand-new European Airbus the John Logie Baird, so that his name would be carried across frontiers.

The riddle endured, however. It remained difficult to track down the real man. Most of his story continued to be based on the 1933 version by his first biographer R. F. Tiltman, which only took Baird's story to that year. Much of the information in this book was supplied by Baird at a time when he was embroiled with competitors and it is therefore full of convenient generalizations and gives several misleading pointers. For Baird it filled the purpose of needful publicity without betraying much of his real work and intentions. Anyone seeking further information had to rely on technical papers and academic summaries of Baird's life or on another biography, written six years after his death by his friend and sometime colleague, the journalist Sydney Moseley. This affectionate cameo was based mainly on the author's dealings with the inventor and, as will transpire, the research involved left Moseley with some baffling and at that time unanswerable questions. It has frequently been noted how difficult it is to trace any accurate technical details of Baird's inventions and how uncertain and contra-dictory are the details and the dates in his career. This was no accident - it was largely due to a smokescreen which the inventor cast round his own life, one that worked only too successfully, so that it has clouded his story to this day.

The bones of the traditional tale were that this son of a Church of Scotland minister had since childhood shown an interest in the possibility of television, and as a youth had enrolled at the Royal Technical College in Glasgow. Afterwards he seemed to abandon his early enthusiasm in order to make swift and easy money through a number of erratic enterprises, which included a specially medicated undersock and the sale of soap.

Always subject to crippling poor health, and unfit for the military service for which he had volunteered, he had nevertheless suffered several gruelling and unhealthy years during the First World War as an electrical engineer at power plants in Glasgow. On the close of hostilities he had headed for the warmth of the Caribbean, where he started a jam and preserves factory in a ramshackle jungle hut in Trinidad. Overcome once more by illness, he had headed home and, while convalescing in the south coast resort of Hastings in 1923, he is supposed to have resurrected his old idea of television. In a room above a shopping arcade and aided by one companion, an old schoolfriend, Guy Fullerton Robertson, he is believed to have produced within a couple of months the televised outline of a Maltese Cross, a truly brilliant achievement if he had indeed just begun.

By August 1924 he had moved to a new laboratory in Soho, London, and in 1925 gained publicity by demonstrating televised silhouettes to customers in Selfridge's store. Later that year he claimed a major development. Instead of silhouettes he had managed to see clearly the head of a wooden ventriloquist's doll on his screen, and he had followed this by focusing on the face of an office boy who he claimed was the first human being to be televised. A few months later, in January 1926, he gave what was said to be the first public demonstration of real television, cramming into his small premises batches of selected guests who included several prestigious members of the Royal Institution.

This demonstration was hailed in America, where *Radio News* acknowledged that it was the first time real television had been achieved in any part of the world. Other developments followed, including the use of infra-red lighting which enabled his cameras to see in the dark, a system he called Noctovision.

Backers now arrived and the Baird Television Company was formed. Even the B B C helped him unofficially and secretly. For a brief period in 1926 they cooperated in transmitting over distances, accepting Baird pictures by wire and returning them through the air to his base in Soho. But this was stopped on the orders of some unspecified source from above. Undeterred, Baird secured a licence from the Post Office for his own transmitter, 2TV, in London, and a similar transmitter, 2TW, in Harrow, the first television stations in the world.

A series of well-publicized experiments followed. He sent pictures by telephone line from London to Glasgow in 1927, and in the following year, from a new and bigger laboratory at Long Acre near Leicester Square, via an amateur shortwave station in Coulsdon, Surrey, dispatched 30-line pictures across the Atlantic to New York. He then capped this by transmitting images to a liner in mid-Atlantic which was bringing his technicians home.

Despite these successes, Baird found the BBC still reluctant to spare him any airtime, even grudging one quarter of an hour three times a week. They finally relented, though, following pioneer pictures to and from the continent, and granted him limited cooperation. He was allowed to televise from the BBC station, 2LO, from September 1929. The broadcasts were experimental, lasting half an hour in the morning with sound and vision alternating every two minutes, and they marked the BBC's first official historical involvement with television.

The next few years brought many innovations including the simultaneous transmission of vision and sound in 1930, the successful televising of the Derby in 1931 and 1932 to cinemas in London, and continuing advances in colour, which he had demonstrated as early as August 1928 before the British Association in Glasgow. Meanwhile the Baird Televisor, with its small, 30-line, faintly rose-tinted picture, was now on sale to the public at £25.

By 1936 he had produced a mechanical scanned 240-1ine picture. Others, though, were now competing, using electronic methods, particularly Marconi-EMI in Britain and the Radio Corporation of America, who Baird suspected were quietly conspiring to oppose him. And indeed

Marconi-EMI were chosen to test alongside the Baird Company from February 1935, in a competition to select which system the BBC would ultimately adopt. This technical contest at Alexandra Palace was to last two years. In November 1936 Baird lost much precious equipment, including a special electronic camera, when his laboratories were burned down in the famous Crystal Palace fire. A couple of months later the advisory committee recommended the closure of the dual transmissions. The Marconi- EMI system was chosen and the last programme from the BBC using the Baird system went out on 30 January 1937.

It was a body-blow, and Baird disappeared from the public imagination, though his name continued to crop up in reports of technical innovations and television to cinemas. As Britain eventually concentrated on war, few noted in 1941 that Baird was demonstrating a 600-1ine 3D-colour television set, and later up to 1,000-line 3D-colour. But the government was evidently aware of his work and it was his 1,000-line service, eventually to be in colour and stereo-scopic or 3D, that was recommended in a white paper by a parliamentary committee set up in 1943 to investigate which form television would take after the war. This system, which would have given Britain a world lead in television, was eventually turned down as being too ambitious.

After Baird's death ideas about him became so confused that he was often portrayed as down-at-heel, always working in a garret. In fact in the days of the Great Depression his salary from various sources topped £4,000 annually. His homes included a stylish converted hunting lodge in the Surrey hills overlooking Dorking, which had been built for a Duchess of Marlborough and where he must have raised quizzical stares from neighbours through his custom of wearing a cloth cap, a hangover from his days on Clydeside and a reminder to himself of a promise never to lose his working-class sympathies. He had headed a company with a shareholding of £1 million and had connections with foreign firms, one of which he had helped found in Germany. His wife was a pretty and promising concert pianist.

Misunderstandings about Baird can be excused, however, as his life, when examined, proved to be riddled with inconsistencies. His friend Sydney Moseley noted one of the most puzzling of these, the apparent almost total neglect of the inventor by the British government during the Second World War, at a time when scientists and technicians were greedily commandeered for vital work.

The research undertaken for this book uncovered facts indicating that this neglect was only apparent. Baird's pocket diaries for the war years have survived and are in the possession of his son, Professor Malcolm Baird, of McMaster University, Ontario, Canada. The entries are brief and enigmatic, but rich in references to meetings with prominent military and scientific figures involved in highly secret war work. They include Sir Robert Watson-Watt, to whom the British invention of radar has been attributed, and Sir Edward Appleton, destined to head Britain's atom bomb effort. Baird's pencilled comments beside some names reveal a knowledge of their participation in extremely confidential war experiments.

Also mysterious was the total absence of any mention of Baird in the writings and biographies of certain figures with whom Baird had been deeply involved. By a strange quirk of fate, in 1906 John Logie Baird found himself at college in Glasgow with John Charles Walsham Reith, the giant figure who headed the B B C during the period when Baird was trying to interest the Corporation in television. Though poles apart in temperament, they had to deal with each other in negotiations regarding the infant television. Yet, oddly, in his autobiography *Into the Wind* Lord Reith absolutely ignored the existence of this acquaintance of his youth, who presented him with what must surely have been the most momentous development during his rule at the B B C.

Equally curious is the non-appearance of Baird in *Three Steps to Victory*, by Sir Robert Watson-Watt, a fellow Scot from Brechin, civil servant and meteorologist who had developed British prewar radar, and who was well acquainted with Baird. Watson-Watt bought hundreds of cathode ray tubes for Britain in the early thirties from a German firm of which Baird was a director. He was present in 1926 at a demonstration by Baird of a system which bore a strong resemblance to radar, the invention which Sir Robert claimed for himself nine years later, and was associated with a special committee appointed in 1934 to study Baird's television. Yet there is not a hint in Sir Robert's writings that his path had ever crossed that of the man without whose discoveries radar would not have been possible.

Faced with such glaring neglect, the search for the real Baird necessitates the bypassing of most of the posthumous accounts which, with so many omissions, remain ill-balanced. The yellowing files of contemporary newspapers and magazines supply another view of the inventor, a man who gained international recognition. They also reveal that Baird had another enthusiasm, allied to television, which he pursued with perhaps even more passion. There had been hints of this in several publications in the months before and after his death in June 1946. One of the more tantalizing was an obituary in the *Daily Herald* of 15 June 1946, which said: 'But the full story of Baird cannot yet be told. During the war he was working in his bombed house at Sydenham, not only on an invention for the Government which is still on the secret list, but also on a new research of his own'.

Still on the secret list? Radar, was, by that time, an open secret and had been for five years. Though it can now be shown that Baird's television work led directly to the development of radar, it also seems to have infiltrated into some other spheres. The weight of evidence must fall in favour of another of his major interests, signalling. Baird had swiftly grasped the important part that television could play in this field and towards the end of his life had been concentrating on facsimile televison and the dispatching of thousands of words per second. Could Baird and others have been waging a secret intelligence war against the Axis powers, using, not just very slow radio codes, but ultra high-speed signalling by television? The coding battle has been kept so secret that even the startling tale of the secret German coding machine called Enigma was not told for almost thirty years after the end of hostilities. The question now arises whether the coding duel, which included Enigma, was an even more complex and dangerous affair, involving high-speed television transmissions and supercodes. It is clear that the techniques were available to both sides. The Wehrmacht certainly ordered such equipment and the material now uncovered on Baird indicates its almost certain use by the Allies.

Baird hated violence and was realistically aware of the Pandora's box he had opened on the world, of the effect of his inventions on war as well as on peace. In an article in the *Philadelphia Ledger* in May 1927, in which he is quoted alongside the future President Hoover, he states: 'Airplanes need no longer wireless scanty reports; equipped with an electric eye they can reproduce the entire field of battle, the very shell bursts, moving troops, every tiny detail, will be stripped of concealment.' Statements like these were soon to peter out and his work on detection systems were to go underground and become almost completely forgotten, something which this master of dissimulation probably intended in the period of crisis leading up to the holocaust in Europe. Little or nothing has been known of the part he played in signalling, or of the fact that either side used television secret signalling during the war. There are indications that Baird expected at least some of the story to emerge at the end of the war. But he died in 1946 at a crucial moment, just as honours and financial awards were poised to shower down on the previously faceless scientists, then emerging, who had helped save the world from a new dark age.

The true story of John Logie Baird is one of courage and single-mindedness from boyhood - the goal, television, achieved and pursued further until he produced gifts even more vital for the Allies at bay in the Second World War. His reputation until now has languished, and his name has been unjustly coupled with failure. In fact his life was a victory over adversity, racking bad health and distasteful and disgraceful sniping from within his own country. For too long the real story of one of the twentieth century's greatest inventive minds has remained unknown. Perhaps his name can now reap the harvest he began to sow as a boy in a seaside town in the west of Scotland in the twilight of the reign of Queen Victoria.

True vision achieved. The birth of a new technology. Two studies of Baird with the worlds first workable television, 1925.

1

Child of the Future

One night at the start of the century a remote control device was triggered in a bedroom of a villa in a Scottish seaside town, photographing a boy tucked up in bed. The picture revealed an impish face framed by a Victorian metal bedstead from which wires trailed to a corner of the room. The device, which allowed him to photograph himself even when asleep, was his own creation. The wires were part of another project, a private telephone exchange linking him with four friends who lived hundreds of yards away. In a curious foreshadowing of the future, using electricity, a camera and a means of communication he was, at the age of twelve, already handling the raw materials which, when combined, would make his own peculiar destiny.

John Logie Baird, born in Helensburgh at 8 a.m. on 13 August 1888, was the youngest of the family of two sons and two daughters of the Reverend John Baird, a scholarly, bearded patriarch who was Church of Scotland minister of the town's West Kirk. Mr Baird had bought the square-built, grey stone house in West Argyle Street nineteen years before, in preference to living in the customary manse that went with the job, as a safeguard for his wife and family should he die. The Lodge, as it was called, remained in the family's hands for more than ninety years until 1971, when Annie, the minister's elder daughter and last surviving child, died.

Intriguingly, young Johnnie Baird had no scientific training whatsoever at school, a fact he was to remedy later, as a young man. Instead he was enmeshed in the typical classical education of the time. He escaped the toils of tenses and declensions by playing intellectual truant, finding relaxation by making his own way into the endlessly fascinating world of science. As he later recognized gratefully: 'If they had taught me science at school instead of Latin and Greek, I should probably have become a minister like my father. There is nothing like a classical education to turn a boy's mind into really practical channels.[1]

He tasted early the sweetness of research, of practical problems tackled and overcome. From *The Boys' Book of Stories and Pastimes* he gathered instructions on how to make a simple telephone with thread and cocoa tins. This fired his imagination, but where it would have satisfied most children, it left him disappointed. He could not be sure whether the voice travelled by the thread or just carried through the air from close by. He decided to go a stage further and in 1900 constructed the real thing, complete with electricity and long-distance cables.

The town of Helensburgh with the nearby village of Rhu, just twenty-five miles northwest of Glasgow, boasted ninety-two official telephone subscribers that year. The number of users was in fact ninety-seven, for, unknown to the Post Office, the home of the respected local minister had become the base for a concerted inroad into their monopoly. The scale of young Baird's operation was impressive. Cables led from the Lodge to the homes of four schoolfriends, no mean feat as these houses were at least two hundred yards away in different streets. Wires spanned roads and neighbouring gardens, snaking over tree branches and winding round chimney pots. His exchange was a home-made varnished wooden box (now in a private collection in Hastings) on which the names of his four 'subscribers' were punched out on tin plaques of the sort available from end-of-the-pier machines. His improvisations included household nails wrapped round with wire to make magnets. At the end of the Victorian era the boy was already displaying the determination and ingenuity which would enable the man to achieve the world's first practical television.

He was, however, to encounter a snag, just the first in a career which he later admitted was freely punctuated by such problems: he had not taken the barometer into consideration. One stormy night in November a horse-drawn bus clattered noisily down West Argyle Street on the last of its regular trips of the day between Helensburgh and Rhu. The top-hatted driver, a local worthy named McIntyre, sat huddled in a damp plaid and holding the reins from his seat ten feet above the ground. Bending his head forward to avoid the worst of the weather, he failed to spot a cable looming directly ahead, sagging from the wind and rain, and in the vicinity of the Lodge he was lifted clean from his perch and deposited smack in the soaking gutter.

Shaking with anger and drawing on a rich reserve of curses, he made for the home of the Post Office's local agent, a mild, inoffensive character called MacDonald, whom he almost strangled. What the devil did they mean by having wires cluttering the thoroughfare? He had a good mind to wring MacDonald's neck and sue the telephone company. It had all the makings of a first-class legal row. Investigations were made, however, and a relieved MacDonald was able to trace the Lodge as the source of the renegade cable. Luckily McIntyre was a friend of the minister, and when apologies were duly proffered by both the young inventor and his parents he let the matter drop. It did, however, spell the end of the Baird Telephone Company. He was ordered to remove his wires, though the exchange itself remained and was still there when Baird visited his old home almost forty years later.

So ended the first encounter between vested interest and the lone pioneer who was to revolutionize communications and a great deal more in the troubled decades ahead. If it was a blow to Baird, he seems to have absorbed it with the resilience on which he drew so prodigiously in later years. Within weeks the Helensburgh Times was describing his latest project - to make the Lodge one of the first houses in town with its own electric light supply.

The town of Helensburgh was then a fashionable resort on the Firth of Clyde, nestling at the spot where the Gareloch merges with the Clyde estuary. It was a dynamic and growing community with 9,000 inhabitants and 3,000 more in nearby Rhu, most of them the families of successful businessmen who had taken advantage of the new rail link with Glasgow that had opened in 1851, enabling them to commute to work in half an hour. During the summer months it was a favourite watering place for the middle classes. It was, though, no mere backwater or dormitory town, and had a distinct character of its own. Glasgow was then the second city and prime workshop of the British Empire, and the number of outstanding men who preferred to work in the city yet make their home in Helensburgh is one possible explanation of how such a small township managed to produce so many impressive figures in science and the arts.

Though he would have several homes and spend much of

his life hopping between lodgings and hotel rooms, Baird never again identified himself with any other spot. Helensburgh was close to his heart, though he disliked the name. His streak of romanticism would probably have preferred something more Gaelic. However, it remained his image of home. Little has changed since his boyhood. Loch Lomond and its lyrical scenery lies close to the east while a couple of miles north of the town rise the craggy ramparts of the Argyllshire mountains, the foothills of the Scottish Highlands. In summer these mountains tower purple and green, and the salt waters of the Gareloch and the Clyde sparkle in the sun as though covered with a billion fireflies. Helensburgh becomes a place to warm the heart and stir the imagination. In winter, however, the mountains hang bleakly on the horizon and the waters turn black as slate, relieved only by the occasional day of pristine clearness. It becomes a place where the shadows of life have to be faced. Such alterations of mood can shape character and certainly seemed to affect young Baird. A strong sense of fun and enjoyment in the simple, straightforward aspects of life had to compete with a deep, almost tormented questioning of the values of society and the worth of the path he had chosen. He was an imaginative child and in manhood one such dark moment still lingered. One Sunday morning when he was a very small boy the family had gone to church. He was standing with his head just touching the window-ledge, the house intensely quiet, when he saw an aged man, bent over his stick, tottering round the comer of the Lodge and into the garden. The man stopped and looked directly at the child who, terrified, jumped back in horror. Baird wrote of the incident:

> *A strange idea took root in my mind that the old man was myself grown old and the horror that I should one day become such a creature made me turn and run from the window. Who the old man was I do not know, probably some visitor wandering round the large garden as they sometimes did, or was it some child's daydreaming vision? Sometimes I wonder if one day, revisiting the old home, I will look up and see looking from the dining room window a horrified little boy.[2]*

Helensburgh's ambivalence continues with the seawards view. Tankers and liners lie at anchor in the middle of the Firth, known as the Tail o' the Bank, a starting point for Atlantic convoys in two world wars. The town's trim villas look out over a long promenade to the opposite bank of the Firth, to the industrialized waterfronts of Port Glasgow and Greenock, where giant shipyard cranes are dwarfed by distance. A tall obelisk on the promenade commemorates the man who made both ships and industry possible, the town's first Provost, Henry Bell. His tiny steamboat, The Comet, launched in 1812, proved to be the first commercially viable steamboat and led to a shrinking of the world, a process that would be speeded even further a century later by his fellow townsman, Baird.

Helensburgh was not an organic community - it had not grown naturally from the needs of the area. It had been grafted onto a small fishing village at the end of the eighteenth century by Sir James Colquhoun, 25th Chief of Luss and 15th baronet, scion of a house which had held the territory for several centuries against marauding clans, including the bands of Rob Roy. Sir James planned to make his reputation in a more urbane manner and dreamed of a town to house bonnetmakers and stocking, linen and wool weavers, who would capture the wool and flax trade from the Highlands before it reached Glasgow. The tradespeople were not attracted, however, and so Sir James' new town, called after his wife, avoided the industrialization that completely changed the characters of nearby Dumbarton and Glasgow. Instead it had time to grow in a planned and leisurely fashion. As the shipowners, whisky barons, lawyers and top engineers discovered its attractions and took up residence, the best architects arrived in their wake to build them even more imposing mansions. One of these was Robert Smith, whose daughter Madeleine gained nationwide notoriety from a court case in which she was accused and acquitted of poisoning her French lover. She became a member of the Fabian Society and a friend of George Bernard Shaw. Later Charles Rennie Mackintosh, Scottish pioneer of art nouveau, designed the exquisite Hill House on the outskirts of town for Blackie, the publishing family.

By the time of Baird's birth it had become a neat and prosperous town, unlike any other in the area, with wide, tree-fringed streets laid out in a grid system. This profusion of trees and the variety of building styles gave it more of an English than a Scottish aspect. Helensburgh, with its influx of the well-to-do, had social pretensions. As the nineteenth century rolled on, the social mores could be seen to change;

the number of billiard saloon owners was eventually outstripped by piano tuners. Baird's father helped to lift the cultural tone by founding a literary society, one of whose members was the future Prime Minister, young Andrew Bonar Law, orphaned in Canada and then being brought up in Helensburgh.

At about the same time East Argyle Street, an extension of the road in which Baird lived, contained the home of a youth who would become Sir James Frazer, anthropologist and author of The Golden Bough. When he was an old man Sir James wrote of the town with deep nostalgia: 'Tonight with the muffled roar of London in my ears, I look down the long vistas of the past and see again the little white town by the sea, the hills above it tinged with the warm sunset light. I hear again the soft music of the evening bells. . .'[3]

Baird, looking back at the age of forty-eight, also waxed nostalgic but leavened this with a dose of realism. Some things had changed, though not the extreme and remarkable beauty of the place. But it also had its sharp contrasts. In a magazine article of 1936 he wrote wistfully:

> *I remember, I remember the place where I was born . . . It was known as Helensburgh with a capital 'H' to the aristocrats and the county and Elensburgh with a capital 'E' to the middle classes, and 'eelensburgh' with two small ee's to the working classes. I lived sometimes in Helensburgh and sometimes in Elensburgh, hovering between the two, Helensburgh at school which considered itself aristocratic and county, and Elensburgh at home.*[4]

It was a place of pronounced class distinction at that time, a fair microcosm of the attitudes and manners of Anglo-India, though divisions tended to blur at the fringes. As Baird wrote:

> *It is difficult to convey the social atmosphere of those far away days in that little village. The caste system, though already in a precarious condition, still survived. In the lowest caste were the beggars, tramps and gypsies, analogous to 'the Untouchables'; then came the dustmen, labourers and navvies and next, but quite a distance removed, the smaller tradesmen such as butchers, bankers and grocers. These again merged into the small businessman and the businessmen in turn expanded into the city magnate. Mixing into the stratum and oscillating between its extremes were the professional men, doctors, lawyers and clergy.*[5]

At the top of the tree were the country gentlemen and kingpin among them was Sir Ian Colquhoun, a descendant of the town's founder and a famous sporting shot. Young Baird witnessed the county types flitting on the margin of his vision, opening bazaars and public functions in a riot of tartans, eagle feathers and clan badges. Sir Ian's photograph frequently appeared in the newspapers and years later the memory afforded Baird some light relief. He wrote: 'I was so impressed by a picture of him which appeared continually in the society papers, showing him a fine figure of a man in Highland costume with a short kilt, bare legs, striding over his native heather, oblivious to thistle, cow pats and press photographers.[6]

Baird's boyhood impression of the county caste was one of standoffishness mixed with a hint of aggression. As a minister's son, he had access to most sections of society, and one can detect in childhood the peculiar tensions which this built into his sensitive nature. In a still rigid social framework the Bairds were an open group, related to and friendly with one of the wealthiest shipbuilding families on the Clyde, yet hardly rich themselves. Young Johnnie Baird went to fee-paying schools but for a time his closest friend was Willie Brown, son of 'Auld Broon', the pound-a-week gardener to a local magnate. In contrast, another bosom pal was Jack Buchanan, son of a well-to-do auctioneer and a distant relation of a famous Scotch whisky family, later a singing star in films and the West End.

Baird's response was to evolve a classless personality. This would create an identity crisis, not for Baird himself but for others dealing with him, a factor that would bedevil his encounters with the establishment. What today would pass as unremarkable behaviour seemed eccentric in the twenties and thirties. Baird had little time for social niceties in a period when they were still expected.

Diverse strains mingled in the Baird blood. Some episodes in their history echoed Galsworthy's Forsytes. They were stolid people, earnest and hard-working, who looked back to a grander era. They claimed descent from the kings of Ireland. The name itself derived from bard, a singer; and, as Baird said, they were apparently a musical and romantic tribe. He certainly inherited the romantic strain, but seems to have missed out on the musical one. Ironically, he was to fall in love with and marry an accomplished concert pianist who remembers with affection: 'Logie didn't have much of an ear for music. One day he surprised me by saying he recognised a tune on the radio. It turned out to be "God Save the King."[7]

As a clan the Bairds were enduring and prolific and migrated in large numbers from the west to the east coast, so that today the name is almost as common in Edinburgh as Brown. Baird himself, who inherited an almost Rabelaisian sense of humour from an unlikely source, his minister father, delighted in embroidering the theme of his ancestry. He was descended, he claimed, from one Sodbann, archly adding that his hero had been expelled from Ireland 'for an act of indescribable obscenity'. He could in fact trace his ancestry back to his great-grandfather, John Baird, who at the time of the Napoleonic Wars farmed at Falkirk, a market town halfway between Glasgow and Edinburgh where the great Carron ironworks manufactured its famed carronades for Nelson's navy. The inventor's middle name, Logie, arrived in the family through John's wife, Elizabeth Loggie, who outlived her husband. She must have been remembered fondly by her grandson, Baird's father, who gave her maiden name to his son.

In 1801 John and Elizabeth had a son, James, who was to live eighty-seven years to the very year of the inventor's birth. Little is known of his early days, but his marriage certificate of 1839 describes him as an engineer and family tradition says that he built bridges in Turkey and other parts of the Ottoman Empire. A daguerreotype portrait of James and his young wife, Jane Simpson, daughter of a prosperous Falkirk builder, shows him staring out with confidence at the world, looking remarkably youthful for his forty years. At just about the time that this daguerreotype was made, Henry Fox Talbot had invented the calotype, forerunner of the modern photographic system. An odd string of coincidences was to link Fox Talbot with James Baird's famous grandson, via William Friese-Greene, the inventor of cinematography.

Soon after his marriage James abandoned engineering and acquired a farm called Sunnybrae near Falkirk, probably close to Sunnyside, his parents' farm; it may indeed have been a gift from his mother. Life was spartan. Five children were born, and one, Robert, died aged three; when the grieving parents had another son and gave him the same name, he too died, though he survived to the age of sixteen. Their next son, though, proved more robust. Born in Glasgow on 31 July 1842 and christened John, he would live to become a minister, leave Falkirk for Helensburgh and see his son world-famous. But firm links with Falkirk would remain, to play an intriguing and hidden role in the story of Baird and television.

Baird's maternal grandfather, George Inglis, was at the other end of the spectrum in both character and chosen profession. He was the artistic one of a family destined to cut a wide swathe in the Victorian industrial scene. Born in 1815, the son of John Inglis, a Glasgow innkeeper and carting contractor, he was the youngest of three sons and one daughter. Whereas his older brothers, John and Anthony, founded the major Clyde shipbuilding firm of A. and J. Inglis, George avoided family involvement and became apprenticed in 1832 to a copper engraver. While his brothers turned into industrial barons of considerable wealth and influence, he made a precarious living from his paintings and engravings.

A hidden scandal surrounds Baird's maternal grandparents. George was a dashing fellow with a fine set of mutton chop whiskers framing sensitive features, just the sort of aesthete who would melt under a pair of pretty eyes, no matter how unsuitable the owner. And in the late 1840s he met his Waterloo in the comely shape of Jane Caroline Robertson. Little is known about her but family legend says she was a beautiful but flirtatious Creole girl of French descent, from the West Indies. She and George married and in the 1850s had four children, two of whom died young. Someone, however, obviously answered the challenge in her roving eye and Baird's grandmother shocked the Inglis family by absconding with a fellow countryman who, rumour said, was a mulatto. Down went the Victorian blinds on the subject. Her name was struck from family records and she was never mentioned again by a family yearly growing in social prestige. A haunting echo of this incident is a letter to Baird's mother, Jessie Inglis, then a young girl, living apart from her parents and being brought up by wealthy relatives in Scotland. This is addressed to 'my dear granddaughter' and is signed by a Helen Dodd, living in the West Indies in 1873. Some link with the West Indies would remain. A maid in the Baird household in Helensburgh came from the area, and Baird himself would head for the Caribbean at a turning point in his quest for television.

Tragedy in the meantime haunted the deserted George. He moved to Southampton presumably to avoid wagging tongues. One of his daughters, Sarah, fell over a breakwater there and drowned. George himself died of pneumonia about 1870. His two daughters were separated. One, Mary Jane, was adopted by a Mrs Breen, wife of the Italian consul in Glasgow, while Jessie joined the family of her wealthy uncle, John Inglis.

The exotic background of Baird's mother contrasted strongly with the youthful life of his father. John Baird moved from the Falkirk farm when he was sixteen to study at the old Andersonian College and Glasgow University. He was an intelligent lad and, as Baird wrote later: 'In those days there was only one thing to do with bright boys and that was to put them into the ministry.

The great ambition of every Scottish family in the middle classes was to see their son wagging his head in the pulpit.'[8]

Remnants of Mr Baird's diaries for the late 1850s are still in the family's possession. He emerges from their pages an honest and dutiful youth, the very epitome of the type extolled by Samuel Smiles in his Self Help, the bestselling textbook for the Victorian go- getter. Anxious to be a burden to none, ever respectful of his parents and determined to improve himself by dint of his own efforts, he taught himself French and German while grappling with arduous studies in theology and the classics. On top of this he squeezed in elocution lessons, paying for his studies by tutoring pupils in the evening and working several days a week in Nisbet's, a hardware shop in Glasgow.

From this store he would trudge in all weathers carrying heavy loads to other shops or to the homes of customers in all parts of the city.

The diaries reveal this earnest character's touching preoccupation with survival and independence. He shrugs off a snub from a better-dressed relative, darns a tear in his trousers and sits at home one Sunday, not going to church because his jacket is 'at the menders'. He has an obsession about his boots, made of gutta percha, a rubber-like substance, which he is constantly patching. His jottings conjure up a picture of cobbled streets glistening in the rain, carthorses and the uncaring clamour of the big city. In the evening the country lad sits alone in a gaslit flat, studying.

As a respite from duty he reads *Oliver Twist* and finds it has 'a lot of merit'.

He breaks into print himself, penning a warning in grave style to the citizens of Glasgow concerning petty crooks like the individual who entered his apartment and stole a clothesbrush. This appeared in the Glasgow Herald and it must have satisfied him as he is soon contemplating an epic poem for the paper, one hopes not on the hairbrush. The young man was obviously testing his powers, feeling how far he could go. He made his own writing desk and, when visiting the farm in Falkirk, bought a jew's harp for his sister from his meagre pocket money and then settled to sowing wheat and helping with general chores. In 1859 he sent his parents the political campaign pamphlets of the candidates for Lord Rectorship of the University, Lord Elgin for the Liberals and Independents and Mr Disraeli for the Conservatives. He still felt like a fish out of water and wrote home:

'At present I confess that I am like a leek in a flower garden or a whinstone among rubies.'[9] But he realized that confidence would come and added: 'I have no doubt that in two or three years, having during these wrought pretty hard, I may traverse the College halls with as great a freedom and composure as lately I did the porch of the Grammar School.'[10]

For a time it seemed that he might become a doctor, but he opted for the ministry and wrote to his parents from lodgings in Sauchiehall Street: 'I feel my mind quite at rest now - I have chosen the only profession which in reality I could have liked and I would not have felt contented with any other.'[11] Within six years he had gained his Bachelor of Divinity degree, and two years later his MA. A photograph of the university student of 1865 depicts a serious young man with a disconcertingly frank and wryly humorous slant of mouth. That mouth would soon be submerged in the depths of a beard as the public persona of a Victorian kirk minister took shape. He developed into a complex character whose rough but incisive humour became a byword in the parish. Those hard days of youth left their mark. His farmer's instinct for laying deep roots held him in Helensburgh for the rest of his days, apart from occasional cultural forays abroad - he was in demand by his more well-heeled parishioners for his knowledge and wit and was the perfect companion on trips through Europe and even Africa.

In contrast his inventor son would lead a restless gadfly existence. This was possibly a revolt against the staidness of home, but such a life was made easier by the comforting background presence of a seemingly indestructible father. The farmer's son who was a student in 1858 when Palmerston was Prime Minister and the Indian Mutiny was still being fought, lived on to see Britain's first Labour Prime Minister, Ramsay MacDonald, lead a coalition consisting mainly of Tories, the birth of Nazi Germany, aeroplanes crossing the Atlantic, and his son's television. His home in Helensburgh gently mellowed with him, assimilating the decades, its identity hardly changing from 1881 through the reigns of six monarchs until 1971 when his last-surviving child, Annie, died aged eighty-eight. When John Logie Baird's own children prepared to sell it, they were confronted by books and Victorian artefacts which had lingered on through the decades - a croquet set, a stereoscope, relics of a family who kept their communal soul intact.

From comments later in life it is clear that John Logie Baird was eager to prove himself to a much-respected father.

There was a tinge of resignation in Baird's observation that his father was not interested in telephones, television or any branch of science. 'His passion was German literature. Philosophy meant more to him than experimental science. "What does it matter, what does it matter? Suppose you can see through a brick wall, what good does it do to the soul of man?".[12] It sounds like rather a put-down for the brilliant inventor, but Baird understood and remembered with gratitude: 'Yet a few years ago at a time when I was hard pressed for money to carry on experiments, he came to my rescue with £50. He did this for my sake, not for the sake of science. I am glad he lived to see me do what I set out to do, even if the result made not the slightest impression on him.'[13]

The newly fledged minister received his call to Helensburgh in July 1869, to the West Parish Church.

A young and energetic man was needed to play Moses, build up the congregation and lead his people out of their temporary 'tin tabernacle' to a place of worship of more substance. He succeeded. The membership swelled and soon they intoned the psalms in a handsome grey stone kirk topped with an elegant steeple, quite the envy of the rival Episcopalians nearby who had run out of funds so that they had no soaring stone aerial to God. A measure of Victorian faith was the amount of 'brass' you were prepared to put out: the West Kirk parishioners had excelled.

The Reverend Baird continued his self-improvement and, though he devoted his life to the one congregation and held fast to the strict tenets of the Church of Scotland, he explored the heavy profundities of German culture and the intricacies of philosophy and theology. It is not on record what his more orthodox parishioners made of their pastor's library on religions of the east. Mohammed, Krishna and Kipling's Great Lord Bud were odd companions for the Shorter Scottish Catechism.

The minister also found time for socializing: with his wit and good looks he was much in demand at tea parties and balls. But it was during a summer visit to his church that he met Jessie Morrison Inglis, then in her early twenties and staying with her rich uncle John at 23 Park Circus, Glasgow. Romance blossomed, and in 1876 the couple were engaged. Jessie Inglis was a good catch for any man. But the farming Bairds back in Falkirk were not over-impressed by wealth and connections, and Mrs Baird sent her son a rather equivocal letter on the subject.

After referring to the crops and the weather she writes:

> *We were glad to hear that you were well and have got the business settled that seemed to engross your thoughts most when last at home; we trust you have made a good choice and that you may both be blessings to each other. She is an entire stranger to us and therefore we can say nothing, neither with nor against. It was our wish that you would marry a respectable lady being the only representative of the family and those that wear the coat should choose the colour.* [14]

Whatever was in the mind of the minister's mother, she need not have worried, for Jessie Inglis proved a sterling character. She had blended well with her adopted family. Though she lived the life of a privileged young lady of the time, with trips by carriage through the Highlands and voyages round the islands on a steam yacht, her head remained unturned. It was no society beau who captured her heart but the striking and slightly gruff minister with the hypnotic gaze. There was some initial opposition from the Inglis family, who probably had reservations about the suitability of a struggling man of the cloth. But the couple's determination prevailed and both families were eventually won round.

The new Mrs Baird put fripperies and girlish ideas

behind her. She developed into a fitting spouse for a Presbyterian clergyman, a regular visitor to the poor and a good mother, constantly worrying about her offspring. She had a particularly sweet nature. Pictures in middle life show a frail figure in a plain tweed skirt and knitted shawl with a face mirroring suffering known and overcome. It is her features which predominate in the face of her famous son. Many years later, in the Second World War, tired, overworked and recovering from a heart attack, Baird wrote: 'Of my mother I find it difficult to write. She was the one experience I had of unselfish devotion. Her whole life was taken up in looking after others, particularly after myself, with very little reward, unless one can accept the wholehearted love of one small boy.'[15] The minister and his wife moved first into 'Clarkfield', a spacious house in Campbell Street, Helensburgh, where their first child, James, was born in 1879. James seems to have been born under a dark star. A rebel at odds with his father and his boyhood environment, he would suffer a great deal and break out of the close family circle, taking himself to the other side of the world. In 1881 Mr Baird moved from this official manse to the substantial one-storey villa in West Argyle Street known as the Lodge. This edifice had been built for a *grande dame* of Helensburgh whose ambition was to have the biggest drawing room in town, which aim being achieved she died fulfilled. Jessie's dowry helped to pay the purchase price of £1,100, and the new family moved into what would be home for the rest of their lives.

Children then arrived at fairly regular intervals; Annie in 1883, Jean, nicknamed 'Tottie', in 1885 and John Logie Baird on 13 August 1888. At first he was a healthy and energetic child, but when he was two he contracted a serious illness, a stoppage of the bowels. He took several months to recover and for some time afterwards was delicate, with very little strength. His parents, suspecting they might lose him, had the golden-curled baby of the family painted in oils by the prominent Scottish artist Muirhead Bone. A naturally pugnacious spirit seems to have pulled Baird through, but the ogre of illness was to dog his whole life; it would worry and exasperate him, but he repeatedly called on a remarkable inner strength - he tended to regard recurrences of bad health as some look on a gnatbite, to be noted and ignored. His first memory was of lying under an apple tree on a red blanket in the lush green garden of the Lodge. Life was calm, with little noise except the jangle of occasional carriages. Half a century later, at a low ebb in his life, in the summer of 1941 Baird penned autobiographical notes while recovering from his heart attack in a health establishment in Bedfordshire.

He wrote:

> ' *In those days life moved far more slowly and with much more dignity than it does today. There were no motor cars, no wireless sets, no aeroplanes; the telephone was a novelty possessed by a few of the more wealthy; the gramophone, a strange instrument, appeared occasionally in booths at fairs held in the village. Mysterious cylinders revolved beneath a great glass dome; those who paid twopence had the privilege of inserting rubber tubes into their ears and hearing a squeaking voice proclaiming some dissertation.* [16]

The revolving cylinders were a hint of the very tools Baird would use to create his early mechanical television.

The sight of them and the excitement of their sounds made a deep impression on the child.

Baird grew up in the high zenith of British imperialism, when the British were still embarking on little-known wars throughout the globe. Britannia's vice-consuls were still being dispatched by sword and dagger, by dusky tribesmen in the deserts of the Sudan and the mountain fastnesses of Afghanistan. Prophets like Kipling, in his poem 'Recessional', could feel in their bones the dawning of a new age with all its promise and threat, but middle-class society stuck to its long-accepted totems. Baird, however, seems to have had his eyes firmly set on the future. He showed little, if any, interest in tales of military glory. His mind, even as a boy just out of knickerbockers, was cast in the mould of the next century, in which he would play such a startling role. He ignored Henty-style tales of derring-do. Instead his luminary was H. G.Wells, whose enthusiasm for science spilled forth in a flood of vivid tales. With his visions of what was possible, Wells helped to germinate the fertile mind of the minister's son in the quiet Scottish village.

The family had unwittingly set their youngest son on a course which, by the laws of probability, should have killed off any scientific talent. At the age of six Baird was dispatched to his first school, Ardenlee, an establishment for young boys which he later termed 'an extraordinary Dickensian menage', kept by a Mr Porteous and his wife.

Mischief at the Manse. Young Baird, seated experimenting with vision even then, poses in an automatic picture triggered by himself, around 1900.

The Argyle Street cricket team, Helensburgh. Baird, top left; future entertainer and film star, Jack Buchanan, bottom right

There was certainly more than a whiff of Dotheboys Hall about the place, with Mr Porteous spreading terror throughout the classroom with his cane, which he used 'vigorously and indiscriminately'. Baird was considered too young to be taught by Mr Porteous himself and managed to have a comparatively happy time as a day boy, learning with ease to read and write under some gentler teacher.

Mr Porteous went bankrupt before young Baird qualified for the sting of the cane. It was a sad business. The strong-armed master could not even pay his pew rent in church. Baird was now sent to Miss Johnson's Preparatory School, a move he always considered an unmitigated disaster. He later claimed that the lady was a fierce, middle-aged spinster who ruled her pupils with a rod of iron. Said Baird: 'It was for me the most miserable time. I was terrorised and the years spent at that school are among the most unhappy of my life.'[17]

There was little relief when he went at the age of eleven to Larchfield Private School, founded in 1845 for boys between the age of eight and eighteen 'to prepare them for the Universities, the Services and the Commercial Life'. The school, as described by Baird, could have come straight from the pages of Evelyn Waugh.

To be fair, his memories may have been coloured by his own need to pursue an individual path and to have adequate mental elbow room. At least one relative, who attended the school not long after, thought it a fine institution. Baird considered it a really dreadful place, a poor imitation of a public school with all the worst features and none of the best.

It was run by three men fresh from Oxford and Cambridge. These masters were of the robust, back-slapping variety known at the time as 'hearties', who believed in no nonsense and plenty of cold showers.

Their intention, it would seem, was to create a conveyor belt of young 'hearties' to provide a backbone for an imperial nation. To this end the boys trundled out every afternoon between two and four to play cricket in summer and rugby in winter. After the game they stripped and leapt into a cold spray to prepare for their studies. For Baird the showers were the culminating point of a tortured afternoon. In his autobiographical notes he wrote: 'In winter it became an unbearable ordeal. I went to every subterfuge to escape, but only to be found out in the end. Sooner or later a dread voice would be heard shouting "Baird! You have not had your tub", and I would be caught by the hair of my head and held under the icy douche until I became numb and blue with cold. Then I caught chill after chill and spent most of the winter months in bed.'[18] In a newspaper article of the thirties he wrote 'I believe that most of the ill health which has interrupted my work has been caused by too much cold water in my school days. The shower baths helped undermine my already delicate constitution. '[19]

Sport was paramount. There was no teaching of science and maths was sketchy. Latin and Greek were learned parrot-fashion, undermining any veneration Baird might have had for the classics, much to his father's disgust. They crammed so much Latin into his head that he hated the sound of it. He stayed bogged down in one class so long, translating the same poem so often, that he came to know *two fabulae faciles* (easy fables) by heart. Years later, at the height of his fame, he had a sort of revenge. He was asked to make a speech at the opening of the White Rock Pavilion at Hastings and afterwards to his surprise was joined on the platform by his old classics master. 'Well,' said the master, 'I don't suppose you remember me?' 'I shall never forget you,' replied Baird, shaking his old torturer warmly by the hand. 'You once gave me three marks for a Latin paper, possibly an all-time record for the school. Thank you very much.' He then launched into the first page of the fables. '*Hercules Alcmanae filius olim in Graecia habitabat. At Juno regina deorum Alcmanae aderat et Hercules necare voluit illigita immedi nocti* ' etc. etc. Baird confessed that after thirty years of the 'accursed rubbish' clogging his brain it gave him infinite pleasure to throw it back at its instigator and watch his astounded face.[20]

Baird's academic record at Larchfield was not impressive. Repeated illness frequently kept him from school. A school report from Christmas 1900 places him thirteenth out of a class of fifteen in English, fourteenth in maths and fourteenth in French. He was tenth in drawing. The consensus of opinion among the masters was that he was eager to learn, industrious and persevering, but absence had largely handicapped him. The headmaster referred to a timidity which prevented him from asking questions. This would seem to be a misreading of Baird's character which recurred frequently throughout his life. He was a shy, sensitive youngster, but the evidence suggests there was a strong dash of the imp in him. Despite ill health he was the leader of a volatile band of rapscallions, fellow pupils who lived nearby and who appeared sometimes in the guise of the Argyle Street Cricket Club or the Photographic Society. A craze for photography seized the school and Baird, smitten by the bug, saved and begged every spare penny. Finally he bought his dream camera - a Lizar's Quarter Plate Perfecta. He was so proud of it that he never forgot its specifications, and forty years later could roll off its virtues: 'Triple expansion, rack and pinion focusing, rising and falling front, folding back, Taylor and Hobson F.7 rapid rectilinear lens, Bausch and Lomb roller, blind shutter, 1/100th to l/10th second.' He might be slow at assimilating the classics but his mind was now homing in unsolicitedly on a subject in which, he may even then have sensed, lay the clue to his future. This impressive piece of equipment led to his election as president of the Photographic Society. They were an unruly lot and included the elegant soft-shoe shuffler Jack Buchanan, he of the top hat and tails and dark velvet voice who danced on film with Fred Astaire and Ginger Rogers. Buchanan, who lived directly opposite Baird and remained a friend for the rest of his life, was also a bit of a dandy. Other members included Jimmy Bonner, killed in the First World War, Jack Bruce, who became a prosperous shipowner, Bony Wadsworth, who became a leading London accountant, Neil Whimster, a Glasgow shipowner, and the tragic figure of Guy Robertson. Guy, Baird's lifelong friend 'Mephy', killed himself, driven out of his mind by the events of the Second World War.

But extracurricular activities led to the demise of the Photographic Society. One of its meetings was interrupted by Jack 'Chump' Buchanan. The future film star had, it appeared, just suffered what he considered a terrible insult. Baird writes: 'While innocently passing the time by instructing young Sonny Forbes how to climb a lamp post and stimulating Sonny with the application of a rubber strap, old Forbes had appeared and, unthinkable insult, boxed his ears. The club there and then were enlisted to wipe out the insult and avenge themselves on old Forbes.[21]

The boys borrowed a builder's ladder and surreptitiously lodged it against the side of Forbes' pigeon loft on a clear, moonlit night. Some versions of what then happened are squeamish, suggesting that they merely removed and sold the pigeons. The action taken was in fact more drastic. In his autobiographical notes Baird reveals how he clutched the ladder in position in cold terror while 'Chump' Buchanan, muttering imprecations against its shaking, scaled it and, amid squawking and fluttering, wrung the necks of the hapless birds. Shivering from the enormity of what they had done, they nevertheless headed for the fishmonger in due course and cashed them in at fourpence a head. Having gone that far in bravado they were spurred on to more devilment, this time a devastating attack on the poor man's prize tulips, which were ruthlessly cut down and laid in a row at his steps. The doorbell was then jangled by means of a string, and when Forbes senior duly appeared he was pelted with a fusillade of mud balls. The pace had now grown too hot for the other members. Resignations poured in and despite a last-minute ordinance that all resigning members be fined five shillings and submit themselves to five strokes of the cane, the Photographic Society disintegrated. This desperate streak in Baird which made him, despite delicate health, a leader of his local Wild Bunch, is worth remembering. He later cloaked ruthless   drive beneath an exterior of benign eccentricity.

He pursued his interest in photography after the break-up of the Society and compiled a record of his family and schoolfriends. There are pictures of the Cricket Club, portraits of himself and friends, and even one of breakfast time in the Lodge. A posed action photograph has Baird himself, aged twelve, in Eton collar, reading in his room while brother James lurks behind, about to slam him on the head with a book. A self-portrait of 1900 shows him in his Larchfield blazer. The traditional cap has been ignored and he wears a wavy-brimmed sou'wester, the flamboyant headgear he favoured in these early years.

That later in life Baird was not keen on flying is probably the legacy of a boyhood scrape. In 1895 Percy Pilcher, a lecturer at Glasgow University, took to the air in a glider in nearby Cardross. Pilcher persevered with The Hawk in the south of England and died from injuries in 1899 when his glider collapsed in on itself while being pulled into the air by horses. Undeterred by the fate of their hero, Baird and a close friend, Godfrey Harris, decided in 1900 to tackle the new element. It was a bold decision, considering that the first powered flight by the Wright Brothers at Kittyhawk, North Carolina, was still three years hence.

They studied the available literature and modestly

decided to glide first, before attempting powered flight. After weeks of clandestine work somewhere in the Bairds' large and leafy garden, a contraption emerged resembling two giant kites held together by a narrow middle section. A suitable time was chosen, presumably when the rest of the family was out, and the rickety glider was manhandled onto the flat portion of the Lodge roof. Baird confesses he had no intention of flying, an honour he had designated for Godfrey. The latter, however, had similar ideas. As Johnnie clambered across the framework preparing for action, Godfrey gave it a hefty push and the junior member of the Baird clan was launched, shrieking, into the air.

He never did have time to master the primitive controls. For a few nauseating seconds he hung in the air while the machine heaved and juddered and then with a rending crack it tore in half, depositing Baird with a tremendous bump on the lawn. Luckily no bones were broken but there and then the world probably lost for ever a pioneer of flight. He later remarked: 'That was the first and last time I have ever been in an aeroplane. I have no desire whatever to fly and, unless forced by circumstances, will probably never do so.'

The family grew accustomed to the string of happenings that occurred with increasing frequency wherever Johnnie directed his attention. It had struck at least one of them, however, that, despite his poor academic record to date there was already a mind to be reckoned with in that touslehead. His sister Annie, five years older than himself, a firm-minded character who became a colonel in Queen Alexandra's Imperial Military Nursing Service, noted with monotonous regularity in her diary her young brother's victories at chess. 'John and I had a game of chess which he won through taking my queen.' And two days later, 'John and I played at chess and he won again.'

Brother John afforded this stern but kindly soul considerable light relief. He was, she noted, always carelessly dressed, as though drawn through a hedge backwards. He had two lop-eared rabbits that escaped and were caught again. He forced her and her friends to see his one-man theatre shows. She comments: 'We escaped as soon as we could.' She took John along to a lecture on South Africa, illustrated by magic lantern and the new cinematograph, possibly another milestone in the process which within a couple of years would have the schoolboy searching for a means of sending pictures by electricity.

The Bairds' home was in the main a happy one, though there was no doubt that, as in most households of the day, father ruled the roost. As Baird himself indicated, it was not the era of romping dads in shorts. In his early fifties Mr Baird's large beard was still brown. His voice boomed like an oracle. Children peered from the cover of bushes as the dark-suited minister strode round the perimeter of the town, book in hand, muttering what sounded like curses. Even his youngest son found him a source of uneasiness and embarrassment. Perhaps he felt that that penetrating gaze could read his mischievous mind. In fact, Mr Baird was merely reading one of his many languages. As well as Latin and Greek, he was strong in several European languages, particularly German. It is clear that his bark was worse than his bite and his young family seemed, for the times, to have had remarkable freedom to pursue their own ideas and enthusiasms. Mrs Baird dutifully complied with her husband's somewhat eccentric household regime. From dawn to bedtime she looked after others. One of Mr Baird's peculiarities concerned the time of his lunch. Like Noel Coward's Englishmen he went out in the midday sun. The best time of day to go out walking was between 11 a.m. and 3 p.m., when it was warmest and brightest, qualities treasured in the erratic and chilly northern climate. The logical outcome of his belief, however, was the introduction of a tiresome shift system for meals. The schoolgoing children had their lunch prepared for 1 p.m. and two hours later Mrs Baird supplied a second lunch for her homecoming husband. The inventor himself tried later in life to emulate this custom of his father's, but characteristically abandoned it when he saw the appalling trouble it caused in the home. A notable strain of eccentricity ran through the family. Baird recalled an aunt Eliza Baird who married an Australian millionaire. He wrote:

> *She developed a mania for attending auction sales where she bought lavishly. The whole of her large house was stacked to the roof with rubbish bought at such sales, her prize bargain being~ twelve dozen chamber pots. My other aunt was not fortunate in her marriage. She married a poor farmer and their mania took the form of pets. Her house was infested by innumerable dogs, cats and fowls. She had a particular hen called Lizzie which slept on her bed.[22]*

Mr Baird himself had a reputation for wry humour which was legendary in the area. Marriages of necessity he did not like, though they were common enough at the time. When called to officiate at one, he did so reluctantly, arriving half an hour behind schedule.

'You are very late,' said the bridegroom. 'Yes, about six months late I should think,' retorted the minister with a swift glance at the figure of the blushing bride.[23]

His mind, however, was far from closed. Baird said his father had ceased to contend for the truth of stories in the Old Testament. He recalled that when a favourite theological student, a devout youth called Willie Milne, stated that he believed in the literal truth of Jonah and the whale, the minister boomed: 'Aye, Willie, you and the whale rival each other in swallowing capacity.'[24]

A wealthy parishioner of solemn countenance, known to local children as Old Coffin Face, told young Baird of his admiration for his father. Many times, he intoned, he had felt the power and emotion of that Sabbath evening service. Impressed, the boy told his father, who bluntly dismissed the flatterer as a posturing old humbug.

Not surprisingly, as his son later pointed out, the higher dignitaries of the kirk looked on this phenomenon in their midst with some apprehension. As the years passed and contemporaries moved from one preferment to another, Mr Baird remained, growing old in his little parish while those who in youth had looked up to him, like Bonar Law, moved on to apparently greater things. Towards the end of his life this state of affairs embittered him to an extent, but such a fate was almost unavoidable for one so continually questioning while at the same time part of an uncompromising organization. His situation contained an element of tragedy, the possibility of someone who had outgrown the bound of his particular calling but found it difficult to move on. He kept his fierce eye and lively wit to the end, none the less.

The stark solemnity and Old Testament thunder of Presbyterian church life had its effect on Logie Baird. The church dominated him and those around him. He was an implicit believer in those days, thought that God floated overhead, a stern man with a beard not unlike his own father, only 'of enormous dimensions, infinite, powerful and fearsome'. Fear crept into his imaginative young mind and hung over his childhood like a black cloud. He describes the fear as 'not only of God but of intangible evil, ghosts and spirits creatures of unimaginable horror, waiting and watching for an opportunity to get at me'.[25] He was put to bed at eight every night and would huddle in terror under the bedclothes, completely covered except for a little hole through which to breathe. He later wrote: 'While the grey lady crept up to my bedside or the two supernatural old men crouched at the bottom of my bed, waiting and watching, a burglar or tiger would have been a welcome intrusion.'[26] Later, his fear centred on God whom, like the Children of Israel, he tried to placate with interminable prayers and gestures of propitiation. This attitude continued for some years even into a period when his reason regarded such behaviour as altogether contemptible and ridiculous'. Later he swung to agnosticism and later still the pendulum moved back, if not to his early beliefs, at least to a suspicion that the universe was filled with more wonderful and mysterious possibilities than a cocksure young man could imagine.

The darker side of his early life was intensified by his weekly trips to the poor, when he accompanied his mother. Mrs Baird, up each morning at dawn, made time each day to call on those who might need help. The boy from the comfortable home long remembered some of the strange and pathetic characters he encountered on these visits. Old Mrs McCaul could only be dimly seen in the gloom of an old-fashioned cupboard bed, and even then he only glimpsed a head in a not-too-clean nightcap. Her single room was a combined kitchen, sitting room and bedroom. She lived on charity, in constant terror of the poorhouse. As Mrs Baird handed her parcels of food, Baird felt the pins-and-needles roughness of her horsehair sofa where he sat gazing at a lithograph of Jesus walking on the sea. This was followed by visits to similar old women, to poverty-stricken younger ones and to squalid families headed by drunken husbands.

These visits had an unsettling effect. In his autobiographical notes he writes:

In Helensburgh the poverty was, for the most part, not the open horror of the Glasgow slums but a horror hidden beneath the cloak of genteel respectility. The condition of the poor in city slums in my youth was appalling. I have seen young children running about in the backyards of Glasgow tenements, clothed only in old sacking in the icy wind and rain of a Glasgow winter. My blood boiled when fresh from such sights, I used to read the society notes and see photographs of the idle rich in the pages of The Sketch and The Tatler, (usually read in dentists' waiting rooms), ski-ing at St Moritz, sunbathing at Monte Carlo and flaunting their overdressed persons at race meetings and house parties. The country could not afford to spend enough on its children to give them even the comforts and protection of the lower animals, or so the wealthy rate-payers insisted. In the Great War however, when the security of these same wealthy rate-payers was menaced, they contrived to spend as much in a week on destruction as would have banished every slum in Glasgow.[27]

Baird puzzled over the extraordinary phenomenon of apparently decent, respectable people being reduced through poverty, misery and despair to nothing better than the poorhouse and then the cemetery. He writes: 'A continual and embittered struggle for a livelihood was all around me. The poor people I visited with my mother lived in continual privation and fear, whereas the upper classes appeared in some mysterious manner to be secure beyond the reach of want.'[28]

He inquired and found out about dividends and interest and money among families who enjoyed an income which often bred faster than the family to which it belonged. Baird there and then decided that some day he would make enough money to leave his four children (four seeming a reasonable number) a capital sum providing an income of £1,000 per annum each. The sum would be invested at compound interest and would be sufficient to allow for each of the children to live to eighty years, at their deaths it would have been augmented by compound interest for each of their children to have £1,000. The foundation fund, he said, was to be so large that at $2^1/2$ per cent interest it would provide for all his descendants. The schoolboy calculated that in a few hundred years the whole of Scotland might be inhabited by independent gentry He wrote:

It seemed straightforward enough, but even to my childish mind there appeared a limit. Suppose my family spread over the whole earth and the world was entirely peopled by independent gentry, who would do the work? Still, it could be alright if confined to Scotland and I saw no reason why Scotland should not be peopled by independent gentlefolk. Nothing would be heard throughout the land but the whizzing of swinging golf clubs and the plop of tennis balls and the fruity voices of the gentry declaiming 'love-fifteen' and shouting 'fore', and their happy bell-like laughter as, in battalions, they shot down the grouse and pheasants, would ring across the glens and bens of their Scottish paradise.[29]

This utopian plan which offered the grown-up Baird the opportunity for satire on his favourite bugbear, the idle rich, was nevertheless a significant expression of the boy's increasing awareness of poverty and the need to provide against it. From the start his mind restlessly sought a way of making a name for himself and a living that would always keep the wolf from the door Ironically his boyish quest to develop and improve television and a string of other key inventions made the man throw caution and possible fortune to the winds. The spectre of poverty may have been the spur but it was soon jettisoned like the first stage of a rocket as he recklessly laid everything on the line, including his life, to achieve his goals.

These encounters with social reality also left their mark on another member of the family. His sister Annie was not impressed by the Bairds' prestigious connections and commented acidly that the wealthy shipbuilders, with a few exceptions, seemed 'a nasty lot, thinking of themselves and very little of their fellow-men'.[30] But such were the ways of many Victorian families who practised their own form of 'laissez faire' and kept kindness and consideration and their money within family bounds. It was a shrewd, hard- headed approach which provided some stability but sustained the status quo, offering little hope of advancement to those who did not already have a foot in the door.

The Bairds, however, did not share this convenient philosophy. At the turn of the century they had a cross of their own to bear- the problem of James, whose troubled character was already rocking the family boat. From 1899 onwards several poignant episodes occurred for Mrs Baird, involving her in a weary odyssey round the west of Scotland in search of her lost sheep of a son. In August 1898 a detachment of the Royal Scots Greys came down from Glasgow and gave an exhibition of dancing and tent-pegging at the first-ever Highland Games in Helensburgh. James, then nineteen and itching with discontent, must have been entranced by what he saw. Soon afterwards he determined to take the Queen's shilling.

The following year saw sabre-rattling as Britain and the Boers headed for a collision course in the Transvaal. In July 1899 James packed his trunk and slipped unseen out of Helensburgh. Mrs Baird's journal makes heartbreaking reading. On 26 July she writes: 'James ran away to the Barracks at Maryhill (in Glasgow) to join the Royal Scottish Fusiliers. He took my little tin box but did not tell us where he was going.' Some days later: 'I have been seeking for James all week but cannot find him.' The distraught mother followed every clue, talking to soldiers, checking with relatives, until at last she traced James 'in a situation' near Langbank, a small village on the Clyde almost directly opposite Helensburgh and easily reached from Glasgow. There seems to have been some hitch in his army plans and he had undertaken some very heavy work, possibly farming or labouring. She left him there, happy at least that he appeared to be in good hands, though under a very strict master. She writes in her journal:

> *I got a letter from another James Baird in the Scots Greys. He had got my letter to our James and thought it was for him. He hates the army and wishes he was out of it, poor fellow. Some young men have a very hard struggle in life. It is not a bed of roses for them, especially soldiers. As to James, I wish he was here and I could make his food and mend his stockings, besides seeing how he gets on. He is a very peculiar boy, he hates books and learning, the very things I love so much.*

And on 10 August: 'James hates his new work and is determined to leave it.' He did indeed return home. In October, as President Kruger eventually tugged the British Lion's tail and the Boer War was declared, James had a strange dream. Mrs Baird's journal reads: 'He went to bed tonight and I heard him saying loudly "What do you want?" I thought he was dreaming, but he says not, that he saw a soldier in Scots Greys uniform staring at him in the dark. The figure was surrounded by a pale light and when I entered the door, it vanished.' James may have been indulging in some genuine Celtic feyness but it could have been a ruse to condition his mother to the inevitable. She managed to prevail for another couple of years, however, and it was not until 29 January 1902 that she wrote: 'Aged 22 years, James left here today to go to Stirling Castle to be trained for active service for a year's work in South Africa. A Company, 1st D.R.C. "Private Baird".' In fact, James joined the 3rd VS Company, Argyll and Sutherland Highlanders and sailed for Capetown on the *Cawdor Castle*. He entrained for Pretoria and was on trek in the Mafeking district for two months. But dreams of military glory vanished because the war ended in May that year, and by July he was on a troopship back home.

When he left the army soon afterwards James kept a service revolver which he toyed with in the house, to his mother's alarm This weapon was removed one day when he was out, broken up and buried in the earth-floored cellar of the Lodge, where its pieces probably lie to this day. Mrs Baird worried about John's health, but she sensed something more vulnerable in the apparently robust James, over whom she fretted like a caring child over a broken-winged sparrow. He seems to have been an impulsive character, a Steinbeck hero as played by James Dean, eager to achieve something, to shine, to please, but unintentionally putting his foot in it, breaking his mother's heart and eventually his own.

Baird senior had ecclesiastical ambitions for his younger son but it was soon clear that Johnnie was veering in a quite different direction. The telephone service linking the Bairds' home with those of his schoolfriends Neil Whimster, Jack Bruce, Ian Norwell and Godfrey Harris had just been summarily terminated through the interference of the Post Office when he made print in the local newspaper, the *Helensburgh Times.* The article informed readers that the Lodge was now enjoying the amenities of electric light, 'thanks to the ingenuity of a youthful member of the household'. Thirteen-year-old John had put his pocket money to good use once more and bought a secondhand oil engine and made a small dynamo. Ingeniously he created accumulators, wrapping lead plates in flannelette and placing them in jam-jars filled with sulphuric acid, a process-that gave him lead poisoning and left a scar on one finger for the rest of his life. These accumulators were charged from the dynamo and in turn lit up the house. Helensburgh citizens were becoming aware of a prodigy in their midst, though it is anyone's guess how this child, working with no specialist guidance at home or school, found his way to the practicalities involved. When his father suggested he might think of becoming a minister, Baird remembered in his notes: 'With the impertinent insensibility of extreme youth, I had the audacity to tell the old gentleman that I did not think I could be a sufficiently good hypocrite.[31] If Mr Baird had been a typical Victorian father his son might have found his head buzzing from a firm cuff on the ear. Instead, probably with a wry expression suppressing a smile, and recognizing a chip off the old block, his only reply was: 'I think you might manage that alright.[32]

The matter was dropped for the time being and Baird continued his experiments in several fields. At the age of thirteen he was pondering the possibility of transmitting pictures electrically by wire. His electrical telephone exchange was meant as a first step, and he wanted to delve further into the exciting possibilities of electricity. At the turn of the century people talked of telectroscopy, the possible art of seeing over long distances by electric wire. And in 1900 a paper was read to a meeting of the International Congress of Electricity by a Frenchman, Constantine Perskyi, coined a new word for it, 'television', a term that did not catch on until reintroduced nine years later by Hugo Gernsback in his American magazine *Modern Electrics*.

In the quiet Scottish town Baird heard little of this, but common sense and a natural flair set him travelling along a visionary path which would to his last breath be an overriding obsession. In a newspaper article thirty-six years later he wrote:

> *Even at that time I had begun to think about the possibility of sending pictures by telephone. So far as I knew, nobody before me had even conceived the possibility of TV. Now of course I know that others much older and more learned than myself have been thinking about it and even writing about it. But whenever I mentioned it, the very idea struck other people as fantastic. They must have thought me a crank.*
>
> *To me, seeing by telephone always seemed as reasonable a possibility as hearing by telephone. If sound waves could be converted into waves of another sort and sent over wires, why not light waves.[33]*

Almost simultaneously in 1873 two men had come up with a major constituent for making the dream come true. Willoughby Smith, chief electrician of the Telegraph Construction Company had found in 1866 that selenium was unsatisfactory when used for high-resistance rods to make continuity checks on the Atlantic cable. Tests showed that the resistance diminished when the selenium was exposed to light. Smith announced his findings in 1873, the same year that Joseph May, a young telegraphist working in a terminal station for the Atlantic cable in Ireland noted that his receiver failed to work properly when the sun fell on it. May excitedly studied the effects of sunlight falling on selenium resistors in some of his circuits. These were meant to control the flow of electricity, but in fact too much escaped whenever sun fell on the selenium. His discovery led to the development of the photo-electric cell, light values could be converted into electrical values. Light shining onto selenium in a cell connected to a battery would increase the flow of current in proportion to brightness.

Shelford Bidwell, an English amateur scientist who specialized in obscure scientific problems, turned his attention to selenium and devised a practical selenium cell. He worked on for fifteen years and eased the path for others, prophesying in 1881 that it might one day be used in facsimile transmitters to react to the black and white variations of messages and pictures. The first big step had been taken in giving man a magic eye.

Young Baird must have kept an eye on the scientific journals of the day. He knew of the light-sensitive properties of selenium, and at about the time that he was running his telephone exchange resolved to create his own selenium cell, which he started on the black-leaded range of the Lodge kitchen. He wrapped wire round a piece of porcelain, heating it and rubbing it steadily with a stick of selenium. The trials were many, resulting chiefly in burnt fingers for himself and odious smells that must have put the rest of the family off their food. He wrote: 'But I did learn one thing, which was that the current from a selenium cell was infinitesimally small. Before anything could be done, some means of amplifying this must be found. I made all sorts of attempts at amplifiers but could get nothing sufficiently sensitive.'[34]

That would have to wait until 1906 when the American Lee de Forest produced his Audion valve, the amplifier which paved the way for both everyday wireless and television, now called the Triode. J. Ambrose Fleming had produced his Diode valve shortly before - the first time that amplification had been possible. It has generally been believed that the idea of sending pictures by wire was just a schoolboy fad which Baird recalled many years later and started once again, this time successfully, in Hastings in 1923. The facts, however, point to a continuing interest that not even the amplifier barrier stopped.

For many good reasons, Baird was less than frank about the realities of his work. Even in his autobiographical notes, where they concern his professional work he sticks largely to popular legend. Yet behind it lie traces of a clear and sustained plan to generate pictures by electricity. Much of his thinking on television was already being done as a schoolboy and, if this sounds incredible, it is worth recalling that in America Philo Farnsworth was to make an extraordinary stab at electronic television in the 1920s while still a teenager.

It is probable that with his father's help Baird acquired a passable reading knowledge of German. In his autobiographical notes he writes: 'In my early efforts to make selenium cells I got hold of Ernst Ruhmer's *Das Selen und seinen Bedeuten in Electral Technique*, which gave a very full account of Ruhmer's experiments. He really laid the foundations of talking pictures with his work on recording sound on cinema film.'[35]

Ruhmer also undertook television experiments with twelve selenium cells fixed to a wall, each cell connected to a shutter. By this means he could make spots appear or disappear in accordance with the illumination of the cells and transmit figures or numbers made up of dots. All this was not lost on the young Scot, who became so engrossed in his thoughts and calculations that he now began to earn a reputation for eccentricity. A cousin remembers:

His head appeared always in the clouds. When his name was mentioned, relatives would smile and shrug, saying 'puir Johnnie, puir Johnnie'. At breakfast one day everyone sat gaping. He was so immersed in thought that with one elbow on the table, he unconsciously used the other arm to scratch his head with the porridge spoon, mixing lumps of porridge through his hair. However, we had to admit that he had the last laugh. He knew what he wanted and he achieved it.[36]

As the years passed Baird developed into a tall youth with a earnest face, cool, blue-grey eyes and a shock of gleaming fair hair. That sense of gravitas, the sober quality esteemed by ancient Rome which predisposed an individual to carry a purpose through against all odds, was certainly his. But a sense of mischief never deserted him, though his humour remained largely deadpan. His ingenuity also sought other outlets and this led him in 1905 while still at school, to purchase for £4 a tri-car, a perfect scrapheap on wheels which he put into some form of running order. The battered vehicle, a Kellycomb Antoinette, was still a novelty in the streets of Helensburgh where it was nicknamed 'young Baird's Reaper and Binder', because of the volumes of sound emitted coupled with choking clouds of smoke and fumes. He swiftly graduated to a real car, though it too had only three wheels. These tri-cars, popular for a time, and also known as fore-cars, were a kind of cross between a car and a motorcycle. A model similar to Baird's second purchase had a 1,222cc engine and managed to run non-stop between London and Edinburgh in 1905, carrying a 22 stone passenger. Baird himself steered from a seat just above the rear wheel, while his passenger or passengers (it could take two perched precariously in front in the equivalent of a fireside easy chair, feet resting on a curled footrest which resembled the front of a toboggan. The passenger, thus poised between the two front wheels, faced the hazards of the road unguarded, like a ship figurehead racing to meet

Wrapped up against a Scottish winter, teenage Baird with a girl cousin aboard his motor machine nicknamed by locals - 'Baird's Reaper and Binder.' 1906.

the waves.

Baird, ever vigilant of the weather because of his health, dressed in oilskin jacket and fisherman-style helmet. He tucked his trousers into the warmth of knee-high felt boots and thus hermetically sealed, explored the breathtaking hill country round Helensburgh in his rickety chariot. His passenger was usually the old friend Guy 'Mephy' Robertson, though sometimes it was a relative, Jeannie Coates, who lived nearby. Jeannie, too, swathed herself in clothes for such expeditions: she wrapped a scarf round her neck and chest and another under her chin and over her head, pinning down a bonnet and protecting her ears. The total effect was one of complete incongruity which Baird is unlikely to have missed. While charging down hill roads in a whirl of smoke and dust, it must have looked as though he was risking the life and limb of some maiden aunt perched up front.[37]

These trips were boneshakers, on roads built for horse-drawn vehicles; but the rewards were boulder-strewn corries, rushing whitewater burns and mountainsides where the curling mist transformed the scattered trees into the vanguard of a ghostly army. On a clear day, from a high vantage point they could gaze out on the Firth of Clyde where plied the finest fleet of pleasure steamers in Europe. The sleek Clyde vessels were so renowned for their speed and grace that half a century before, during the American Civil War, the Confederate States had sneaked several across the Atlantic as blockade runners. Some of the greyhounds of the north ended as skeletal wrecks on tropical Caribbean reefs. During Baird's youth, rivalry among the various steamer companies had reached such a pitch that they were still racing each other to gain harbour first and scoop up more business. This was accomplished heedless of the comfort and sometimes the safety of the passengers, who in fact joined in the fun which, on occasions, ended in collision and a court appearance for the captains.

The ventures on wheels continued for a couple of years. Baird managed to coax his vehicle almost 1,000 feet up the Rest and Be Thankful, an old Redcoat military road through the mountains, once visited and lauded by Wordsworth but on a trip near Loch Lomond the car met with some unspecified disaster, gave up the ghost and had to be abandoned.

Baird was an accomplished painter but significantly the

land- scapes which exhilarated him in real life were not the subject of his brush. He concentrated on still life. His studies might include a glazed brown jug, a couple of frayed antique books or an old phonograph. Their most-striking feature was the attention to light, how it bathed and outlined form - important, of course, to all painters, but of special fascination to someone battling with the problem of sending images by electricity. His lone experiments continued as he struggled to create a light-sensitive cell powerful enough to help him project his images. This, he knew already, was the touchstone to success. Books too were a passion. He read widely and variously mixing the austere with the frivolous. He wrote later:

It is interesting to consider what out of all this reading has been retained. I remember much of Goethe's Faust, something of Tolstoy, much of Voltaire, Macbeth and Hamlet, not that these classics were my favourites. Favourites came and went, Boothby, Max Pemberton, W.W. Jacobs, Jerome K. Jerome and many others, but not one line of any of these has left a trace whereas, even today, after over thirty years I remember whole pages from the classical authors; their words bit deep.

One writer, though, scored far above the rest. 'In my boyhood youth,' he said,

he was a demi-god and the reading of any new book by him was regarded as a feast; today he still occupies a high place although he is no longer a demi-god. I have met him in the flesh and not many can submit to this ordeal and remain gods, certainly not H.G.Wells, that pleasant, stubby little man with a squeaky voice. None-the-less, apart from a few classics, he is the only one among the popular authors of my youth who survives recollections and actually takes his place among the classics

The long late Victorian and Edwardian idyll was drawing to a close. Life at the Lodge was changing. In 1903 Annie left to train as a nurse. Later his sister 'Tottie' went to university. James wandered off to New Zealand in 1903, and returned three years later, only to leave again, this time to lay bricks and work silvermines in New South Wales, Australia.

Larchfield had become even more irksome. Most of his contemporaries had left while Baird studied on, recouping time through illness. But at last, in 1906, to his heartfelt relief, schooldays ended. By then his father was reconciled to the idea that science, not the ministry, called his son, and it was agreed he should attend the Royal Technical College in Glasgow to study electrical engineering.

The years spent at the Lodge had been happy ones but there were signs that, latterly, Baird had been feeling the constraints of life there, where he considered the regime 'most strict'. His move to Glasgow certainly offered freedom of a sort. But he had made an odd choice for someone with delicate health. His new life was to bring him hard up against the grim realities of making a living in a harsh industrial world. He was heading for no ivory tower. Part of the training would involve apprenticeships in dank city engineering shops. The experience would make him more introspective and put iron in his soul.

NOTES

1   Baird, quoted in *The Sunday Chronicle* series, November 1936.
2   Baird, autobiographical notes, *Sermons, Soap and TV*, written from summer 1941, ch. 1, p. 3. This unpublished material is now in the hands of Baird's son, Professor Malcolm Baird.
3   Sir James Frazer, *Sir Roger de Coverley and other Literary Pieces*, Macmillan, 1920.
4   Baird, quoted in 'Talks with Great Scots', *Scotland* magazine, summer 1936, p. 46.
5   *Sermons, Soap and Television*, ch. 1, p. 2.
6   *Sermons, Soap and Television*, ch. 1, p. 2.
7   Conversation with Mrs J. L. Baird, summer 1979.
8   *Sermons, Soap and Television*, ch. I, p. 7.
9   Letters to his parents by John Baird sen., now in the possession of Professor Malcolm Baird.
10 Letters to his parents by John Baird sen.
11 Letters to his parents by John Baird sen.
12 Baird, quoted in *The Sunday Chronicle* series, November 1936.
13 Baird, quoted in *The Sunday Chronicle* series, November 1936.
14 Letters now in the possession of Professor Malcolm Baird.
15 *Sermons, Soap and Television*, ch. I, p. 8.
16 *Sermons, Soap and Television*, ch. 1, p. 1.
17 *Sermons, Soap and Television*, ch. 1, p. 3.
18 *Sermons, Soap and Television*, ch. 1, p. 9.
19 Baird, quoted in *The Sunday Chronicle* series, November 1936.
20 *Sermons, Soap and Television*, ch. 1, p. 9.
21 *Sermons, Soap and Television*, ch. 1, p. 10.
22 *Sermons, Soap and Television*, ch. 1, p. 11.
23 *Sermons, Soap and Television*, ch. 1, p. 4.
24 *Sermons, Soap and Television*, ch. 1, p. 4.
25 *Sermons, Soap and Television*, ch. 1, p. 5.
26 *Sermons, Soap and Television*, ch. 1, p. 5.
27 *Sermons, Soap and Television*, ch. 1, p. 9.
28 *Sermons, Soap and Television*, ch. 1, p. 7.

29   *Sermons, Soap and Television*, ch. 1, p. 7.
30   Annie Baird's diary.
31   *Sermons, Soap and Television*, ch. 1, p. 12.
32   *Sermons, Soap and Television*, ch. 1, p. 12.
33   Baird, quoted in *The Sunday Chronicle* series, November 1936.
34   *Sermons, Soap and Television*, ch. 1, p. 12.
35   *Sermons, Soap and Television*, ch. 1, p. 13.
36   Personal conversation, summer 1978.
37   *Sermons, Soap and Television*, ch. 1, p. 6.
38   *Sermons, Soap and Television*, ch. 1, p. 6.

2

Apprentice Years

When King George V visited India in 1911 for the Great Durbar, he met the engineers who had built the bridges and railways and constructed dams and factories throughout the subcontinent. He found to his surprise that large numbers of them were alumni of a single institution, the Glasgow and West of Scotland College of Technology. So impressed was he by their monumental achievements that he conferred the prefix 'Royal' to the College in the following year.

The College was justifiably proud of itself. In the nineteenth century Britain had led the world in the Industrial Revolution, but there was a strange lack of opportunity within British universities to study the new technology. For years the Glasgow college remained pre-eminent in the field, offering students a chance to study practical applied science and engineering up to university level. It was therefore no ordinary parrot learning institution that the young Baird joined, but a forcing ground of innovators and world beaters, and the inventiveness of its founder seemed to have rubbed off on him. He was John Anderson, Professor of Natural Philosophy at Glasgow University in the latter half of the eighteenth century, a radical and prolific inventor, known to his students as Jolly Jack Phosphorous. During the French Revolution he gave the National Assembly a model of a gun carriage which absorbed the shock of the recoil. Later he invented a secret alloy for his guns, two kinds of perforated bullets, and time fuses for howitzers. In his will he left instructions for the setting up of the university with the enlightened clause that there should be a course of lectures for the ladies of Glasgow, with such a stock of general knowledge as would make them the most accomplished in Europe.[1] Though Baird became known through his mainstream interest, television, he too produced a scatter of inventions with applications in peace and war.

It is unlikely that anyone spotting the pale, seemingly diffident youth, at that time as thin as a beanpole, would guess that he was the respository of teeming ideas and apparently boundless determination. Certainly not someone whose eagle gaze was fixed on his own destiny, a fellow student, John Charles Walsham Reith, the future Lord Reith, first Director-General and founding father of the BBC. That Baird, the man who first developed and introduced television, should attend college with the figure who would one day have power over his fate is a striking coincidence filled with irony. Superficially they had a lot in common. Both were sons of the manse. Reith's father was a Free Kirk Moderator. Both were to experience the rigours of heavy work in bleak engineering shops. There the similarity ends. Whereas Baird was fascinated by science, and eventually immersed his personality in his work, Reith, who trained as a civil engineer, would have chosen to be almost anywhere out of engineering, preferably in the field of politics or organization. Despite the fulfilment of many of his ambitions, his remained an austere and lonely ego.

At an early stage he had shown a tendency to bully, which surfaced at Glasgow Academy, where he was a pupil for eight years. Two smaller boys were absent from the school following bullying and Reith's father withdrew him, after consultation with the staff.[2] Reith was sent to Gresham's School in England and returned very much a public school type. As Baird later observed, the students at the technical college were mostly poor young men, desperately anxious to get on. Most of them worked with enormous tenacity and zeal. He added:

There were, however, a few exceptions, gentlemen's sons, well off and with no real anxiety as to their future. Among these was a tall, well-built youth, the son of the Moderator of the Presbyterian Church, by name, John Reith. I met him for the first time in rather unfavourable circumstances. I was, and still am, very short-sighted and, at the beginning of one of the classes, the Professor asked if those who were short-sighted and wanted front seats, would hand in their names. When I went up to the platform to give him my name, three large impressive young students were talking to him. They talked in terms of equality; in fact there was a distinct aroma of patronage. The young gentlemen were of the type we would today call 'heavies', and they boomed with heavy joviality at the poor little Professor, who was distinctly embarrassed and ill-at-ease. I interrupted, timidly, and handed him a piece of paper with my name on it. As I did so, the heaviest and most overpowering of the three 'heavies' turned round and boomed at me 'Ha! What is the matter with you? Are you deaf or blind?' I simpered something in inaudible embarrassment, and he turned his back on me, and the three 'heavies' walked out of the classroom booming portentously to each other.

This was the first time I saw Reith. I did not see him again for twenty years. Reith did not distinguish himself in examinations; he was worse than I was, without the excuse of ill-health, but now we see him as a Cabinet Minister and a national figure while those who soared above him at College are lost in obscurity, little provincial professorlings, draughtsmen, petty departmental chiefs and the like, hewers of wood and drawers of water. The examiners awarded no marks for impressive appearances, no marks for oracular booming voices, no marks for influential relatives. To the examiners an overpowering 'heavy' and a lean rat-faced little cad were all alike. All they were concerned with was the capacity to absorb knowledge and regurgitate it on to an examination paper. Had marks been given for personality, and for moving in exclusive circles (superlatively valuable in the business of getting on) Reith would undoubtedly have topped the examination list. The great acquisition of knowledge counts for little in the battle of life. Francis Bacon has summed up the matter in his essay on Metaphysics: 'Wouldst thou acquire riches? The rule is simple - make many friends.' That is the first rule, it being understood that the friends move in the right circles, influential friends, but any friends are better than none. God help the recluse who lusts for worldly success.[3]

This passage fairly seethes with untypical bitterness. Baird usually spiced his bad-tempered references with humour. Mrs Baird says her husband was never quite able to rid himself of the mixture of awe and dislike which Reith had created in him. This brush between two eighteen-year-olds, with its echoes of Tom Brown and Flashman, obviously rankled with Baird, though it is probable that Reith never gave it a second thought. However, the bitterness is more likely to have stemmed from adult experiences when Baird had to threaten to turn pirate broadcaster in 1929, before the BBC under Reith deigned to take notice that television had arrived and was begging development.

Baird was probably unfair, however, in casting the young Reith in the role of the super-privileged. At the technical college Reith was reported as a nuisance, and withdrew without completing the course.[4] In fact he, too, had to struggle to achieve. There is little doubt that Reith gave Baird a hard time during the crucial early years, and he probably found the inventor a much tougher character than he would have remembered from college days. The feeling between the two, though described only by Baird (Reith seldom mentioned television, except to say that he disliked the idea), has bedevilled the story of Baird and television ever since.

Baird gradually settled to the discipline of college life. For a time he still travelled to and from Helensburgh, but he probably abandoned this around 1909, when, as part of his studies, he started working as an engineering apprentice with a motoring company. He tackled the intensive work of the college, attending daily classes in chemistry, technical chemistry, natural philosophy, mechanics, engineering drawing and electrical engineering. In August 1907 he toured Italy, one of several trips he seems to have made to the Continent when in his teens. Altogether he spent eight years at the college, five of them studying for the Associate-ship and the Diploma in Electrical Engineering. Baird later commented that the course would have taken an able and energetic youth three years. But his studies were frequently interrupted by the old curse of ill health. Like many brilliant people, he was impatient and overcritical of his own shortcomings, and he therefore blamed what he termed his 'simple lack of ability and stupidity', but almost in the same breath he is critical of the course and writes, 'The first year I was there I learned a good deal that was useful and interesting; the remaining years were, I think, almost entirely a waste of time. I learned, with great pain and boredom, masses of formulae and tedious dates, much of which was never used and soon forgotten. But what I learned in that first year has remained with me all my life.[5]

This was the quicksilver man of ideas speaking. He never was the perfect technician. After those early days he tended to sketch out what was needed, and leave the making of nuts and bolts to others. The meticulous college training jarred on someone who instinctively grasped that his realm was the exploration of possibilities. Some technicians who later worked with him considered this a weakness; in their opinion they carried out the particular task better than he would have done. Few grasped, or were allowed to discover, the wide range of his work and breakthroughs. He was the pathfinder. As frequently happens, once the way was shown it seemed obvious.

Baird learned something really valuable at the college, though, and that was the discipline of consistent effort. He had gone there feeling sure he would distinguish himself, but wrote,

> *I found it not so easy. There were plenty of other youths there, filled with zeal and determination. How those youths worked They were, for the most part, working men, bright lads out to make a career for themselves. They were not the intellectual cream (those won scholarships and went to the University) Nevertheless, they were doughty competitors. Nothing could approach the frenzied concentration. There was no pretence at social life - there was no time for it.[6]*

Over the years the spindly adolescent turned into a lean handsome young man, grave of visage, with a disconcertingly intense gaze. At home in Helensburgh he compared notes with his friend Godfrey Harris on the intellectual upheaval common to young men. Baird wrote:

> *The growing doubts as to religious beliefs, interminable arguments on metaphysics and philosophy - when I remember the long, interesting talks we had together in our student days.*
>
> *I think then my brain was clearer and better than it has ever been since, and the conclusions I arrived at then are the same today only perhaps less clear, less well understood. We discussed the everlasting problem of free will, how every cause must have effect, and therefore the future must be as fixed as the past, and the events of tomorrow as fixed as the events of yesterday. Free will is a myth, an illusion, such was the thesis.[7]*

By the age of twenty he said he knew, or thought he knew, that he was just an animal, a mechanism, a cousin of the arboreal ape and added,

> *The clergy who told me I was an immortal spirit imprisoned in mortal clay, I regarded as hypocrites and humbugs. The journey of life was, I knew, a meaningless pilgrimage from nothing to nowhere, 'let us eat, drink and be merry for tomorrow we die' and now, after some 30 years, can I add anything to these youthful beliefs? Only this - that now I am*

less sure. What seemed pitifully clear then is less clear now. As the end grows nearer, I become less certain that it must be the end, less certain of everything.[8]

He tried time and again to convert to agnosticism the flow of young clergymen who called on his father, but found them fresh from university with plenty of theological arguments. 'They met my confident spear thrusts with vast, verbal smokescreens, pompous evasions, references to authorities, references to the original Greek Testament; they twisted and turned far into the night until the discussion died with the exhaustion of both parties. The older clergy baffled me by repudiating reason and intelligence alike, and appealing to faith.[9]

It is not on record what Baird senior thought of these attempts to suborm his young associates. With his own questing mind it is probable that he believed that any faith which could not hold out against his son's intellectual sparring was better re-examined anyway. He may even have enjoyed his son's forays into humorous literature, in which he frequently parodied biblical and ministerial style. Baird was soon a regular and much-read contributor to the college magazine, and gained a reputation for wit and skill with words. For his pseudonym he took the chemical formula for water, H_2O, a joking reference to his abstemiousness which was noticeable among young men who were beginning to enjoy the freedom to indulge in strong drink. At this stage Baird was teetotal, and there are many references in the magazine to his predilection for aqua pura. H_2Os offerings, which appeared from 1909 to 1913, ranged from the earthy to the ethereal, from the whimsical to the downright belly laugh. Under the solemn exterior lurked a rich vein of deadpan humour. The editor singled him out for special attention, referring to pen pictures which could only be handled by literary geniuses such as H_2O. Baird occasionally acted as sub-editor. Had his energies and ambitions not gone elsewhere, he might well have become a writer.

The articles contained many 'in' jokes and references, but they reveal something of Baird's preoccupations and characteristics at that time. In 'The Soul of Dominic McSharkey' a student's note- books are filled with caricatures of his acquaintances and professors. He dissipates time at music halls and ice rinks, and as a result finds himself doomed to follow lectures in hell under a clock which measures years and centuries instead of hours. In 'Zerubabel and the Mirror Galvanometer' Baird brings biblical cadences to bear on the prosaic operations of the machine for measuring electrical currents. "Wherefore smiteth thou the Galvo, knowest thou not that thou destroyest it?" says the master. Now Zerubabel was sore afraid and answered "The galvo sticketh, some mucilage hath gotten within it, I do but loosen it."

In 'The Temple', a story about a visit to a famous Glasgow music hall, Baird is back with the Old Testament. 'And first will I show thee that temple of Vaudeville; even the Panopticon which lieth hard by the gate called Tron. And immediately I heard a great voice calling "Enter ye in, enter ye in", and behold Miss McPhee of Port Dundas. The hairs on her head be six cubits long or thereby notwithstanding the days of her life, which be three score and seventeen years.'

There is a disquieting piece simply named 'A Parable', written in November 1912, which may have mirrored Baird's inner turmoil over the constant tug between pleasure and duty. He was aware at that particular time that the golden days of youth were slipping by. He reveals in his notes that he was suffering very much from repressed desires. However his situation, financial prospects and the need for study made any permanent relationship unlikely. His parable starts humorously but shows eventually how much he was aware of just what sacrifices would be entailed if he pursued work and duty. It was the path he chose, and for so sensitive and warm-hearted a character the cost was great. He wrote:

Mine eyes were opened and I beheld a young man, and in his hands were many books, and he walked neither looking to the right, nor to the left, and maidens very fair smiled on him, but he passed them with scorn and to the temple of 'Wines - John Boyle- Spirits' he entered not in. And again he was in a very large chamber, with many like unto him, and an aged man vexed them sore with the writing of strange symbols and much words. And again he was within his chambers and the night was far spent, and deep did he study with many repetitions from a book of great learning, and at last in sore travail, he cried, 'I am a weary, I am a weary', and immediately a cloud of great darkness arose and covered the earth.

The vision passes and the youth is now old. His face is stern and he sits at a desk. Men come and go and bow before him and bring him milk in a glass, and mouldy bread. A voice from the darkness orders him to 'Work; work for the night cometh, when no man can work, and much study is a weariness of the soul.' Baird is prophetic here, and almost predicts the pain-filled last years of his life during the Second World War, when his health was so poor that he could take only the plainest of food and drink.

The carefree days of tri-cars and boyhood mayhem in Helensburgh must have seemed light years in the past when in 1909, aged twenty-one, Baird embarked on the first of a series of jobs as an engineering apprentice, part of his college course. The experiences were traumatic and instilled in him even more deeply a horror of poverty and of the grinding necessity which made men, capable of intellectual pursuits and of joy, into cogs in a souless industrial machine. This turned Baird into a lifelong socialist, a conviction which, in his case, was more emotional than practical. By natural inclination he was the lone pioneer with more than a hint of the enterprising capitalist, but, endearingly, he never forgot his links with the men in the workshop and later in life, while travelling by Daimler, he still donned a cloth cap as a symbol of solidarity.

The dark atmosphere was stamped on his memory, and he described it thus: 'the years of romance and youth were lost in sordid and mean lodgings, in soul destroying surroundings, under grey skies.' He trudged to work in the cold dawn through cobbled streets flanked by tenements where families lived on the breadline. Smoke from giant chimneystacks fouled the air, making the glimpses of the green slopes of the Campsie Fells on the skyline even more tantalizing. He was frequently coughing, choking with a cold, or just recovering from one. He wrote: 'What a wave of resentment and anger comes over me, even now, when I think of the awful conditions of work in those Glasgow factories - the sodden gloom, the bitter, bleak, cold rain, the slave-driven workers cooped in a vile atmosphere with the incessant roar and clatter of machinery from six in the morning to six at night, and then home to lodgings surrounded by sordid squalor, too worn out to move from my miserable bedroom.'[10]

Baird did not exaggerate. Glasgow, the busy industrial cockpit of the Empire at that time, had some of the worst working conditions in Europe. People laboured hard and faithfully for meagre return. During the First World War their efforts were second to none. But when they decided enough was enough, and organized themselves for industrial action, they were branded Bolsheviks and Red Clydesiders.

Working in the same conditions, though encouraged by the knowledge that for him it was probably only a passing phase, Baird understood how anarchists are spawned, and wrote:

> *But if I had been like most of the poor creatures who worked for me, in for a life sentence, I would certainly have become an anarchist and taken part with zeal in anything which would have mended - or ended - my lot. I would have joined any modern Guy Fawkes and blown to hell his Most Gracious Majesty, the King, the Royal Family, and all the Lords and Commons, in the firm belief that, whatever happened, nothing, not even death, could be worse than the fate to which these, my callous, indifferent rulers had doomed me. Such was my embittered outlook. The men themselves were not Socialists. They were, for the most part, indifferent, and took their conditions as an inevitable, natural phenomenon, like long and bitter winter weather, miserable but unalterable.* [11]

His first job was at Halley's Industrial Motors of Yoker, Clydebank, makers of vans, lorries and charabancs, in an era so close to coaches that their telegraphic address was 'Horseless, Glasgow'. And there he was under the direct supervision of a fierce old journeyman, known simply as Old Gibson, regarded by his workmates as 'a callous old bastard'. Baird said he was an independent, vindictive socialist with the most lurid flow of unprintable foul language.

Work started at 6 a.m. and normally stopped at 5.30 p.m., but incessant overtime meant he was rarely home before eight in the evening. He arrived full of ardour, willing to do well, but soon found his enthusiasm draining. He wrote: 'The work was absolutely soul destroying, monotonous drudgery. The first job I got was to chip, with a chisel, little grooves in a great pile of castings. I remember they were called "spring housings". Week after week, I chipped these little grooves, with all around me the most sordid conditions, in the winter, icy cold. The result was that my work was punctuated by perpetual ill-health.'[12]

Halley Motors shaped more than piles of castings. The youth from the manse and college found himself toughening, as, smarting under old Gibson's rasping tongue, he learned to fight back, to do a day's work with the best of them, and to discover a rough form of comradeship. In the years to come, people who had not known such hard labour were impressed by his appetite for work. Baird had the chance to.learn many lessons in practical survival; how, for example, the polished bourgeois could be routed by the unsophisticated tough guy who, in turn, was crushed by the rules of society. As big Gibson roared his abuse, 'Whit the hell are ye standing gaping there for? Dae ye take this for a bloody Sunday School treat?' there was no disputing the supremacy of the royal stag in his own domain. But this had its limitations. Baird wrote:

The chief of the research room was a public school and university man and endeavoured to keep some of his refinement. On one occasion he had the temerity to offer a piece of advice to Gibson. Big Gibson considered this an insufferable impertinence. I remember to this day the storm of abuse which descended on the superior research gentleman who fled, followed by a roar of 'Get to hell, ye hauf-biled toff.' He complained to the manager who got on well with big Gibson, and rebuked him gently- 'Aye, George, that's fine!You knock the bloody guts oot o' the stuck-up bastard. Then you get the sack and your wife and weans starve. Keep your daunder doon, the poor beggar does his best' There it was - lose your job and you and your family starve. There was no dole in those days.[13]

When Baird left Halley's in 1911, the reference from the shop foreman read: 'During the time J.L.Baird was in our employ I always found him most attentive to his duties. I have the greatest pleasure in recommending him as a very industrious, sober and efficient workman.' 'Industrious', 'sober' and 'efficient' were underlined.

Perhaps superfluously, considering his financial condition at the time, Baird and some friends, including Godfrey Harris and Guy 'Mephy' Robertson, made a bachelor's agreement signed at the Lodge, agreeing that, in the event of the marriage of one previous to the marriage of the others, he should pay ten shillings to the remaining signatories. The spirit of the boyhood camera club lingered.

Baird moved on to another famous automobile firm, Argyll's of Alexandria, Dunbartonshire, where he spent six months in the car drawing office and worked mainly on engine and chassis details and fittings for motor bodies. The reference from the chief draughtsman said he was persevering and industrious and anxious to get on. It ended, 'I shall be very glad to hear of his success and to answer any questions as to his ability.' Then it was off for a near two-year stint, until May 1913, as an apprentice draughtsman at the Springfield Electrical Works in Baltic Street, Glasgow. There he was mostly employed in the design and layout of switchgear and switchboards of all classes, both high and low tension. His new reference stressed that he had undertaken certain extra work of his own accord, to get further experience in other classes of work. Somewhere in between he managed to work in a shipyard and helped build the liner *Aquitania* on which, world-famous, he was to make a momentous trip to America twenty years later.

The long spell of hard labour in Clydeside workshops drew to a close, and Baird returned to college with relief, to receive his Associateship and Diploma. His hands were calloused. His jaw was set more firmly. He was twenty-five, an age by which some men were married, had children, and had settled into their lifelong mould. Baird was hungry for life, anxious to make his mark. But a deep-seated horror of the monotonous employment he had just endured made him postpone a decision about his immediate future. He knew what he intended that future to hold. It should be the fulfilment of a technology not yet invented, the boyhood dream of vision by wire, an obsession which never faded. His schoolboy experiments with the selenium cell had continued in a concentrated manner. The popular belief that television was something which just flitted back into his life in the early 1920s has no substance. He never lost sight of his goal. All his actions were designed to help him advance on that path.

The breakthrough had not yet arrived in 1914, and so he chose to spend another six months studying, this time as an undergraduate at Glasgow University. From 1913, much of the Royal Technical College's work was recognized to be of the level offered in independent universities, and an affiliation agreement dating from then meant that some college students were able to take degrees granted by the University of Glasgow. Baird's Associate-ship qualified him to take his BSc at the university after six months' attendance.

He started university just as Europe entered the throes of a convulsion which would forever destroy the measured, stately pace of western civilization. When the First World

War ended, the world would be a forcing ground of new scientific processes accelerating at an unprecedented speed, with John Logie Baird one of the foremost pacemakers.

NOTES
1   'A Decade of Progress 1964-1974', University of Strathclyde, Andersonian Library.
2   Andrew Boyle, *Only the Wind Will Listen,* Hutchinson, 1972, p. 37.
3   Baird, autobiographical notes, *Sermons, Soap and Television,* ch. 2, p. 1.
4   *Only the Wind Will Listen,* p. 46.
5   *Sermons, Soap and Television,* ch. 1, p. 14.
6   *Sermons, Soap and Television,* ch. 1, p. 14.
7   *Sermons, Soap and Television,* ch. 1, p. I 1.
8   *Sermons, Soap and Television,* ch. 1, p. 6.
9   *Sermons, Soap and Television,* ch. 1, p. 6.
10   *Sermons, Soap and Television,* ch. 2, p. 2.
I I   *Sermons, Soap and Television,* ch. 2, p. 2.
12   *Sermons, Soap and Television,* ch. 2, p. 2.
13   *Sermons, Soap and Television,* ch. 2, p. 3.

3
Diamonds and Undersocks

As the guns of 1914 opened up on the continent of
Europe, the Rev John Baird, now seventy-two, preached a
dark and fiery sermon from his Sabbath pulpit in
Helensburgh. While the mood of the nation was generally
one of optimism, with the prospect of an early victory, he
donned the authentic robe of the Old Testament prophet,
and thundered about the agony that lay ahead. He spoke
with a special sense of sadness and betrayal, as one who
loved German culture and philosophy. Just as the Hebrews
had had to stand against their tyrants, their Tiglath Pilezers,
their Sennacheribs, their Shalmanezers. The Germans now
had to face their Hohenzollerns. 'Watchman, what of the
night?' he thundered. 'It is indeed a dreadful night which
we are passing through. We have not gone this way
heretofore, with the future of our native land and of the
British Empire - we might also say - trembling in the
balance. The foundations of the Kingdom are shaken, and
when this war is ended, it will be a different Europe, for it is
a war of life or of death, for the one side or the other.'[1]

This ominous vision of the true nature of the conflict
which would lay waste the lives of a generation did not
filter through to many areas of society in the first few
months of the war. At Glasgow University Baird found the
atmosphere bright, even jolly. It proved to be one of the
happiest periods of his life. After the disciplinary
restrictions of the college and workshops, he was tasting
comparative freedom. He wrote: 'I had the sense not to
endeavour to cram and did the absolute minimum of work,
while heartily enjoying the society of my fellow students.
We had innumerable outings in the happy atmosphere that
can only be found among students.'[2]

Though he did not cram, he worked efficiently as usual,
tackling problems in his own distinctive way. Brigadier
A.Prain, then a fellow undergraduate in the university

engineering laboratory, recalls that part of the lab work entailed the writing up of experiments, illustrating them, when necessary, with diagrams of the apparatus used. Says Brigadier Prain:

John Baird scoffed at those of us who laboriously produced drawings and sketches. His notes were illustrated by photographs taken by himself. He was really an outstanding sort of person, even then. I treated him with a very great deal of - respect. He did better and knew more than most people and did not suffer fools gladly. When he tackled something he gave the impression it was being done better than anyone else could do. This was not something he tried to convey. It was a quality you noticed. One felt here was a man who knew where he was going, what he was doing, and just exactly how he was going to go about it.

Another fellow undergraduate was Archibald Thom, later Emeritus Professor of Engineering at Oxford, who remembers Baird as an inventive genius even then. He and Baird were part of a triumvirate who took turns copying lecture notes, had them duplicated and handed them round afterwards. Baird's efforts, says Professor Thom, were 'pretty awful'. He adds: 'He was really quite a fellow. The pages frequently had drawings round the edges and extremely rude, though often funny, remarks on various points made by the lecturer.'

The BSc should have been attained almost as a matter of course, as Baird was on top of his subjects, but, like many of his companions, he was fated never to take his degree. As the war rolled on, with the retreat from Mons, the hard-won victories on the Marne and the Aisne, and the First Battle of Ypres, Britain's young bloods clamoured to volunteer. Baird wrote: 'It was expected at first, and confidently predicted, that it would be over in a few months. Germany would give way. Germany would crack. Germany could not stand the strain; but it dragged on.' Early in 1915 he decided to join up, and wrote in his usual self-mocking vein:

Urged by some sense of duty, or possibly by the desire to appear well in the eyes of my friends, I presented myself at the recruiting office. A red-faced Glasgow 'keelie' in a badly fitting uniform stood at the door.

'Upstairs, first to the left', he shouted in a very broad accent. Upstairs a very raw and nervous young man sat by the door,

while at a desk a young officer filled up forms one by one. 'Take that pipe out of your mouth ' he roared at one lout, who was endeavouring to show his sangfroid by puffing at a pipe 'Name, age, occupation? Now then. In there for a medical examination.'

The medical examiner, a shrewd-looking old gentleman examined my skinny form with sad and disapproving eyes tapping my scanty chest and placed his ear to listen to my wheezy breathing. An assistant ran a tape measure round me and shouted the paltry inches with contempt.

'Do you suffer from colds very much?' said the doctor.

'Yes,' said I, 'a great deal.'

'Every winter you are knocked up, I suppose?' he asked, then grunted 'Aye, aye, umphm! You can dress now.'

He went to his desk and wrote something on a piece of paper then stamped it with a large rubber stamp. When I examined it, I read in large red letters 'Unfit for any service'. I buttoned up my waistcoat and went downstairs. The red-faced 'keelie' was surprised.

'Hello,' he said, 'What's up? You're back quick.'

'Yes,' I said, 'I am unfit for any service.'

'You are lucky,' he ejaculated, 'what about the price of a pint'. [2]

I gave him a shilling and took my way to the tram - lucky to be unfit for any service.[3]

At an unexpected loose end, Baird answered an advertisement and became assistant mains engineer with the Clyde Valley Electrical Power Company, which was vitally linked with local munitions work. It must have seemed like a bad dream, for he was back again in the daily and nightly grind of the miserable workshop. Though authorized to wear the War Service badge, it is not clear under what auspices he held this post. Despite the failure of his first attempt to join the forces, he received on 25 February 1916 a card stating that he had been attested and transferred to the Army Reserve until required for further service. Other such cards, still in existence, show that two months later he appeared before a recruiting board in Glasgow, which declared him unfit for any military service, while on 28 December one in Stirling passed him for service at home. There may have been more; he never mentioned this string of medicals. It is probable that, with word of friends killed or wounded at the Front, he felt that he too must go. Local newspapers of the period published pages of obituaries of those who had been killed, emotions were subsequently at fever pitch, and many young men who, for one reason or another, did not at first pass muster, tried their luck with medical boards elsewhere.

This early link with Army Reserve had an intriguing sequel some years later, in 1928-9, when he mysteriously appeared as a reserve officer in uniform at a time when he was supposedly wholeheartedly engaged in developing television. Baird reputedly wore the double pips of a lieutenant, the same modest commissioned rank given to another inventor, Guglielmo Marconi, when he joined the Italian Army in 1915 to help with communications at the Front. For a time Baird seems to have worked in the Yoker area, where once he had been an apprentice at Halley Motors, but for most of the war he was based at Rutherglen, near Glasgow, operating from Farme Cross Sub-Station.

I had a telephone in my bedroom and, if the electrical supply failed, I had to get out of bed and attend to it. It was a horrible job. My memory conjures up visions of standing the whole night in the rain, cold and miserable, while Stibbs, the chief ganger, and his men dug holes in the road to find faulty cables. Trying to placate a gang of angry Irish labourers at 4 o'clock in the morning, when they wanted to stop the job and go home, was anything but pleasant. Sometimes in the night drunken fights started. I remember one particular night, Jimmy McGauchy knocking Billy Macilvaney down a manhole and both finally departing with roars of pain and anger, and volleys of cursing, and all the time steady rain falling and a bitter wind blowing. Sordid, miserable work, punctuated by repeated colds and influenza. I wanted more money. I got 30 shillings a week and I was unable to get a better job because I was always ill. Finally I decided it was hopeless and I had better try and start some business which was less strenuous and in which I would be my own master.[4]

Baird and his favourite writer, H.G. Wells, had more than science in common. There was a definite streak of the Kipps-style Wellsian hero in the inventor, which made him seek a fortune in anything from boot polish to pots of jam. Had he been content to sidestep his destiny, he would have been a marked success as a buccaneering commercial opportunist with a flair for advertising. Back in 1913 his college magazine had published a humorous article of his entitled

J.L.B. at the Rutherglen Sub-Station of the Clyde Valley Power Company 1915.

First woman sandwich-board carriers advertising Baird's undersock venture in Glasgow 1915-18.

'How to Make Money', which foreshadowed some of these bizarre ideas which he actually put into operation. There was frequently a vein of near-Keystone Cop comedy in some of his ventures. Though some of his products were amusing, they nevertheless made him a small fortune. For a period his 30 shilling wage at the power station was augmented by an enormous £200 a week. His first thought was a cure for piles. The idea came from Billy Barnes, a power station attendant and former stud groom, who had a specific cure which he swore by. Baird wrote: 'Unfortunately for Billy's pile cure project, I was a chronic sufferer and tried it on myself, with devastating results - I was unable to sit down for some days.'

He did find a marketable commodity when he tackled another of his infirmities - cold feet! This ailment was invariably caused by damp, and Baird mused that while civilization had come up with the watertight boot, it had neglected another fundamental, the watertight sock, so he set about remedying this oversight. He heated socks to burning point, but found them damp again within a very short time. Wads of paper between the foot and the sock did the trick, however, and the relief was great. A bewildered landlady found him with sheets of toilet paper wrapped round his feet, but clearly the project had to be advanced beyond this rudimentary and impractical stage.

Papers under socks were not feasible, so I broached the sock maker and, after many peregrinations, discovered two things. Firstly, the Trade does not recognise such things as socks. Socks are 'gent's half-hose'. Secondly, the home of 'gent's half-hose' is Hinckley. From Hinckley I got six dozen specially made unbleached half-hose. Then I sprinkled them with borax and put them in large envelopes printed with 'The Baird Undersock' and containing a pamphlet describing their advantages and containing testimonials.[5]

Baird's product was worn beneath the ordinary sock and was damp-proof. He rented a one-room office at 196 St Vincent Street, in Glasgow's busy city centre, where he masterminded the project, even adding a few home-made testimonials to speed the under- sock on its way. He turned a back-street attic above an hotel into a tiny factory, churning out the socks himself by night and going round the shops with them, when he could find time, the following day. An advertisement for representatives in the *Glasgow*

Herald brought dozens of replies, and soon he had men travelling all over Scotland and as far south as London, where Selfridge's bought six dozen pairs. Old cronies found socks arriving through the post in the hope that they might push them among friends. Archibald Thom got a pair, and even the future Brigadier Prain, now at the Front. Baird made advertising history when he sent a squad of women round the city streets with sandwich boards. Newspapers used pictures with the caption 'First Sandwich Women in Glasgow'. He followed this with another eye-catching stunt, a lifesize wooden model of the new armoured tank, standing almost nine feet high and almost twice as long, with realistic side guns, which trundled through the streets propelled from inside by two hard-working men. The tank bore the proud legend: 'The Baird Undersock Keeps the Soldier's Feet in Perfect Health.'

The undersocks sold in chemists' shops, but the biggest sales were in drapery stores. When the Polytechnic, the Selfridge's of Glasgow, bought a dozen pairs apparently more out of curiosity than need, Baird was perplexed to find they were not on display. He swiftly rallied his friends, handed them money for purchasing, and had them wend their way to the store, where the astonished sales staff found themselves facing an unprecendented demand. The result was immediate and gratifying. A buyer was rushed to St Vincent Street where three times he found the office closed. A note was left and Baird obligingly turned up and sold fifty dozen pairs on the spot. The store had a special table set up in an entrance and a front window bedecked with the Baird undersock. 'The result, of course, was an immediate rush by the inquisitive public. Not only so, but Copeland and Lye and the other big stores wanted to be in on this new line, which was booming at the Polytechnic! My whole stock was sold at once and I booked further substantial orders.'[6] Word of the commercial activities of their assistant mains engineer had meanwhile reached the Clyde Valley Electrical Power Company, and there were irritable rumblings from top management. He worked well enough, but it was unsettling having an employee who looked set fair to make much more than they did, and who they probably thought was growing too big for his undersocks. Matters deteriorated when Baird used the Power Station for an experiment more befitting to a medieval alchemist. He decided to imitate nature and create a diamond. The idea was not as far-fetched as it may seem, for the Royal Society had recently discussed methods of making diamonds, and it is possible that Baird even had a link with a prolific Helensburgh inventor called James Ballantyne Hannay. Baird is known to have sought financial backing for his early TV experiments from local businessmen, and it is a fascinating possibility that support, and the idea for the diamond, may have come from Hannay.

A self-taught chemist and metallurgist, Hannay was thirty-four years older than Baird, lived at Cove, near Helensburgh, and was an old boy of Baird's school, Larchfield. He had a factory in Sword Street, Possilpark, a district of Glasgow, not far from the Royal Technical College. His most controversial invention consisted of what could be the world's first artificial diamonds. These were produced in 1880, and were sent to the British Museum where they caused heated debate. Only recently the whole question of Hannay's diamonds was raised again, with experts stating that they were indeed valid stones. It is unlikely that two such restless innovators, living in such close proximity, were unaware of each other. In nature diamonds are created by extremely high pressure and temperature. Baird tried to duplicate these conditions artificially by electrically exploding a rod of carbon embedded in concrete.

> *I got a thick carbon bar and filed it down into a thin rod in the centre, then I attached a wire to each end and embedded the whole thing in a large iron pot. I connected the wires to a switch which, when closed, put them straight across the power station bus bars. My idea was to pass a stupendous, sudden current through the carbon, so as to generate enormous heat and pressure. I chose a good time and then, when no-one was about, closed the switch. There was a dull thud from the pot, a cloud of smoke, and then the main current breaker tripped, and the whole of the power went off.*

A sizeable section of Glasgow was plunged into darkness, but Baird had anticipated the possibility of the experiment backfiring, and soon had the plant going again. He did not manage to remove his tell-tale wires, however, and 'some unpleasant explanations followed'.[7] The experiment proved inconclusive. In the excitement Baird forgot about the pot and it vanished. He commented: 'Perhaps it is today lying in some forgotten rubbish heap, a pot of cement with a priceless diamond embedded in it.' What the hard-headed senior engineers made of this Arabian Nights exploit in their down-to-earth power station is not on record, but from then on their junior engineer was regarded, in his own words, as rather a dangerous character. The diamond episode occurred just after the end of the war. Now that hostilities were over, Baird scented freedom, though friends and relatives thought that discarding his 30 shillings a week job was irresponsible madness. He would disrupt his career and throw away all his expensive training. He believed, however, that if he had remained on the engineering path he would have died. 'If the choice was between hopeless slavery and madness, I preferred madness; there seemed no middle course.' Colds and chills helped him make the break. His health was so precarious at the time that Nairn, the chief engineer, had summed it up by writing: 'We cannot give Baird a better job - he's always ill.' Also, news of his extracurricular commercial activities was continuing to rankle. Baird decided: 'I had read Matthew Arnold's poetry and I determined, in his words, to "depart on the ocean of life anew." ' He tendered his resignation just in time, he believed, to forestall getting the sack.[8]

The year was 1919. His undersock business had become so successful that in September 1918 he had officially formed the Baird Undersock Company. The registration certificate, No. 15348, was located recently by the authors in Register House, Edinburgh, and gives Baird as sole partner, his address at the time 17 Blairbeth Road, Rutherglen. He had been in business since 1 May 1917. When he was released from the power station he was approaching his thirty-first birthday. Business was booming, netting £200 a week, of which he was able to bank £195. And, perhaps even more important, he had found romance. The pretty, dark-haired girl was more than ten years his junior. They met in a library, and both fell deeply in love. Marriage, though, was out of the question at that time because of his poor health. They never would be man and wife, though she would play a strange part in his life for some years to come.

He was now supporting himself solely from his business enterprise. To undersocks, he added sidelines ranging from 'Osmo' boot polish to solid scent, and other aids to civilized living. It seemed that the world was his oyster, but the old enemy swooped. A crippling cold which developed bronchial complications knocked him out. He landed in a nursing home and watched in mounting frustration as his business, so much a one-man show, suffered. There was no alternative; he wound up his company, found he had £1,600 profit, and realized that in a year and a half he had made more than he would have done in twelve years at the power station. The urgent problem was now his health. He must escape the Scottish climate. Like his fellow countryman, Robert Louis Stevenson, he bade farewell to Scotland's mists and rain and, heading for a place in the sun where he might labour in comparative peace, set sail for Trinidad. Baird's departure for the Caribbean affords an opportunity to appraise not only his own progress towards the realization of his goal, but also the steps which other pioneers had taken along the same road. Many of his contemporaries believed, wrongly, that after he had struggled for so many years in order to become a skilled electrical engineer he threw it all away in the pursuit of quick profits. To them his work on television in Hastings a few years later seemed to be merely the latest and most promising of a string of schemes designed to make a fortune. It will be seen, when the competition he encountered is examined, that it suited Baird to allow this view to persist. He found it politic to pretend that his work on television had very little substance prior to his experiments in Hastings. In fact the reverse was true, as will be demonstrated by details which have now come to light. Of course, he hoped that television might one day make him rich but, when he had to make the choice, he showed his true colours and threw out the chance of becoming a millionaire. He left others to cash in on his early work while, untrammelled by their demands to stand still and consolidate, he wandered into new lines of research. It now appears that from the start Baird basically sought money for the prime reason of gaining freedom to persevere with electrical vision. College had taught him the fundamentals of his calling, but his dream subject was not on the syllabus. There was little that anyone could teach him in this field, and so he researched alone. His hotch-potch of commercial ventures were merely stepping-stones to television.

One looks in vain through his autobiographical sketch for any mention of his early experiments, but occasionally he let facts slip elsewhere which show that work had been going on steadily since 1912, and there are people alive today who can corroborate this. Baird was often several jumps ahead of the position he chose to reveal, and when his veil of secrecy is pierced an exceptionally single-minded, arduous and long-term operation is revealed. An article in the *Daily Express* of 8 January 1926, in which Baird predicts that before long he would be able to transmit the finish of the Derby and other topical events, contains this revelation:

> *He began his experiments in 1912. He met with great difficulties - lack of capital, shortness of time caused by the need to earn a living, and the knowledge that all over the globe, some of the best brains of the scientific world, backed by the possession of splendidly-equipped laboratories and limitless capital, were trying to complete the discovery in front of him. He saved his earnings, however, and worked far into the night, sometimes having to stop experimenting because of the strain.*

So much for tales, many of them encouraged by Baird himself, that television was an enthusiasm that he just happened to remember in 1923, and started on almost from scratch. The same article makes another telling point. One of Baird's leading business partners in television was Belfast-born Captain Oliver George Hutchinson, whom Baird consistently describes as having met for the first time in London in 1922. Yet the press article states: 'Then Captain Hutchinson, who had met him at the Argyll works in 1912, came to his assistance and found capital when the inventor was in financial straits.' Close associates confirm that they gleaned the impression that both Baird and Hutchinson had been apprentices in the same workshop, adding credence to the press story.[9] This sort of anomaly makes one wary of accepting at face value those accounts of early television which Baird intended for public consumption. The scenes described are probably accurate enough, but the dates, places and even the people were changed on occasions to protect the inventor's interests. He compiled his autobiographical notes in the summer of 1941, but portions were rewritten from articles already published in newspapers and magazines years before, versions to which he was therefore committed. The birth of television had already become something of a legend and had passed into the history books. It would have been difficult, and at that time, with the war raging, pointlessly controversial to do an about turn and change those often quoted facts and dates.

One of Baird's earliest biographers, R.Tiltman, writing in 1933, managed to draw Baird on some of his early attempts.[10] He described how Baird carried out a great deal of experimental work involving electricity and the construction of selenium cells while attending college and university. This was not undertaken in the academic laboratories; the regular curriculum precluded original experiments. He depicts Baird, instead, operating in the makeshift lab of his boyhood, the kitchen of the Lodge in Helensburgh. There he apparently tried to devise a system of talking pictures and made sunlight ring a bell. Egon Larsen, who was to know Baird over many years up to 1946, the year of Baird's death, also recounts some of Baird's early work in television. [11]

Renewed interest in Baird in his home town recently brought to light a significant incident of 1911, which strongly echoes the telephone scrape of 1901 and also involves a horse-drawn vehicle. It seems that for over a decade Baird, with his equipment, was the unwitting scourge of Helensburgh horse bus drivers. The event suggests that at twenty-three he was extending some form of communication experiments, though hard-pressed by studies and long hours at the workshop in Glasgow. Mr Alex Grierson, of Arrochar, near Helensburgh, was then employed as a bus boy collecting threepenny fares and applying the wheel brakes when necessary on the horse bus, a two-in-hand owned by Waldie & Co. Mr Grierson recalled in 1979 that Baird had erected aerials and antennae on the side of a building in William Street. One of these sprang forward, buffeted by high winds gusting up from the Clyde estuary, and whacked the hat from the driver, 'Tartan' McWilliams, forcing young Grierson to haul on the brakes to stop the horses bolting. He recalls that the air was blue when Baird appeared and was reprimanded. Mr Grierson was adamant about the date, 1911. This story is so similar to Baird's, set in 1901, that one might think that Baird had transposed a good story. This, however, is unlikely, as he first recounted the 1911 story in an article entitled 'My Tough Times' in *Answers* magazine on 19 February 1927, a date early enough for locals to dispute it and for his own immediate family to recall the incident. Sir J.J. Percy, later a director of Baird Television Ltd, wrote an article for *Motor News* of 26 June 1926 in which he quoted Baird as saying that he had been carrying out experiments more than ten years before (i.e. 1915). This is supported by a startling account of the inventor in Yoker, Glasgow, in 1915 . In "*Both Sides of the Burn*", published in 1966, the author, W. Imrie, a history master at the local secondary school, states that Baird was in lodgings at a terraced house, Kildonan, 17 Coldingham Avenue, Yoker, the district where he had once worked as an apprentice and was now employed at the local power station. In this house, he is said to have achieved the first practicable method of transmitting live pictures. The equipment comprised a tea chest, a biscuit tin, scraps of cardboard, fourpenny lenses bought at Turners cycle shop, some darning needles, string, sealing wax, wire, glue and a secondhand electric motor. The total cost was a few shillings. It was also claimed that the picture he obtained, though indistinct, covered the distance between one room and another, 'but the achievement was unquestionable'.[12]

Attempts to trace Mr Imrie have been unsuccessful. The equipment he describes is almost identical to that used by Baird eight years later, and one might think that the account had been confused with the Hastings experiment but for the mention of the local cycle shop. That house in Yoker was the scene of the first of many clashes between Baird and landlords. These long-suffering individuals watched and listened in trepidation throughout Baird's career as explosions rocked rooms, smoke seeped under doors, and blinding light flashed through windowpanes. He was not the ideal lodger. The son of Baird's landlord at Yoker, a prominent doctor living in Sutton Coldfield, remembered how his mother quarrelled with Baird when he chipped the sink in his room after dropping objects into it. Several later accounts make the point that in TV experiments at Hastings Baird tended to use the sink as a toolbox. Evidence for the experiments at Yoker may seem circumstantial, but reinforcement comes from Mrs Marguerite Key, of Bournemouth, who was acquainted in the late twenties with a Miss Buchanan, an aunt of Baird's. This aunt, once a missionary in China, recalled that in his student days and afterwards her nephew tinkered with makeshift materials that sound distinctly familiar. Mrs Key says: 'One time she spoke of the great disappointment he had been to his family. (This at a time when he was at the height of his fame.) When he should have been studying or applying himself in some way to his advancement, he was forever occupied with his biscuit tins and bits of wire.'

So it seems that, even while he was embroiled with his under- sock business, Baird persevered with the equipment usually associated with his later experiments. Mr Colin

Graham of Ibrox, Glasgow, worked as one of Baird's salesmen from the office in St Vincent Street. As well as the Baird undersock his wares included black boot polish, unsweetened chocolate from Cowan & Co., and Pall Mall cigarettes. Mr Graham said that Baird rented an attic in the Bath Hotel, Bath Street, a short walk from his office, where Mr Graham helped him punch holes in cardboard discs, which he now recognizes as Nipkow discs for TV scanning. The time was 1918-19. And it was about this period that Baird apparently drew a boyhood friend in Helensburgh into a mysterious scheme involving the utmost secrecy. Alex Horn was the founder of a prosperous local plumbing firm. The family lived first at Stanwix Villa in East Montrose Street, not far from the Bairds' family home; later, they moved to a larger house on the banks of the Clyde, previously occupied by Andrew Bonar Law, the future Prime Minister. Young Alex Horn was one of the gang who used to gather at the Lodge to decorate the walls of Baird's room with paintings and drawings, or to go boating on the Clyde. Alex became a civil engineer but on the death of an elder brother he entered the family business and about 1919 found himself spending much of his spare time working on a particular task for Baird. His widow, Mrs Ruby Horn, remembers how her husband, sworn to absolute secrecy, made components for his friend.

The work had started before Mr Horn's marriage in 1919, and Mrs Horn says that even at this juncture Baird was being helped financially in his project by two of her husband's wealthy clients. Alex Horn laboured on his clandestine task well into the night, sometimes until 3 a.m. He died in an accident in October 1926, and in retrospect Mrs Horn was not too happy about the time he had spent away from her and the family. She recalls that he turned out hundreds of meticulously made components, about half an inch by five-eighths of an inch, of either nickel or chrome, mostly between 1920 and 1922 after Baird had returned from Trinidad. They were rectangular in shape, no bigger than a postage stamp, but she never did discover their purpose. However, in a strange sequel she described them to an engineering lecturer at Melbourne University, who told her that they sounded remarkably like radar components.

This startling remark, and Mrs Horn's account, were made before anyone had suggested a link between Baird and radar. Mrs Horn dismissed it at the time, but if this story seems unlikely, in the light of the date and of accepted history, readers will find that the facts grow stranger still when the details are investigated more closely.

Those who believe that he developed the world's first true television pictures in just a couple of years at Hastings in 1923 quite illogically proceed to write him off and relegate him to the minor league of television pioneers. There is something distasteful about the way many of Baird's learned contemporaries virtually fell over themselves praising foreign inventors, most of whom had accomplished far less, while they consistently belittled him. His detractors were saying, in effect, that scientists and researchers they vastly admired, who had laboured without success in well- equipped labs and workshops, had been beaten to the draw by someone who then proved at a loss to take his invention much further. Baird was a brilliant synthesizer, as well as an innovator. Random possibilities that had struck blind alleys in the hands of others, he made work. He was to prove this repeatedly throughout his life. Nevertheless the suggestion that his first pictures were not just the result of a few months' intense effort, but the fruit of almost a decade's work, does sound surprising at first, considering that in 1912, when Baird probably started, a talking radio service was still almost a decade away.

Though Marconi made his famous transmission of the letter 'S' 1,700 miles across the Atlantic from Poldhu in Cornwall to St Johns in Newfoundland in 1901, the letter was tapped out in morse. The first real radio broadcast, as we know it, occurred in an almost random experiment conducted by the American Lee De Forrest and his assistant John V.L. Hogan from a laboratory in Manhattan. De Forrest, a Yale graduate who had been turned down for a job by Marconi and went on to form a powerful rival company, capped the work of the Englishman, Sir J. Ambrose Fleming. Fleming created a two-element thermionic valve, the Diode, which could detect and amplify radio signals. De Forrest, showing Baird-style improvisation, used a piece of wire and a lamp from a Christmas tree to make his three-element thermionic valve known as an Audion or Triode, which proved to be the amplifier the world was seeking. The year was 1906. The following spring he and Hogan let loose their first 'broadcast', as De Forrest called it: 'We'll just let her go free. We'll broadcast it.' A record of the William Tell overture went out over the air to land, like the proverbial archer's shot, 'they knew not where'. In fact, the first recipient was an astounded wireless operator at Brooklyn Navy Yard four miles away, who heard the rousing tones of William Tell ringing through his earphones instead of the usual monotonous dots and dashes. [13]

In fact the quest for television had been following fast on the heels of radio, and had been under way for half a century when Baird announced his breakthrough at Hastings. For centuries mankind had dreamed of seeing from afar. Through legends and fairytales the crystal ball that conjured up images, or the magic mirror that clouded and cleared to present a picture of a far-off scene, proved firmly rooted in the mind of man. The theme was so persistent that it appears to be an almost Jungian archetype, one of those all-pervading, collective ideas with the power to shape events. It came flooding up in the nineteenth century from the subconscious of the men of many lands, Americans, Irishmen, Italians, Germans, Russians, Frenchmen and Britons. Even Sir Walter Scott joined in the act. A prophetic short story, set in Edinburgh featured an Italian doctor who showed visitors moving pictures of their friends. His magic mirror oscillated until the picture grew steady and clear, just as in modern TV. In the 1880s Albert Robida, a French author and illustrator, fantasizing on the future, came up with some astonishingly accurate predictions. These included the 'Telephonoscope', set in a viewing booth in which a caller could see the person he was telephoning. Robida also depicted a form of Open University in which a girl student sat at home with her books gazing at an oval screen on which a lecturer appeared with a blackboard. As a change he portrayed light entertainment, with comely dancing girls on a screen. In 1878 a cartoon by George du Maurier in *Punch 's Almanack* showed an elderly victorian couple holding telephone mouthpieces, talking to their daughter in Ceylon. She appears on a wide screen with her family playing tennis in the background.

Though impressive, these examples were nevertheless only dreams. However, for years a few practical people had been systematically laying the groundwork. Baird's initial success does not seem quite so singular when one realizes that some of these vital first steps were taken by fellow Scots. As early as 1753, the year after the American philosopher-statesman Benjamin Franklin demonstrated the electrical nature of lightning with his famous kite and key experiment, an anonymous writer to a Scottish magazine suggested, probably for the first time, that electrical currents might be used to transmit messages. By 1816 the Englishman Sir Francis Ronalds had set up what was probably the world's first working telegraph in his garden at Hammersmith in London. A mixture of lettered discs was moved by clockwork at one end, while electrical impulses triggered and lifted lettered pith balls which appeared in synchronization at the other. A German mathematician, Karl Gauss, later used different strengths of current to deflect a magnetic needle indicating different letters of the alphabet; and in 1837 Samuel Morse, an American artist, built and demonstrated his electric telegraph using the system of dots and dashes now known as morse code. These were produced primitively at first by electrical impulses activating a lever with a pencil on the end. But it was a little-known Scotsman, Alexander Bain, who made the first big leap towards television with his plan for messages by facsimile, or accurate reproduction of an image transmitted from one place to another. This was announced in his British patent of 1843, and was intended to avoid the need for coding.

Bain, one of thirteen children of a crofter from Watten, Caithness, was barely educated, yet soon he was posing a threat to the American hegemony of the great Samuel Morse. As a child he made imaginary clocks, using bits of heather as springs and mechanisms. He became apprenticed to a clockmaker, but, after hearing a lecture on light, heat and electric fluid in 1830 when he was twenty, he grew fascinated by electricity. He moved to London where he produced the world's first electric clock in 1838 and that same year manufactured a model of his electrical printing telegraph. The process of creativity involved was similar to the famous example of Samuel Taylor Coleridge, who fell asleep in the summer of 1797 while reading a prose passage by Samuel Purchas on Kubla Khan and woke to write without conscious effort the famous fifty-four lines beginning 'In Xanadu did Kubla Khan' Bain dozed off after experimenting unsuccessfully on his telegraph far into the night, and awoke at his bench with a telegraph process complete and clear in his head. Bain's telegraph involved a transmitting metal stylus which traced or scanned parallel lines across metal letters on an insulating wooden block. At the receiver a similar stylus duplicated the motions of the transmitting one, marking out the letters on conductive electrochemical recording paper, so that a word or phrase could be accurately reproduced. In no way was it direct vision, but it was pointing in the right direction. Electricity was being used to recreate an outline miles from its source. As early as 1846 he installed a telegraph line along the railway between Edinburgh and Glasgow. He also used an electric clock in Edinburgh as a 'master' to synchronize a 'slave' in Glasgow, so that both were exactly in step. In 1846, at Lille in France, Bain demonstrated a telegraph system, sending messages at the rate of 19,500 words per hour over a line more than 1,000 miles in length. Two years later he was in America and soon had electrochemical telegraph lines operating between New York and Boston, Boston and Burlington, Ogdensburgh and Portland, Troy and Saratoga, New York and Buffalo. But his American experiences fore shadowed those of Baird's almost eighty years later. He faced constant harrassment from the influential Morse Co., who finally obtained an injunction against him; the Federal Court of Pennsylvania ruled that Bain's patent infringed that granted to Morse in 1840. Back in Britain, he found lesser men afraid of his talent, closing official doors on him. He never gave up, and as an old man sought the secret of perpetual motion. He died comparatively poor in 1877, though the Gladstone government had awarded him a civil list pension and the Royal Society of London made him a grant of £150 for his pioneer work.[14]

An Englishman, Frederick Bakewell, improved on some aspects of Bain's work a couple of years later, adding to the performance by transmitting drawings and maps. But his complex synchronization system made it unsuitable for everyday use. Some years later an Italian, the Abbe Giovanni Caselli, designed a facsimile system incorporating principles developed by Bain and Bakewell. Metal foil was scanned and a reproduction was signalled over a wire, to appear on chemically sensitized paper. The results were excellent, owing to the Abbe's meticulous attention to mechanical detail. In 1862 he successfully transmitted four lines of Dante from an assistant in Livorno to Florence, in exactly the same handwriting. He also sent a portrait of the poet over the wire. Caselli's system was quickly in demand, and he moved to France. Soon his Pantelegraph was operating on railways between Lyon and Paris, and Lyon and Marseilles. At a time when photographers were hiding under cloth covers and taking long exposures, the French public were able to send telegraphed illustrations and even letters in their own handwriting to friends hundreds of miles away. The service, however, was abandoned around 1870, a possible casualty of the Franco-Prussian War.

The scientific base for the growth of television was growing more fertile each year. A Scottish physicist, James Clerk Maxwell, followed the work of Michael Faraday in demonstrating the link between magnetism and electricity. He showed that electro- magnetic waves travelled in a similar pattern to light and estimated that they travelled at the same speed as light - about 186,000 miles per second. He believed, correctly, therefore, that light was part of the electromagnetic spectrum. The natural corollary was that electromagnetic waves too might travel through the air 'wire-less', a fact which was demonstrated practically by the Hamburg-born physicist and engineer Heinrich Hertz in 1888.

Meanwhile another Scot, Alexander Graham Bell, who had emigrated to America, developed a telephone in 1875-6. If sounds could now be sent electrically, why not vision? Bell himself saw the possibilities and spoke of adding vision to his invention. The discovery of the light-variable qualities of selenium just a couple of years before was an added spur. A cell made of selenium would have photoelectric properties, acting for vision as a microphone does for sound. The race was on with a vengeance. At that time the goal was not called television, but a new art which took several names, 'the electrical telescope' or 'telectroscope'. The British Patent Office used the term 'telescopy' until 1908.

As might be expected, the first ideas were sometimes weird and wonderful. They varied from huge mosaics of selenium cells to walls of cells made of electromagnets with silvered surfaces to polarize light beams on a screen. The innovators were a varied crew, ranging from the French lawyer Constantin Senlecq, who in 1877 suggested reproducing tonal shades derived from a camera obscura, to Denis Redmond, of Dublin, who announced plans for a multi-circuit of selenium and platinum. Redmond's scheme of 1879 was ingenious and, though elementary, might have been a basis for true television. [15] Other inventors in the field sound like a roll call from the United Nations: De Pavia, Ayrton and Perry, Le Blanc, Carey, Sawyer, Szezepanik, von

Jaorsky, Frankenstein and many others right up to 1920, when a Major Baden-Powell, a cousin of the hero of Mafeking, also made a bid.

In December 1880 Oliver Joseph Lodge, later Sir Oliver Lodge, pioneer of wireless tuning, lectured at the Royal Institution in London, on 'The Relation between Electricity and Light'. Concluding his lecture Lodge stated, 'I must allude to what may very likely be the next striking popular discovery, the transmission of light by electricity; I mean the transmission of views and pictures by means of the electric wire.' Sir Oliver was to become very friendly with Baird from 1926 on, an important friendship which will be discussed later.[16] The Royal Institution, made aware of television by Lodge in 1880, was to be the first public body who sent representatives to witness J.L. Baird's television demonstration, at 22 Frith Street, Soho, London on Tuesday, 26 January 1926.

Many of the ideas of that time were purely theoretical and never left the drawing board. It was soon clear that the problems were of a vastly more complex nature than the reproduction of a single two-dimensional illustration. Three-dimensional real life would have to be reproduced with the attendant problems of light and shade. Even more perplexing was the question of scanning. It sometimes took up to ten minutes to scan a complete facsimile illustration, yet television would require pictures to be broken up, transmitted and reconstituted at the rate of at least ten per second in order, as in a cinematograph, to obtain persistence of vision. Even today, with twenty-five images per second, there is still a hint of TV flicker. All this would involve meticulous synchronization of transmitting and receiving signals, with the minimum of a million electrical impulses per second. The obstacles must have seemed almost as great as those involved in reaching the moon. In 1890 a publication called *The Electrician* sadly mused that the problem was unlikely to have any practical solution, adding: 'There is more hope of seeing through a brick wall than of seeing through a copper wire.'[17]

The press of the period swung from one extreme to another, one day predicting a brilliant future for electrical vision, the next stressing its impossibility. Individuals, however, were already making significant moves in the right direction. For example, an unknown twenty-three-year-old student of natural sciences in Berlin devised an ingenious and practical method of scanning, which Baird later utilized. In 1883 Paul Nipkow, a cherub-faced young man with a huge quiff of uncombed hair who came from Lauenburg in Pomerania, experimented with a disc perforated with holes; a year later, with German patent No. 30,105, he supplied what the American technical and electronics historian George Shiers has termed 'the master patent in the television field' [18]

Nipkow's scheme for an 'electric telescope' proved to be the basis for all the first television schemes throughout the world, though he never achieved any practical pictures himself. Nipkow suggested transmitting images onto a disc which contained a spiral of twenty-four holes round the circumference. The apertures were so positioned that, as the disc revolved at speed, each hole vertically scanned a line of the image, allowing different light intensities through to a selenium cell. As one hole swept over a segment of the picture, the next in sequence tackled the portion next to it, until the complete subject image had been scanned. Pictures were reconstituted by a similar disc, synchronized and whirling round in the receiver. Like so many others of the period, his effort was theoretical. Nipkow apparently built no apparatus and the patent lapsed. Four years later another German, Professor Lazare Weiller, suggested using a drum with tilted mirrors to scan objects with a spot of light. This idea, proposed even earlier by an Englishman, Llewellyn B. Atkinson, would also be used by Baird in the early 1930s. In 1897 an important new factor intervened. A German, Karl Ferdinand Braun, developed the cathode ray tube. The cathode is the negative terminal of an electrical source; when it is placed in a vacuum, it emits streams of particles which we call electrons. Braun made one end of his tube fluorescent and used metal plates inside to deflect the rays or streams of electrons, which then traced their path with a luminous curve on the fluorescent screen. This was in fact the oscilloscope, which has a wide range of modern uses.

Now, it seemed, the way was clear to abandon ideas of cumbersome mechanisms and to develop direct electronic vision. But this would not be practicable for many years to come. Cathode ray tubes were just not up to the stringent demands of television until at least the 1930s, though this did not deter some notable pioneers from experimenting with them. The first were probably Professor Max

Dieckmann and Gustave Glage, who worked with Braun. It seems that Braun was not enthusiastic about his tubes being considered for television, which at the time was considered on a par with seeking perpetual motion. But these two researchers developed a facsimile-style system for transmitting line drawings and type characters onto a Braun tube. The scheme was bold, but still utilized the Alexander Bain idea of scanning metal templates. [19]

In Imperial Russia the cathode ray tube was also receiving serious attention. In 1907 Professor Boris Rosing of the Technological Institute in St Petersburg combined mechanical scanning with a cathode ray tube and provided the world's first hint of true television. His mixed mechanical transmitter/electronic receiver system resulted in faint patterns with no light or shade. It was a start, however, and around him Rosing gathered a precocious band of students, two of whom, Vladimir Kosma Zworykin and David Sarnoff, were to emigrate to America, where they developed all-electronic black and white television by 1932, becoming rivals to Baird.

Television was taking shape but, despite so many insights into its processes, it remained mostly theoretical. An example of this was the brilliant exposition of a TV system of the future given by a Scots electrical engineer, Archibald Campbell-Swinton, as early as 1908. In a letter to *Nature* on 18 June that year he outlined plans for electronic television. On 7 November, three years later, in an address to the Rontgen Society, he expanded the idea, virtually outlining the basic electronic television system adopted by the BBC in 1937. Some have suggested that Campbell- Swinton may have tried to make the apparatus, but in a secret memo on television made to the Air Ministry in 1928 and discussed later, this humble visionary declared: 'You will understand, of course, that the whole of my description is merely an idea of something like what might be accomplished, and I have never made any apparatus.'[20]

Campbell Swinton's original ideas were instigated by an article in *Nature* `of 4 June 1908. It was written by Shelford Bidwell, the veteran British television pioneer, who at that point had been experimenting intermittently for twenty years. Bidwell summed up the frustration that must have swelled in the breasts of the talented men who felt they were so near the solution in theory, yet so far in practice. Forlornly he wrote: 'Of each of the elementary working parts - selenium cells, luminosity-controlling devices, projection lenses for the receiver, and conducting wires - there would be 90,000.' He thought the cells would need a surface of about 8 square feet. The receiving apparatus would occupy a space of about 4,000 cubic feet, and the cable connecting the stations would have a diameter of 8 inches. The process, he concluded, could probably be done for a cost of around £$1^1/_4$ million. Eleven years later the situation apparently remained the same - only apparently, however. The young man, pale-faced and almost crippled with colds, who sailed out of Britain for the New World on a cargo boat in the winter of 1919 had almost certainly solved many of the problems that puzzled Bidwell. Where others had failed, John Logie Baird was on the verge of a major breakthrough, financed by his own earnings and the investment of a few friends, and using equipment that in itself would have cost little more than a night out for two at the Savoy Hotel.

NOTES

1   Sermon preached by the Rev John Baird on 20 September 1914.
2   Baird, autobiographical notes, *Sermons, Soap and Television*, ch.2, p.3. 3
3   *Sermons, Soap and Television*, ch.3, p.3.
4   *Sermons, Soap and Television*, ch.2, p.4.
5   *Sermons, Soap and Television*, ch.2, p.5.
6   *Sermons, Soap and Television*, ch.2, p.6.
7   *Sermons, Soap and Television*, ch.2, p.4.
8   *Sermons, Soap and Television*, ch.2, p.6.
9   Conversation in 1979 with Mr B.Clapp, employed in 1926 as J.L.Baird's first technical assistant.
10   R.Tiltman, *Baird of Television*, Seeley Service, 1933, p. 35.
11   E.Larson, *Men Who Have changed the World*, Phoenix House/Dent, 1952,p. 186.
12   W. Imrie, *Both Sides of the Burn*, Bell, Aird - Coghill, Glasgow, 1966.
13   R. W. Hubbell, *4000 Years of TV*, Harrap, 1942, p. 70.
14   Caithness Field Club, pamphlet entitled 'Alexander Bain of Watten, Genius of the North'.
15   G. Shiers, 'Early Schemes for Television', I E E E *Spectrum*, May 1970, pp. 24-34.
16   0. J. Lodge, *Modern Views of Electricity*, Macmillan, London, 1907, p.358.
17   'Seeing by Electricity', The Electrician. 24, 7 March 1890, p.448-50.
18   G.Shiers,' Early Schemes for Television', IEEE Spectrum, May 1970, p.33.
19   Bosch Technische Berichte, *5O Years of Fernseh*,1929-1979, Vol.6 1979, No.5/6, pp. 12-13.
20   Letter dated 23 January 1928 from A. C. Swinton to H. E. Wimperis, Director of Scientific Research, Air Ministry; Secret Air Ministry File, Air 2/S24132, Public Record Office, Kew.

4

Land of the Humming Bird

Wherever he travelled, John Logie Baird proved incapable of living the quiet life. His passion for discovery and his knack of setting up his experiments, undeterred by circumstances, geography or suitability of surroundings, earned him a bizarre reputation among the native population in a corner of Trinidad. This pleasant and unassuming man unwittingly struck chill terror into their hearts, and recent evidence reveals that they nicknamed him the 'Obeah' or 'Black Magic Man'.

This nickname, which almost had unfortunate consequences, sprang from hitherto unknown television experiments set up in the bush. It was previously thought that Baird spent nine months in the West Indies merely on a gimcrack project, trading with local communities and opening a jam and preserves factory in the jungle. However, the work he had started in Scotland was continued in a wooden bungalow on a cocoa plantation. From there, it now appears, images were transmitted in 1920, three years before the traditionally accepted experiments back home in England, at Hastings.

Baird did not mention the Trinidad experiments in his autobiographical sketch. In fact, he ingenuously remarks that the idea of resurrecting his early work occurred while on a walk on the cliffs at Hastings - another example of the postdating of milestones in his career in order to confuse competitors. He indicated the genuine sequence of events once, in a newspaper article in 1936, when he dropped his guard and wrote: 'Then my health broke down and I decided to go to Trinidad. There I would not only recover my health, thus enabling me to carry on with television, I would also make some money, which I could spend on experiments.[1]

His schoolfriend, Godfrey Harris, had just been to Trinidad and Baird chose this island after Godfrey had sent him glowing accounts of its possibilities. Baird may at this time have made contact with distant relatives in the Caribbean; his maternal great-grandmother had lived in Georgetown, Guiana, half a century before. His initial interest was reinforced by a swift browse through travel books. He read of 'Eerie, land of the humming bird and eternal summer'.

Later in the 1936 newspaper article he says:

I was going to live in the land of the humming bird, to spend my days and nights free from all cares in an equatorial paradise. I packed two large trunks with calico which I had been assured the dusky inhabitants would fall over one another to buy and a third trunk with books on sound, light, heat, electricity and the latest discoveries that pointed in the direction of my own goal, television. There would be plenty of time to read in the tropics.

He did not merely read, however. For later, describing the failure of his preserves enterprise, he adds: 'The only progress I made in that West Indies year was towards television. I spent my nights in the jungle working out problems, and on my return to England I was ready for new experiments.'

His passport, issued in Glasgow in September 1919, gives his profession as engineer, and describes his hair and skin as fair, eyes blue, chin round and face oval. In the passport picture his arms are folded and he looks confident and at ease. The hair is, for him, unusually short and straight and a pair of alert eyes peer through rimless pince-nez. He looks ascetic, almost stern. It is a good, clean- cut face. The picture is a peculiarity, one of the few that offer a glimpse of the man's true character. Later he would wear his hair longer and ill health would make him bulkier and puffier in the face. The qualities of the lean man of the picture would live on, though, in a personality of unusual dedication and tenacity.

Life had been hard until now, with few opportunities for enjoying himself. But as Baird slapped the labels marked 'Port of Spain, Trinidad' onto the trunks, he must have felt his troubles were over. He had money in his pocket, with more to come. The world was his oyster. Reality, however, soon intruded. The cargo boat on which Baird was a passenger had few home comforts, the weather was rough, and a hard-bitten Venzuelan who inspected Baird's trading

Personal
details from
the Trinidad
passport

DESCRIPTION OF BEARER.

Age 31 Profession Engineer
Place & date of birth Helensburgh
Maiden name of widow or married woman travelling } 13.8.88
singly

Height feet inches
Forehead Medium Eyes Blue
Nose Straight Mouth Medium
Chin Round Colour of Hair Fair
Complexion Fair Face Oval
Any special peculiarities —
National Status British born subject

PHOTOGRAPH OF BEARER.

SIGNATURE OF BEARER.

J. L. Baird

Baird's passport
photograph for the
trip to Trinidad
1919.

samples informed him that they stood little chance of selling. The West Indies had progressed a little from the days when a penurious merchant venturer might arrive and lay the foundations of a fortune by selling cotton and safety pins to the locals. He thought Baird mad to have thrown up a prospering business at home.

On arrival he headed for the Ice House Hotel, where Godfrey Harris had booked him a room. Moist heat rose from the pavements. He was jostled by bustling crowds of negroes, Chinese, Caribs, Hindus and Portuguese. He felt unwell and was glad to flop down in a tiny bedroom where he languished for a few miserable days suffering a bout of dysentery. He surfaced with his confidence in a promising paradise slightly shaken but, with resilience, set about making himself known. Not one to be overwhelmed by new surroundings, Baird soon had a string of acquaintances whom he roped in to help with his ventures. He never lost the knack of confronting comparative strangers and enlisting their cooperation.

First he moved to Columbia House, a boarding establishment run by a plain but kind-hearted lady named Mrs Brisbane, who took one look at the wan features of the convalescent and immediately promised to look after him like a mother. The other inhabitants were refugees from a Somerset Maugham novel. Besides three bank clerks, one in bed with veneral disease, there was a young commercial traveller from London, the black sheep of his family, sent to Trinidad to recover from dipsomania, and an elderly English governess, prim and proper, who either believed in living dangerously or was stranded flotsam from the colony's more conventional days. Baird shared a large room with the dipsomaniac, who obligingly offered to help with introductions and sell his wares. After three weeks of tramping around the shops and homes of all races, Baird had sold just 5lb of safety pins. He was forced to admit that the trading scheme was a fiasco, and to complicate matters he was struck down for a week by fever.

Undeterred by this inauspicious start, he utilized his time in bed by dreaming up a fresh venture to make a fortune and win himself freedom to experiment with television. The island, teeming with citrus fruit, guavas and sugar, seemed an ideal location for a jam factory. It was so obvious that he could hardly contain his excitement. There seemed no drawbacks. He had, of course, no knowledge of cooking; all he had been required to do in the past was boil himself an egg or brew up tea. Never one to be overwhelmed by such difficulties, he systematically quizzed his landlady and pored over relevant books in the local library. The island was crammed with mango trees. He would add mango chutney to his list of products and build a magnificent export business.

He bought himself as a runabout a 20hp Ford registration number P-12555, and took an exploratory tour round the island. The spot he chose was away from the town, on the edge of the bush at the foothills of the Northern Range in the Santa Cruz valley. The area was called Grand Curucaye and abounded in tall trees known locally as pessie, the wood from which made fine walking sticks. The adjacent village was called Bourg Mulatresse, Mulattos' Village. The climate was wet, cool and suitable for Europeans. Today it is being widely developed for housing, but in 1919 Baird found his forest territory primitive and peaceful. He described his new home as a room in the wooden house of a local cocoa planter, beside a river, surrounded by a clump of giant bamboos. A few Trinidadians remember it as the bungalow of the plantation overseer employed by Albert Stollmeyer, one of the wealthiest landowners on the island and father of sons who became outstanding West Indian cricketers.

The bungalow, which burned down a few years ago, stood about 800 yards from the Stollmeyers' mansion. It is not on record what Mr Stollmeyer made of the strange young man who doubtless enthusiastically drew him into plans for launching a new branch of the preserves industry. He was probably more intrigued, however, when the irrepressible newcomer let slip hints about his idea of transmitting vision. Baird's arguments must have impressed him, as research reveals that Mr Stollmeyer soon joined in the experiments.

Baird started his preserves venture by appointing a motley crew of lieutenants, a Hindu youth named Ram Roop, and Tony, a large, simple individual of Portuguese extraction. Together they directed an occasional workforce of negroes and Chinese. They set to and erected three ramshackle huts or lean-tos *à la* Robinson Crusoe. From a scrap merchant in Port of Spain Baird procured a large copper cauldron which had last seen service as a washtub. It could take 112 Ib of jam and was suspended over a brick

The ramshackle huts in the bush in the Santa Cruz Valley,
Trinidad - Baird's preserves factory.

fireplace complete with chimney. There, with fires burning
all day long and adding to the torrid heat, Baird assembled
his cookery books and recipes. He then filled his cauldron
with cut-up oranges and ladlesful of sugar and boiled it to
make marmalade. With Ram Roop on one side and himself
on the other, the bubbling mixture was constantly stirred
with spade-like sticks; they had to jump clear as the lava-
like stuff spat from the cauldron. The temperature was often
so hot that they had to strip to their trousers.

It was tiring, backbreaking work, especially following so
closely upon a severe illness, but Baird still found time to
pursue his constant dream. No one has ever suggested
before that he attempted any practical television research
during his West Indian period. But a routine letter from the
authors in a British newspaper, asking for any details of his
Caribbean sojourn, drew a swift response that was to lead to
some startling new facts. A West Indian, Mr Philip
Yearwood, of South Norwood in London, wrote saying that
he had been shown a house where Baird was said to have
lived. Mr Yearwood revealed: 'I was told that locals
suspected he was practising Obeah or Black Magic because
of the strange flashing lights in the house at night.'

Quite independently, Mrs Patricia Murrain of Port of
Spain also replied, stating: 'During his experiments, and in
those days people living in the country districts were not as
wise as now - they believed in supernatural things, and
hearing Mr Baird's noise and experiments, they became

suspicious.' She added that flashing lights emanating from the house convinced them he was working Obeah, and their fears increased. One night a crowd from the village gathered to watch the strange phenomena. Their numbers grew. What followed resembled the traditional Hollywood version of an attack by Transylvanian villagers on Dracula's stronghold. One can imagine the scene. Darkness in the bush, the clicking crickets and a frightened crowd, some carrying burning torches, approaching the bungalow shouting insults. Baird was roused to run to the front of the house. Self-preservation might have indicated flight as the best policy but, not one to let anything interfere with work, he stood his ground and threw back the stones and clods of earth and grass which were aimed at him. Any explanation that he was merely trying to project images from one spot to another would only have confirmed their suspicions. They probably wished he would decamp to Haiti where he would be more at home with the voodoo makers.

The event merged into local folklore, and though Baird's identity was largely forgotten, a small group of contemporaries retained memories of those early experiments. A letter from the authors to a Trinidadian newspaper unearthed further evidence of early television. Mr Bruce McLeod, a Port of Spain antique dealer, replied saying that he had read an article in the local newspaper, The Bomb, about a man who had invented television in a shed on the Stollmeyer estate in Santa Cruz. Mr McLeod did not know of Baird's stay in Trinidad and added: 'At the time I thought this to be an absurd claim and didn't think of it again until I read your letter.' Further inquiries revealed that the man who had made the claim for television was a Mr Nicholas Aparicio of Bourg Mulatresse. Mrs Murrain revealed that she had approached Mr Aparicio, who had indeed worked with Baird as a boy, and she pointed us in the direction of Mr Jimmy Bain, chairman of Trinidad and Tobago Television, who said:

From my personal knowledge, Mr Baird did his experiments in Trinidad when I was a boy. He used to make guava jelly to sell and support himself while here, and my father used to assist in selling his jellies. I remember my father mentioning the experiments he was doing here, although I would only have been ten years old at the time. My father arranged for Mr Baird to live in the overseer's house on the cocoa plantation of Mr

Mr Albert Stollmeyer in Santa Cruz, and it is here he conducted his experiments.

Nicholas Aparicio was one of Mr Stollmeyer's employees, a young lad who used to run errands. Mr Bain said: 'Mr Aparico tells me he definitely saw a picture transmitted from Mr Stollmeyer's house to the overseer's house where Mr Baird lived, a distance of a few hundred feet.' Mrs Murrain also said that Mr Aparicio recalled Mr Stollmeyer assisting Baird. 'Cables were connected between the two houses so that pictures were visible. Apparently they were seen hazily but one could recognize the faces that appeared. No sound was used.'

And so, in 1920, Baird was apparently televising people - at least three years before he got round to announcing publicly any success at all. He was playing his cards close to his chest, building a firm foundation of research. If anyone announced a breakthrough before him he could always step in and reveal his work; presumably already a few stages further ahead. This was in keeping with the secrecy that was to confound even close associates in the future, but it was a risky tactic when so many others were trying for a first in television.

He still found time to enjoy Trinidad's social life, and is known to have accompanied a local girl to several functions. It may have been Grace Fitzgerald, daughter of his landlord, who kept house for Baird and his friend, or it could have been Edith Shoebridge, whom he taught to drive his car on a picnic to Manzanilla on the east coast of the island. It is unlikely that he was seeking a permanent partner, for he was still in love with the girl he had left behind in Scotland.

Baird also encountered a likeable character named Harold Pound, who was later to help him set up another commercial enterprise in London. Pound shared the bungalow with Baird, who seems to have temporarily abandoned his teetotal habits. In the land of rum and buccaneering traditions he found himself tucking into gin cocktails and whisky. The results were predictable; sore heads and at least one funny incident. Baird later described returning home to find Pound with a large whisky and soda before him, gaping with alcoholic horror at a 'stupendous, unbelievably large grasshopper which sat on the table gaping back at him. He was immensely relieved when I arrived and confirmed that the creature was real and not the result of alcohol.' The two men then capered around the room and eventually trapped the creature under a wastepaper basket. The locals identified it as a giant locust and Baird and Pound kept it as a pet in a canary cage. The locust joined in with the drinking twosome, but consumed so feverishly that Baird reported laconically: 'It soon died of delirium tremens.'

Meanwhile, mother nature conspired to wreck his jam project, suspected Obeah man though he might be. He soon discovered an almost insurmountable drawback in the operation. As he and his men feverishly stirred the boiling cauldron, sweet and alluring scents drifted out into the jungle and acted like a trumpet call to every wasp, bee and hornet in the vicinity, not to mention columns of voracious marching ants. Baird's first reaction was to run for it but Ram Roop remained, stirring imperturbably. Baird stayed too, swiping the air and stamping the ground, but all to little avail. He watched bemused as the insects buzzed suicidally around the cauldron and then plopped in scores to a swift but happy death amid the bubbling oranges and guavas.

Spiders darted up and down the walls. Mosquitoes plagued them. One night ants made off with 112 Ib of sugar. Bottling the jam proved a particular problem, and not a few jars ended up with the odd wasp entombed, a feature of the products that did nothing to recommend them to shopkeepers in Port of Spain. Baird put his scientific mind to work on the problem and came up with ideas for diverting the hordes, which included ditches filled with water or sometimes smouldering wood, but once again fever struck. Ram Roop and Tony soldiered on. Baird gave orders from bed but began to realize that there was no adequate local market for his wares, so he decided to head back to London. The jam lingered on in local memory and occasionally turned up for sale in local shops. Incredibly, one jar was bought in Port of Spain twenty-six years later.

Baird was disappointed but not downhearted. Television was his goal and advances had been made. He must find a new means of financing his work. In the meantime he decided to salvage what he could and packed a large cask and several kerosene tins full of mango chutney, guava jelly, marmalade and tamarind syrup. These would accompany him home, for sale in England. He sold his copper pan and what goodwill there was for £5. Pound decided to accompany him. They bade farewell to their many friends and embarked for home on the steamship Stuyvesant, via the French Antilles and France. Baird later remarked ruefully: 'The West Indies is an excellent spot for those in robust health who can stay at the Queen's Park Hotel and spend their time in bathing and motoring, but living in the bush, particularly under the trees in a valley near a river, is not at all a wise course of procedure.' Despite knowing all this, he would one day return in strange circumstances to the same area, in the middle of a world war, when tourist traffic was non-existent, when his health was poor and when all his friends were convinced he was a forgotten man at home.

NOTES
1   Baird, 'My Fight for a Dream', *Sunday Chronicle*, 15 November 1936.

5

Into Business

Baird returned to Britain and in London, according to legend, endured another of those sombre periods when he struggled to make a living- almost a carbon copy of his days in Glasgow. In fact his main preoccupation, as always since 1916, was the quest for money to improve the already significant breakthroughs he had made in television. Once this is accepted, his early, almost manic dabbling in one commercial venture after another must be viewed in a new light.

He had tried pile cures, industrial diamonds and Jam in the jungle. Now he resurrected for sale the Baird Undersock, and also embarked on marketing Australian and Guatemalan honey and bars of soap. Nothing if not imaginative, he is supposed to have settled on television as merely the latest and most successful of his wild schemes for making a fortune. On the contrary, his persistent interest in television during this period would lead within the year to his being shown the door again by a landlord, this time a GPO civil servant, who misconstrued Baird's behaviour and suspected him of being a spy.

Even his close friend, the journalist Sydney Moseley, was never let into the secret of Baird's early start on television, and the secret life that ensued. Moseley wrote the first biography after the inventor's death,[1] which sympathetically outlined the familiar landmarks and followed Baird's own autobiographical sketch. Moseley, an experienced reporter, could not help noticing strange anomalies in the story, however, factors that did not square with the inventor's character. He was mystified by the British government's apparent neglect of Baird during the Second World War. He also noticed striking similarities between details of devices like radar, publicized after the war, and Baird's prewar patents. Puzzled, but lacking vital clues, he told a straight story, inadvertently reinforcing the legend of the thwarted inventor, and totally missing Baird's vital contributions to his country in wartime. Moseley accepted the version that in 1920 Baird was just battling to make a living.

At the start, television had been an enthusiasm, a gateway to fame and fortune. By 1920 it had all the signs of a major passion in which the profit motive, though still intact, was fast receding in importance. He had returned from Trinidad, a young man in a hurry. He must have felt on the verge of success, but scientific magazines were carrying ominous reports of others progressing in the same field with plenty of financial backing and more lavish facilities. Life for him at this time is thought to have been lonely, but this view can be taken with a generous pinch of salt. He was constantly in touch throughout his working life with diverse individuals in many parts of the country, who frequently helped him quite independently of each other. More of these unknown aides continue to emerge as one follows occasional reminiscences that crop up in the columns of local newspapers from people who mark Baird's anniversaries or join in the controversy which has always surrounded his name. Even at this early stage Baird was almost certainly making fleeting visits to these unnoticed aides whom he had persuaded to share his dream.

He had returned in late autumn to the fogs, rain and cold of London, and lapsed into one of his recurrent colds; he therefore rested for a couple of weeks at the home in Deptford of his elder sister Annie, then a district nurse. She was already becoming one of those formidable Scots spinsters, whose eagle gaze, nerves of steel and caustic comments disguised a warm nature, susceptible to anyone in need of help. Her war had been distinguished. She had served in France with Queen Alexandra's Imperial Military Nursing Service, been mentioned in dispatches, and left carrying the rank of sister-in-charge. She appears to have looked on at her brother's apparently erratic modes of carving a career with a mixture of affection and trepidation.

Funds were running low. He now joined the precarious ranks of the get-rich-quick brigade, already swollen with disillusioned veterans of the Western Front, young ex-majors selling patent medicines through newspapers ads and former Royal Flying Corps pilots hawking encyclopedias at the door. First, he rented a tiny shop at 116 Lupus Street and tried to market his West Indian produce. It was soon clear that no one was particularly interested in his unbranded mango chutney and guava jelly, not even the cut-price stallholders at Mark Lane and Mincing Lane. Philosophically he surrendered the fruits of his jungle labours for £15 to a sausagemaker, who added it as bulk to the other materials in the sausages. At this point Baird met up with his old schoolfriend Mephy - (Guy Fullarton Robertson) - now an often out-of-work Shakespearian actor. The gentle Mephy seemed to gain confidence in the presence of the energetic and ever-hopeful Baird, so intensely interested in the challenges of the present that he discounted everyday blows and hardships. During Baird's bachelor days, Mephy acted as a sort of majordomo, bringing some order into his domestic life and even helping him choose a wife. His untimely death would particularly sadden Baird at a trying and vulnerable time in his career.

The even earlier death of another friend would also darken his horizons. Godfrey Harris, the former school-friend who had recommended the West Indies, had taken his BSc degree and gone to work for himself. Baird cast some light on his own character when he wrote: 'Poor Godfrey! He was a mass of brain and initiative but, like Mephy and myself, he had a kink. He could not stand routine work, he could not be employed, he wanted freedom.'[2] Harris had lost money in business and gone to America as a draughtsman. There he threw up his job, and bought a few acres of land in the wilds of Louisiana and built himself a shack among the hillsides, where he kept a few goats and hens and planted his own vegetables. His neighbours were religious fanatics of the Holy Roller variety who yelled and moaned in ecstasy at church services, grabbing each other and rolling on the ground. The illegitimacy rate, Godfrey observed, was high but everyone seemed satisfied and happy.

Godfrey spent his time meditating on the old problem that had exercised their minds when boys, the eternal question of free will and immortality. He dispatched the results of his pondering to Baird until they came to a sudden halt. Maybe Godfrey had found his answers. One morning, while he was trying to clear a tree stump with dynamite, the charge went off accidentally, blowing up Godfrey as well as the tree stump. Baird mourned: 'Godfrey might have sat behind a desk in pompous self-important dignity, but he chose freedom and, like Mephy, was labelled a madman.'[3]

Baird moved to the boarding house of Miss Selina Borthwick in Bloomsbury where Mephy, cutting down on expenses, rented a bed in the disused washhouse. This was damp but had the advantage of the original washtub complete with hot water. Baird took a wretched attic for himself, clean but sparsely furnished with a bare floor and a single barred window with broken glass. He now started to answer ads in *The Times* headed 'Business Opportunities', which led to a series of encounters with dubious characters anxious to persuade him to part with his little remaining capital. One individual turned up with an enormous, thuggish-looking man who was introduced as the King of the Barrows. They had a scheme which would have involved Baird in helping to buy surplus army stocks of galvanized iron buckets. When Baird expressed his doubts they proved obstreperous, and he had a problem persuading them to leave Miss Borthwick's establishment. He was certainly learning business the hard way. He had his fingers burned in dealing with characters known as Mark Lane scorpions, smooth operators who would clinch a deal and vanish with the money before delivering, or would sell goods and disappear with the takings.

Nevertheless, he soon started to make considerable money once again. He heard of consignments of Australian honey languishing at the docks, purchased 2 tons and advertised in *The Times* and the *Morning Post*- 28 lb tins, post free. Replies soon streamed in. Another stroke of luck was the arrival of his friend from the West Indies, Harold Pound, who offered him a small horticultural sundries shop with large storage capacity owned by an uncle who was now retiring. Baird bought it for about £100 and now had an over-the-counter trade in fertilizers as well as honey and coir fibre dust. But his old enemy, the cold, now laid him low again and when a friend of Pound's, freshly arrived from Trinidad, offered to buy a half share in the business Baird gladly agreed. The cold worsened, and he was dispatched to Buxton Hydro on his doctor's advice, selling out to his partner for £100 plus £200 worth of shares in an oil company that never proved saleable. The infection was more severe than usual and he was laid low for six months. Fortunately, he had insured himself against such a disaster and was paid £6 a week until he was ready to return to the fray in London.

Baird bounced back from illness with £100 in his pocket

and was attracted by the prospect of selling resin soap, which was advertised in *The Grocer as* cheap if bought in bulk. The soap proved to be rubbish and so Baird did not purchase it, but instead placed an order with another firm for one ton of double-wrapped pale yellow soap. Headquarters were set up at 13 Water Lane. A manager was appointed at £2 a week, an elderly gentleman named Mr Young, adorned with a pince-nez from which one glass was missing, just the sort of idiosyncrasy that appealed to Baird. Soon Mr Young and a team of rag-tag travellers were on the road pushing twin-tablet double-wrapped pale yellow soap under the name of 'Baird's Speedy Cleaner', suitable for scrubbing floors.

Business proved brisk, and Baird was soon able to rent as a warehouse a basement in a tumbledown house on the south bank of the Thames, putting Mr Young in charge. Once installed, Mr Young insisted on having a boy to help him pack the soap. Baird inserted an ad in the local evening newspaper, 'Strong boy wanted to help in warehouse'. This led to another of those comic incidents which afforded him light relief intermittently throughout his life. He was approaching Water Lane the day after the advertisement had appeared and found two policemen struggling to sort out a near-riot among a seething mass of strong boys. Baird pushed his way through the jostling melee and went through a back entrance, only to find more lads pounding on his office door. He yelled above the din and eventually the door was opened by a white-faced Mr Young, thoroughly terrified. Baird immediately took command, appointed the first boy in the queue, hastily scribbled 'Job filled' on a card and hung it on a door. He then locked himself in and sat in a state of siege. Baird recalled: 'For days strong boys hung around the Water Lane office. Glowering and muttering, strong boys banged at the locked doors and threatened to break in. Strong boys waylaid us in the passages and in the streets as we scuttled in and out.'[4]

Hotels, boarding houses, ship's chandlers and barrow boys were now buying his soap. It was very cheap, which was just as well, as he admitted also it was very bad, being more abundant in soda than in fatty acid, an essential requirement for good soap. One day a ferociously angry matriarch erupted into his office clutching a small infant. She pulled its clothes over its head and rammed its raw and inflamed posterior into Baird's face. She was calmed only when he explained that Baird's Speedy Cleaner was intended for use as a powerful scourer for floors and ships' decks, not for the tender rears of infants.

It was also a time of heartbreak. During this period Baird made a bitter trip to Glasgow. The girl who had been the love of his life so far had married another man, presumably reckoning that her wandering admirer was so entangled in his work that he would not surface again. This was a huge blow to Baird, one which saddened and complicated his life for almost a decade to come.

There is little doubt that he had been genuinely in love and it had probably never dawned on him that an absence of a year or two would make much difference. It was now that he displayed those fighting qualities which his subsequent boffin image obscured from the public, a fierce determination not to give up even when the cause seemed lost. He confronted the lady in Glasgow, and both found their attachment still deep. Baird might have attempted a secret affair but instead he took the unusual step of challenging her husband, exclaiming that he was not prepared to let her walk out of his life just like that. Tempers reached boiling point but, surprisingly, after more discussion both men began to respect each other and some sort of agreement was reached. The solution was unorthodox even in the relatively relaxed postwar atmosphere. The two men stayed firm friends, while the lady herself frequently joined Baird for several months a year until he met and fell in love with the woman whom he married in 1931 and to whom he described what had happened. Otherwise the affair was kept a secret, which forced him to be socially evasive and, added to his involvement in secret work with the government and the Armed forces, was to make his life at times positively clandestine.

His stay at Miss Borthwick's boarding house was short and he now moved into a variety of lodgings. A fascinating description of Baird at this juncture reveals again his continuing interest in television. It comes from Mrs F.S.Hawkins, a retired chemistry teacher and graduate of London University, now of Pulborough, Sussex. In 1921 Baird arrived at her parents' home at 57 Ellerby Street, Bishops Park, Fulham, close to Fulham Football Ground and to the moated Palace of the Bishop of London. Bairdy, as the family christened him, lived en famille, occupying a bedsitting room and having breakfast and evening meals with them. They knew nothing about his interest in television, and this led to a misunderstanding and to another of those swift ejections by landlords which were to occur with monotonous regularity in his days of experiments.

Mrs Hawkins was then a schoolgirl called Freda Impett, and like the rest of the family she regarded Bairdy as a distinctly odd bird. Her father had been demobilized late, after serving from 1915 to 1918 in the Royal Engineers, and had decided to take an occasional lodger to help the house hold budget. His first lodger had been a run-of-the-mill civil servant who had stayed for two uneventful years. The family were hardly prepared for his successor, the strange Scotsman who, to their bewilderment, did not have a job and who frequently spent all day in his room. His habits were tantalizingly odd. He seemed to read a lot, as cheap books were regularly consigned to the wastepaper basket, each one with the right-hand corner of the fly-leaf torn off. This was probably the price tab, which he would reuse on his jars of honey, but the family were naturally mystified.

It was his behaviour at evening meals that made them even more uncomfortable. Mrs Hawkins says: 'My parents sat at the head and foot of our large dining room table while Bairdy sat at one side and my brother, five years my junior and killed in the Second World War, and I sat opposite him. Behind us was the Victorian sideboard with the mirror above the cupboard portion. Bairdy faced it and screwed up his eyes and made faces into it between and past the two of us.' As the family cast discreet glances at each other and got on with the meal, Bairdy continued his odd behaviour. Mrs Hawkins adds: 'I don't mind admitting that, as a shy teenager, I was frightened of this peculiarly-behaved Scotsman sitting opposite. With his shock of hair, thick glasses and a fierce way of talking, I did not find him particularly attractive.' In all likelihood, Baird as usual oblivious to his surroundings, was using the mirror to check some image theory for his television experiments.

Mysterious parcels arrived, including large ones full of honey and molasses from Guatemala. He also marketed his patent under-socks, which he admitted to the Impetts had large layers of newspaper interlining them. Family foreboding grew during the hot summer weather. As Mrs Impett prepared coffee after meals he would pace up and down the garden muttering audibly: 'The wo-rr-ms are coming up.' Whether he was philosophizing aloud on the brevity of life or just being impish, adding spice to their bewilderment, we shall never know.

Mr Impett was a clerk in the Post Office Engineering Office in London where he ended his career as chief cashier in the Chief Engineer's Office. And it was this employment, and Bairdy's seemingly excessive interest in it, that brought matters to a head. Mrs Hawkins says:

Baird tried to pump him on several occasions as to conditions there. It was a great pity that Bairdy did not confide in him at all, for it was now that the misunderstanding occurred. The more he cautiously probed, the more my father began to think he was a spy trying to extract from him secret information, and the more he resented it. So in the end Bairdy was asked to leave. With hindsight we realized that he was wondering whether he could get a footing for a studio in the GPO for the invention he was contemplating, and the grimaces in the mirror must have had something to do with the images he was later to transmit.

He seemed to convey a sense of sadness to the young Freda, but she remembers:

One night he was really excited and loquacious. He had hired a dress suit and was to meet Jack Buchanan on stage after a show. At last he showed himself to be really human! This is all I can recall about a strange, taciturn man. We were surprised to hear later that he had married. Presumably he was able to unburden himself to his fiancee. It is a pity that he seemed so lonely previously for, although my mother was very quiet and shy, my father was known as a friendly sort of man.

Baird's mainstream soap business prospered until one day a bothered Mr Young arrived bearing a cake of rival soap labelled 'Hutchinson's Rapid Washer'. In his autobiographical sketch Baird implies that this was his first encounter with 'the jovial Irishman' who was to play a major part in the launching of his television company. He says Hutchinson had been undercutting him and so he telephoned and arranged a parley. They met and dined that night at the Café Royal, and over old brandy arranged a merger.

But this does not fit the facts, as we have seen. In early newspaper interviews Baird said that the two had known each other from apprentice days in Glasgow in 1912[5] Captain Oliver George Hutchinson had served in the army in the First World War. It is likely that he was one of the few who over the years had known just what Baird was up to. As his work became more involved, and the need for secrecy increased, Baird apparently found it necessary to pretend that Hutchinson and he had just met by chance. However, 1922 was most likely just the tip of the iceberg and they had probably been in touch at that point for almost a decade. The morning after the Cafe Royal meeting Baird was laid low with a cold in an icy room in his latest residential hotel. Hutchinson visited him and, alarmed at his condition, called a doctor. Baird grew rapidly worse and was ordered out of London to recover. Mephy had moved to the seaside town of Hastings and Baird decided to join him there in the winter of 1922. His company had become limited, with a capital of £2,000, and he had two co-directors, young businessmen introduced by Harold Pound. They bought the remainder of Baird's shares for £200, and he headed for the town which was to be hailed as the first public milestone in the history of Baird's television.

NOTES

1   S. Moseley, *John Baird: The Romance and Tragedy of the pioneer of Television*, Odhams, 1952.
2   Baird, autobiographical notes, *Sermons, Soap and Television*, ch. 1, p. 11.
3   Baird, *Sermons, Soap and Television*, ch. 1, p. 11.
4   Baird, *Sermons, Soap and Television*, ch. 3, p. 6.
5   'Broadcast Pictures of the Derby', *Daily Express*, 8 January 1926.

6
Seeing by Wireless

One evening just before dusk, early in 1923, a curious procession wound its way up West Hill in the Sussex resort of Hastings. Above the shore, close to where William the Conqueror landed to triumph over the Saxon King Harold, four boy scouts laboriously hauled a trek cart accompanied and aided by a mop-haired man in an overlong coat. The trek cart's contents were bulky and covered, and the man tended and steadied them as though they were precious. On reaching the summit he unloaded his mysterious burden and dismissed the boys with their cart. One, though, was allowed to remain, and what he witnessed gives a rare glimpse of John Logie Baird conducting one of his previously unsuspected secret experiments.

The scout, now a retired radio engineer still living in Hastings, Mr Norman Loxdale, never forgot that odd foray up West Hill, or other encounters with the inventor who deeply impressed him and helped shape his own future career. It was only when he revealed his story to the authors that the implications of that dusk expedition became apparent. As the sun dipped behind the horizon on that windswept hill, John Logie Baird took the wraps off a large, saucer-like metal dish with a spike in the centre, connected through a battery to a small receiver with a glass screen, which appeared to be covered in small metal particles.

Today we have grown accustomed to such dishes. They are a commonplace adjunct to modern centimetric wavelength radar and wireless. Hastings had once been the gateway for invaders from the continent. Now, by a quirk of fate, it was to be the setting for the development of an instrument which would successfully defend those same shores in 1940 during the Battle of Britain. Young Loxdale was almost certainly one of the first people in the world to set eyes on this early prototype of Baird's system, and his account affords an insight into the experiments which Baird managed to keep secret even from close associates, Their very existence is only gleaned through a careful study of contemporary accounts and by piecing together the fragmented memoirs of casual helpers who seldom knew of each other's existence.

The most striking aspect of Mr Loxdale's story is the date. Baird was operating an object-detection apparatus with a screen at exactly the same time as he is thought to have stumbled on the inspiration to investigate his old enthusiasm, television. While there is little doubt that he made vital breakthroughs in Hastings, that town's true link with Baird could well be based, not on television, but on the birth of radar and other detection systems. Baird himself would later encourage these misleading versions of his activities at Hastings. In his autobiographical notes and numerous newspaper features he describes how, in order to swell funds, he made a glass razor blade that would not rust or tarnish- and cut himself rather badly. He then turned to pneumatic shoes.

Inside a pair of large boots he fitted two partly inflated balloons and set off on a trial run. He lurched uncontrollably for a hundred yards, followed by a few delighted children; the episode ended when one of the 'tyres' burst. He continued:

> *More thought was needed. I went for a long walk over the cliffs to Fairlight Glen, and my mind went back to my early work on television. Might there not be something in it now? My difficulty then had been to find a means of amplifying the infinitesimally small current from the selenium cell. Such an amplifier was available thanks to Britain's Ambrose Fleming and the American Lee De Forest. Why not try again? The more I thought of it the easier it seemed. I thought out a complete system and returned to Walton Crescent, his lodging, with an influx of new life. Over the raisin pudding, I broke the news to Mephy.*
> *'Well Mephy, you will be pleased to hear that I have invented a means of seeing by wireless.'*
> *'Oh,' said Mephy, 'I hope that doesn't mean you are going to become one of those wireless nitwits. Far better to keep to soap - you can't afford to play about you know."*[1]

In line with this, Baird's days at Hastings have always been described to show himself and Mephy alone and struggling. The financial hardship was real enough but the two were far from solitary. And 1923 saw Baird not, as described, planted only in Hastings, but also working on television 400 miles away, back in Scotland in his home town, Helensburgh; and later in Folkestone, London and Tunbridge Wells. In Helensburgh he was seen working in the outhouse of a friend, and an edition of the local newspaper of the time reveals that he had the cooperation of a wireless and electrical company, Youdall and Sprott of 78 West Prince's Street. In Folkestone a plaque has been erected at 36 Guildhall Street following the revelation by a retired company director that Baird had experimented in 1923 on the premises of, and with the aid of, T. C. Gilbert & Co., an electrical contracting firm.

The various groups involved seem to have worked in total ignorance of Baird's experiments elsewhere. In Hastings he had brought his not inconsiderable powers of persuasion to bear upon a whole range of people who were fired by his burning enthusiasm. Displaying the same talent for enlisting help from all walks of life that he had shown in the West Indies, he soon had a team of almost a dozen occasional assistants, all acting (unpaid), eager to aid this extraordinary man of vision. They included Ronald Hartnell, a marine engineer, who made a light chopper and discs; Vincent Edwards, a mechanical engineer with Hastings Tramways, who worked on some of the drive mechanisms; Norman Blackburn, a radio engineer; Boyd Alexander, a local radio enthusiast; George Farmer, who worked for a local undertaker and helped Baird with woodwork; a Mr Claude Froude; Norman Loxdale, the schoolboy who had helped him drag his apparatus up West Hill and who was also a radio ham; William le Queux, a prominent wireless enthusiast, journalist and author, who helped Baird generally, especially with publicity; a Mr Wells, a turner by trade; and a Mr Siddell, a chief engineer with the Post Office.

But perhaps the most significant presence was that of J. J. Denton, then an engineer with the Municipal Corporation of Hastings. This fascinating individual, twelve or more years older than Baird, was to work alongside him in a sort of freelance capacity until his own death in 1944. Other colleagues of Baird's never quite figured out Denton's role, but it is now clear that this staunch ally was one of the very few people who were privy to the inventor's secret aims. Denton was largely self-educated, but had shown such original talent that in 1895 he was accepted as a lecturer in physics at Morley College, London, with which he remained connected for the rest of his life. The two men met at Hastings through a common interest in a technical book available at the local library. Baird had tried to consult the book several times, without success, and one day asked the librarian when he might possibly obtain it. Pointing to Denton, the librarian replied: 'Ask him. That's the man who's got it.' At that meeting common ground was established and a lifelong alliance formed.

Another of the assorted band of helpers named by Norman Loxdale, one who played an outstanding role in the work at Hastings, was Victor Mills, who, when he died, was a retired schoolteacher still living in Hastings. Mills gave Baird invaluable help with the selenium cell. They frequently disagreed, but it is clear that Baird respected the judgement of the young radio enthusiast. Mills described Baird's recruiting methods in a 1978 newspaper article.[2] The inventor had read reports of the sophisticated wireless set built by the schoolboy at Hastings Grammar School. One day in February 1923 he turned up at Mr Mills' parents' home in Hughenden Road. Mrs Mills returned from the front door and told her son: 'There's a funny man at the door asking for you.' The schoolboy then encountered a figure in a long, soiled raincoat who explained he was trying to invent television. Mr Mills wrote: 'I remember saying to him "What's television?"

"Seeing by wireless," he replied. "You probably know something about resonance. I'm getting a picture but I can't do anything with it. I'm getting too much noise..." '

Young Mills was soon a frequent caller at the small room in Queen's Avenue, generally called Queen's Arcade, which by July 1924 Baird had transformed into a lab.[3] This had been sublet from Leighton Brothers, photographers, who had a studio and drying room adjacent to him. Below was a shop selling artificial flowers. Baird was to write later that his landlord in the Arcade was a Mr Twigg, a name reported by others writing of the Hastings period. Baird may have misremembered his name, or it could have been another example of his camouflaging the facts, but certainly no one alive now remembers a Mr Twigg in the Arcade. He may have been the landlord at 21 Linton Crescent, where Baird and Mephy lodged. Baird recalled that a certain tension had arisen in his digs because he used his bedroom as a laboratory. In 1923 he appeared initially to have had a laboratory near Hastings railway station, but had to give this up when the premises were converted into a shop. By January 1924 he had installed the television apparatus at his lodgings in Linton Crescent.[4]

Baird's sketchy accounts of his life in Hastings, sometimes set out in the wrong sequence, are complicated by visits to his woman friend in the north. Neither the husband nor Baird was prepared to relinquish her and she, in confusion, flitted between them. She probably helped nurse him on his arrival in the town, when he was coughing and spluttering and 'so thin as to be almost transparent'. He must have been living on his nerves during this spell of ill health, during which reports multiplied of others pursuing the elusive goal of vision by radio. Hot on the track were Denes von Mihaly in Budapest; Vladimir Zworykin, a Russian expatriate now in the USA; August Karolus, in 1923 assistant professor at the Physical Institute of Leipzig; and C.F.Jenkins, once a humble stenographer clerk, now one of America's most prolific inventors. Also in the act was a Colonel Green, experimenting in special laboratories on his estate near Buzzard Bay, Massachusetts. He was the son of Hetty Green, reputed to be one of Wall Street's most successful woman financiers. Perhaps most amazing of all was a seventeen-year-old Mormon high school boy, Philo Farnsworth, a prodigy already working quietly in Provo, Utah. He would soon shake the big companies of America with his TV patents, and more than a decade later would ally himself with Baird in the fight against the big-money battalions of RCA and EMI.

From this broad field it is Baird who is acknowledged as first past the post, a fact which should in itself have alerted past researchers that his story was not as simple as it was portrayed. They have delighted in dwelling on his eccentricities, his string and sealing wax approach, the biscuit tins and darning needles, the odd assortment of basic materials involved in his early models. Funds were low and he probably had several machines under way at the same time, forcing him to use his talent for improvisation. He started from the same stable as Nipkow, and concentrated on the mechanical method. Others, such as Zworykin and Farnsworth, had chosen the electronics approach foreshadowed by Rosing and Campbell-Swinton, which is now the universal system. Subsequent emphasis on Baird's early mechanical work has dogged his whole story and unjustly damaged his reputation. His research is still often dismissed as a dead end by individuals who ignore or are unaware of his natural development into electronics. Quite apart from this aspect, misleading accounts of the capabilities of mechanical systems are given to this day. The mechanical system was eventually quite capable of supplying high-definition pictures every bit as good as, sometimes better than, the electronic ones.

Baird planned from the start to modify his invention for live television on the big screen in cinemas. By the time that cathode ray tubes and all-electronic systems were available for home TV sets in the 1930s, Baird had already blazed a trail in television techniques by mechanical means, including stereo, colour, outside broadcasts, recording video and even international transmissions. Through this and his flair for publicity and competitiveness he forced the pace and certainly advanced the growth of television by ten years.

Those who, with hindsight, think he should have dallied until he could have tackled the problem exclusively through electronics surely lack imagination. In 1923 mechanical scanning seemed the best path to the first pictures. The romance of radio was still under way. The BBC was only an infant and by 1928 would be flirting with the comparatively dull concept of the Fultograph, a machine for accepting still pictures by radio in the home. How much more promising were Baird's moving pictures, by whatever method. Given his dream and the closeness of rival systems, the choice was obvious. He had to forge ahead by mechanical means. Some of these competitors were already achieving outline shadowgraphs, but the true and extremely difficult goal was to move pictures of actual, living scenes, with gradations of light and shade. Some contemporaries confusedly imagined that television could be achieved by simply transmitting sixteen filmed images a second to give the impression of movement, as in the cinema, but this was dodging the real issue, which was the reproduction in light and shade of actual three-dimensional scenes.

Baird, as revealed, had already achieved some form of television image before arriving at Hastings. Why did he not rush to make a public announcement of his progress to date, and why did he give helpers the impression that he was still only capable of shadowgraphs? He was having trouble with the light-sensitive cell, as witnessed by his conversations with Victor Mills, and he was striving for improvement before trying to impress a financial backer and the scientific establishment. Throughout his life most of his assistants were not allowed to know exactly what was happening. Baird seemed to be satisfied as long as they accomplished the tasks and solved the particular problems allotted to them. An extension of his caution was the doctoring of his inventions when on display, or when revealed in newspaper photographs of diagrams. These were sometimes added to, vital sections subtracted, presumably to send would-be imitators off on a time-wasting trail. All's fair in love and war and, as Baird was soon to discover, the launching of television had all the bitter qualities of a war.

He was tackling a problem that had exhausted the patience of many pioneers. Though various techniques had been theoretically worked out, no one had yet made the magic breakthrough to practicality. There were few reliable guidelines, though he managed to procure the nearest thing to a textbook on the subject, *The Handbook of Phototelegraphy and Teleautography* by the Germans Korn and Glatzel, published in Leipzig in 1911. The principle he chose was straightforward in essence. The subject image to be televised was broken up into segments of light. These segments were then directed one by one rapidly onto a light-sensitive cell which, in turn, transmitted them one by one as electrical impulses to a television receiver. The receiver converted them back in the same order, one by one, into impulses of light and reconstituted a picture of the subject.

His assistants at Hastings believed he was just embarking on the project. All they saw were repeated experiments with a Maltese Cross, first cut from cardboard but later replaced by a solid, enamelled metal version loaned by a local doctor to whom it had been awarded by the St John's Ambulance Brigade. Accounts of the early efforts differ in minor detail, but the machine was described by Baird himself in articles of 1924.[5] The unit had a Nipkow disc containing four spirals of five holes which rotated at a speed of 200 rpm. In future operations, and subsequently in all television, the light would be directed onto the subject from the front, to be reflected from the subject back to a focusing lens at the rotating Nipkow disc. The illumination in this early Hastings transmitter was aimed at the cross from behind. The shadow outline of the cross was focused by a lens through the disc with its series of staggered holes. The first hole of each series of spirals was set at the edge of the disc, the next a little nearer the centre, and so on. Each hole was in a position to transmit a strip or line of the subject image from the lens. Behind the disc was a light-sensitive cell which was exposed to the rapid bursts of light from the disc lens. This cell acted like a microphone in radio and emitted varying electric currents to the television receiving disc, identical to the transmitting one, except that in place of the holes there were small electric bulbs. These bulbs were connected to a commutator in the centre of the disc, to which the transmitting signals were fed. The observer looked through a small aperture at the whirling receiver disc bulbs, which turned in synchronism with the transmitting disc. As the bulb lights twinkled in and out at speed, the outline of the cross could be seen approximately four times per revolution with obvious flicker. Since the disc rotated at 200 rpm, or 3.3 revolutions per second, the image frequency was 3.3 x 4 or 13 images per second, approximately the same frequency as used by Baird in his later 30-line television receivers.

The instrument seemed primitive, with no actual screen. The picture, if played onto a screen, would have supplied a crude 5-1ine image. But it had some remarkable refinements for such an infant. Behind the transmitting disc, and moving in the opposite direction to it, was another disc with serrated edges, a chopper disc. One of the big problems with the selenium cell was its quality of chemical inertia. Baird likened it to the properties of a photographic plate. Though it reacted directly if light fell on it, some time elapsed before the light produced its full effect, and there was a further delay in returning to its original resistance value before the next burst of illumination arrived. Baird attempted to solve this problem by using the spokes of the chopper disc, moving at high speed, to interrupt the light further. The spokes prevented light from reaching the selenium cell, and produced the time delay required to overcome the selenium inertia, thus allowing the cell to cope with the rapid and short bursts of light which came through the gaps between the spokes to reach the cell. The rotating spokes also gave an audio output frequency to be used with the medium wavelengths of radio.

These first receiving and transmitting discs seem to have been synchronized by means of a common shaft. But this method was swiftly overtaken. Descriptions as early as 1924 described an ingenious device which had both discs moving in near perfect synchronism. The transmitting motor sent out a wireless wave which automatically regulated the speed of the reception disc motor. If Baird was the beginner he pretended to be, he had certainly come up with a very sophisticated and obviously well- tried technique.

Rapid changes in the direction of his work led to conflicting descriptions of his machines. Baird's first patent, applied for in July 1923, envisaged a stationary frame of lamps arranged in vertical rows to form a screen, instead of the lights in the rotating receiver disc mentioned earlier. Later in 1923 he described a system with really no screen at all. Instead of a collection of rotating receiver lights there was one neon lamp placed behind a rotating Nipkow disc. Baird peered through the scanning disc and, as it revolved, saw the outline of a cross forming on the lamp.[6] The same disc was being used for both receiving and transmitting, one side for transmitting, and the diametrically opposite side for receiving the image. In this method the selenium cell was connected through an amplifier to the lamp. The lamp flickered in and out rhythmically with the illumination of the cell and the viewer could see the shadow of the cross cast back onto the far side of the same disc. This latter method, modified now by having the neon lamp at a second and separate receiver Nipkow disc, would be the basis of Baird's mainstream mechanical television.

The intriguing factor in all these early accounts is the absence of a proper screen, which was in fact already in existence in the mysterious equipment on West Hill. It is likely that Baird already had his basic television scheme worked out, but was tinkering with modified, simplified versions to suit his own research purposes. Baird was at this time seeking a suitable, stationary receiver screen, not a rotating Nipkow disc. As will be seen later, the West Hill receiver was just such a screen, which could accept radio waves directly from the television transmitter and convert them into a visible image on the screen.

The new receiver required still further development before being patented in early 1927. Baird therefore concentrated on improving his Nipkow disc units. The problems to be tackled included an increase in the number of holes in his discs to provide images with more detail, the provision of better screens, a speeding up of the transmitter disc to give more images per second, and the finding of a more sensitive cell. He struggled to refine his equipment during the Hastings period. One bugbear was the serrated disc which interrupted the light, sending out flashes of light at a frequency which was audible if connected electrically to a microphone. The sounds produced were high-pitched like a piccolo for the brighter parts, deep like a trombone for the shades, and silent for complete darkness. If a telephone was connected across the selenium cell when the apparatus was in use, a high-pitched scream resulted. The strength of this noise was interfering with performance and Baird told Victor Mills: 'I'm getting too much noise.' Mills was not impressed by the primitive equipment he saw in the Arcade.' [7] He realized that the problem centred on the weak response of the selenium cell and the deafening noise arising from it. He was now running a radio business and was able to supply Baird with a good amplifier and other pieces of apparatus, and helped Baird clarify his Maltese Cross. But to this day there is a trace of criticism from Mr Mills that he and the 'hidden' Hastings auxiliaries were never given public acknowledgement or thanks. They were part of Baird's secret story which, even as early as Hastings, was already becoming convoluted. It is unlikely that they were allowed to know the actual stage of his achievement and his projected plans.

Victor Mills never believed that the mechanical system had any future. He advised Baird to join forces with some large firm and do research on cathode ray tubes. In a letter to a local researcher, he described the early experiments he witnessed as 'not radio vision'. The shadow was appearing across a distance of just 2 feet. He still regards these early attempts as 'just a stunt. We could make it better but it could never be good; a bit of fun but a waste of time.' Baird's later progress refutes this opinion, but perhaps Mr Mills' appraisal can be attributed to Baird's deviousness. It is possible that the units used were comparative 'toys' by means of which Baird perfected certain components without alerting his part-time aides to his real progress. A clue lies in Mr Mills' letter to the authors, in which he states: 'What I don't understand is why it took him from 1923 to early 1926 to obtain good images using reflected light from the objects being televised. In my opinion, given a good photo- electric cell, or even better, an electric multiplier tube, we could have had live TV, 30 lines, going by the end of the year- a real stunt.' Baird had been toiling at television for at least eight years and was probably just as aware of these possibilities, if not more so. Given the circumstantial evidence to be described it is logical to assume that he was already using reflected light from the televised subjects and had proper images.

The materials used in Baird's machines were gleaned from a cross-section of everyday life. There were 7 lb biscuit tins, bobbins, darning needles, cardboard from hatboxes, an electric fan motor and a variety of lenses. He soon became a well-known figure pottering around antique shops and scrapyards looking for odds and ends. Mrs A. Coleman of Hastings worked at Jepson's Fancy Goods Establishment, and recalls Baird as a very quiet man who would call in two or three times a week to buy Meccano parts for his invention. Mrs Cicely Englefield wrote from Canada that Baird bought from her father-in-law's cycle shop the entire stock of magnifying lenses used in acetylene lamps for bicycles - all were destined for his scanning discs. Oil-filled lanterns used by the police were replaced by electric torches in Hastings over the period 1918 to 1923, and Baird bought a considerable number of the defunct lamps for their bullseye lenses. He polished bits of tin and used them as brightly shining chambers for his 2,000-candlepower light. A member of a Hastings firm which still runs a scrapyard recalls that his late manager frequently talked of Baird's forays into the yards seeking wheels and spare parts for his experiments. In a letter to the authors Mr R.D.Cott said: 'Mr Gobbett, the then manager, told me he was a nuisance, but when the telly began just after the war he, Mr Gobbett, was one of the first to obtain a TV.' Perhaps the weirdest of his improvised materials were lumps of wood and bits of spare coffin material from an undertaker. They formed the base for his machine.

Instead of using one large stationary lens to focus an object image through the transmitter Nipkow disc spiral or spirals of holes, Baird started using lens spirals. Each lens focused directly onto the cell, the lens images being subdivided before reaching the cell by using extra rotating slotted discs placed between the lensed disc and the cell. He was positively profligate with lenses and in constant need of new supplies. As the discs grew even faster lenses frequently came loose from their sockets and ricocheted around the room like bursting shells. At such times Baird and company dived under-tables for cover, in the knowledge that a direct hit on the head could result in a fractured skull. As he progressed and the discs grew larger and more solid, the lenses too became bigger and more menacing. Sometimes the apparatus itself would tremble, leap off balance and fly from one side of the room to the other as though propelled by a poltergeist. This was a disturbing feature of his experiments that was to continue until the thirties.

The townspeople were soon aware of a wonder in their midst. Baird and Mephy's eating habits drew comment: they seemed to subsist on tea and buns. Their sartorial style also attracted attention. Both walked around in shoes or sandals - without socks - at a time when formalities were usually observed, even in a seaside resort. The presence of an artist named Gerald, who rented a shop in the Arcade and sported the regulation artist's hat and big velvet bow tie, only added to the curiosity value. It was La Boheme, with the scientist-inventor replacing the poet as hero. Baird was living fairly hand-to-mouth but coping valiantly with near-crippling bad health.

A frequent visitor was a small, dapper man who lived at the Marina, William Le Queux, a popular thriller writer who was also one of Britain's keenest radio enthusiasts. Superficially Le Queux was an obvious type, a card. The wife of Baird's landlord in the Arcade, Mrs Louise Leighton, remembers him as a rather fussy little man who obviously knew that history was in the making and wanted part of the action. Mrs Leighton recalled one incident that led to a singeing of Le Queux's dignity. He had asked to be pictured with Baird in the lab. Le Queux never travelled without his poodle which, as expected, was posed for the picture. As Le Queux, poodle and Baird stood to attention, Mr Leighton lifted an old- fashioned flash-powder pan. There was an explosion, and when the smoke cleared it revealed Le Queux and Baird minus eye-brows, and the once-proud poodle looking very ragged. But this fussy little individual may not have been quite what he seemed. His presence may have been a portent of the future secret life of Baird. Le Queux had in fact served the British government in Secret Service work before and during the First World War.[8] Unknown to themselves, the little team working in Hastings were perhaps strongly attracting attention in some unexpected quarters.

Le Queux was still interested in secret matters after 1918. In 1925 he wrote an article on the use of radio by spies for transmitting secret coded messages.[9] He was an early radio pioneer and possessed a license to transmit, call sign 2AZ.[10] In 1924 he is seen standing to the left of Baird in a photograph, inspecting Baird's television equipment.[11] Le Queux was to become first president of the Hastings Radio Society, elected in 1924.[12] Not surprisingly, Baird would be invited to give the inaugural lecture, 'Television', [13] and Le Queux would describe Baird's equipment in an article that year. [14]

Work was progressing, and on 27 June 1923, in *The Times* personal column, Baird made his first public attempt to obtain help. Lodged between an advertisement about shares in the Canadian Pacific Railway and a gentleman driver on European roads seeking to act as chauffeur/courier (own expenses paid) appeared the appeal: 'Seeing by wireless - inventor of apparatus wishes to hear from someone who will assist (not financially) in making working models.' Despite the no-finance clause, this advertisement probably attracted Baird's first official offers of backing. He wrote later: 'I thought it better not to ask directly for money and I think this was wise.'

One of the first to bite was Mr Odhams of Odhams Press. another was W. Day, who owned a prosperous wireless and cinema business. Baird hoped to form a company comprising himself, Le Queux, Odhams and Will Day.[15] Odhams wanted to investigate first, and dispatched two experts, F.H.Robinson, the Director of Broadcasting (an Odhams publication), and Captain A.G. D. West, then chief research engineer with the B B C and later to join Baird's company. Both were impressed with what Baird allowed them to see, but both agreed that he had a long way to go. Baird reported that Mr Odhams was very charming, gave him tea and entertained him with a respect and consideration 'which were a balm to the soul of the struggling inventor accustomed to being regarded as a dangerous crank'.[16]

Day was a Victorian figure, an astute businessman and one-time backer of William Friese-Greene, another legendary British inventor whose career bore a certain resemblance to that of Baird. In 1889 Friese-Greene patented a camera for producing a series of photographic images on celluloid; he also took out patents on colour photography and experimented with three-dimensional images. He even applied for two patents on 'the electrical transmission of images' - television - in 1900 and 1901. Friese-Green seems to have lacked the flair to capitalize on his inventions, though his many commercial setbacks do not seem to have affected his essentially sunny and romantic nature. Though posterity was to eulogize him in 1950 in the film The Magic Box, with Robert Donat playing the part of the inventor of cinephotography, he received scant help or recognition from contemporaries. Just as Baird, too, would oppose foreign influences that threatened to dominate British television, Friese-Greene made his last appearance combating a move to dismember the British Film Industry. He turned up on 5 May 1921 at a meeting of film-makers and distributors, chaired by the press baron Lord Beaverbrook. Under discussion was the question of Britain's continued involvement in making films, or the alternative - accepting ready-made ones from America. Friese-Greene spoke from the heart, demanding that British films should continue. The meeting agreed to help new film production in Britain. Then there was a commotion around Friese-Greene's seat: people rushed in his direction, but he had collapsed and died. Eighteen pence was all that was found in his pocket. Friese-Greene was the epitome of the struggling inventor who beat a path for others to follow. Many of his ideas were sound and it is possible that his work on colour and stereoscopic vision may have stirred and even influenced Baird, through his connection with Day.

Some sources have suggested that Baird and Day became partners in 1924, but Baird's first patent application, dated 26 July 1923, giving his address as the Lodge, Helensburgh, also names Wilfred Ernest Lytton Day, of Highgate, London. The full patent, No. 222,604, for a system of transmitting views, portraits and scenes by telegraphy or wireless telegraphy, was eventually published on 9 October 1924.

Baird found Day's support a mixed blessing. Day's solicitor made the inventor sign a document whereby he found himself bound to pay all expenses in developing the invention, plus patent costs in every country. Baird had not bothered to read the fine print, so keen was he to have an influx of funds. Fortunately, he later discovered that the document was badly drawn up and therefore unenforcable in law. From the start he was experiencing a new dimension to his struggles - the world of middlemen, in which he was frequently at sea.

He was happiest when immersed in his work, and it took a brave individual to interrupt him unnecessarily. With the confidence of youth, Norman Loxdale once made such an intrusion. Early in 1923 one of the wireless sets he made as a hobby refused to function. Someone suggested a visit to Baird and so, filled with apprehension, the schoolboy climbed the steps of the Arcade with the radio under his arm. He knocked on the door.

'It was opened by a tallish fellow, not at all the ogre I had expected,' Mr Loxdale told the authors. 'I said, "Can you help me, sir?"

"What can I do for you, son?" he replied. I showed him my radio and said it would not work.' John, as young Norman learned to call Baird, said he was busy, but took the chunk of ebonite with its valves and tuning coils and examined it. He told Norman he couldn't do it for him, but gave him a piece of string and told him to chew it. 'I thought he was having me on,' said Mr Loxdale, but he did as he was told, and with great patience John proceeded to show him how to use the chewed string to measure the resistance, and how to perform various other tests, until the set was working perfectly - it continued to do so for a number of years.

'I thanked him very much,' Mr Loxdale said, 'and as I was going out of the door I asked, "Do you mind if I come up and see you again?"

'He replied, "Come up when you feel like it as long as you don't touch anything." ' Norman did return again and again, and was soon one of 'Baird's Irregulars'. He says: 'I just couldn't keep away from the place. One day he asked if I was good at making things and set me to cutting holes and making a circle in the centre of a disc.' He also made another disc and other bits of equipment, working in an old washhouse at home in Wellington Street, Hastings, and Baird must have sensed that the boy was a near-replica of himself when young. The young enthusiast watched the comings and goings of Baird's aides, one after another, working on various facets of the experiments. He was particularly struck by the contribution of Victor Mills, and says:

Baird was the sort of chap who would give you something to do and just leave you to it. Afterwards it was either right or wrong. Some people found him rather aloof. His ideas were everything and he related mainly to those who could assist him in that. He was a very clever man. He knew how to construct things but he did have a lot of help with the people around him, though I don't think they really understood what he was trying to do. I think they were as much in the dark as I was.

Norman recalls Victor Mills examining the equipment and telling Baird that he was not going to get any results with a selenium cell of the type he was using (it was 2 or 3 inches in diameter) and that he did not think the synchronization was right. Though Baird initially showed unwillingness to follow advice, he would eventually do so, and in this case the cell apparently came down to the size of a shilling. 'John wasn't too happy,' Norman Loxdale recalls, 'and said we're just going to make it worse than ever', but Victor Mills said they did not have sufficient amplification and offered a three-valve amplifier. Baird first tried two valves but later adopted the three-valve model. Typically, when the equipment was photographed for the local paper he removed the third valve. Pictures for public consumption rarely portrayed his equipment as used.

Mr Loxdale said: 'They did get results eventually on the equipment they were using: a Maltese Cross, slightly distorted at first, but it improved. I think my disc was in the machine that worked and congratulated myself at the time on having something to do with Baird, though I wasn't quite sure what was going on.' But young Norman even at this early date was to pick up a number of clues to the diversity of Baird's work. Baird was quite capable of making his own equipment, as witnessed by his electrical work when a boy, but at Hastings he conveyed a completely different impression. 'J. L. B. was no mechanic,' Mr Loxdale insists. He wouldn't know where to start. He knew what he wanted and how it should function, but I'd stake my life on it that I never saw him make anything at all. He always got someone else to do it for him. I asked him once what some piece of equipment was for and he said, "3D - you know what I mean: vertical, horizontal and depth." The man who was busy refining shadowgraphs of a Maltese Cross was apparently quietly working on 3D as well. Again the answer to it all could be in Mr Loxdale's own words: 'Before he patented or published anything, he had it working. These days people patent it first.'

Norman Loxdale's eye-witness account of Baird at work in Hastings describes a sequence of events that in all probability was being repeated in several other parts of Britain in 1923, where Baird was also at work with entirely different sets of colleagues. One can make an informed guess at the projects: 3D, colour, reflected infra-red and radio-wave object detection systems, all being worked on concurrently. One recalls the small, rectangular components made in secret by his friend, Alex Horn, from 1919 onward, components that one expert many years later thought were for radar.

Baird had returned to Helensburgh in 1922 for the marriage of his second sister, Jeannie ('Tottie'), to a minister, the Rev Neil Conley. He had his picture taken in dark morning coat and flyaway collar, looking remarkably unlike his usual self. He returned to Helensburgh again in 1923 for a forgotten sojourn that figures in no subsequent account of the period. An article in the *Helensburgh Times* later in the year states, under the heading 'A Coming Wonder': 'Recently Mr Baird was in Helensburgh on a visit to his home and, in conjunction with Mr Youdall, of Messrs Youdall and Sprott, carried out several experiments in connection with his invention. Ill health and a lack of material, however, drove him south and he has since been in Folkestone, Tunbridge Wells and London.' Strangely, there was no mention of his headquarters, Hastings. Norman Loxdale remembers the gap and says: 'In 1923 he went away for quite a number of months and he then came back and finished a disc.'

A witness of Baird's 'lost' period is Mrs Elizabeth Honeyman, now living in Coventry. In 1923 she was nineteen, in domestic service when she encountered John Baird in Helensburgh, where it was said, even then, that 'He could see through walls.' Mrs Honeyman frequently spent her days off at a house at the corner of Colquhoun Street and West Clyde Street where her friend, the parlourmaid in the villa where she worked, lived with her step-mother. Beyond the house was a drying area and an outbuilding that served as a washhouse. It was there Baird was ensconced most days, at a time when he was presumed to be in Hastings. Mrs Honeyman says: 'We met him often when going into the house. I learned he was a minister's son, a quiet and studious gentleman who worked a lot at weekends, when you saw him most.' Baird was not particularly acquainted with any of the occupants in the four-storey tenement. He did, however, tell Mrs Honeyman's friend something of what he was attempting. Mrs Honeyman recalls: 'She joked with me afterwards about being careful what boyfriend I took up with as Logie Baird was inventing a machine that was going to throw out pictures and that my mother would see them seated at her fireside miles away in New Stevenston, Lanarkshire.' Mrs Honeyman experienced a moment of poignant nostalgia half a century later when, on holiday with a group of fellow pensioners, she was staying in Glasgow's Sauchiehall Street in a hall of residence belonging to Strathclyde University. It was called Baird Hall. She says: 'I saw a model of his first TV set there and a bust of him, just like I'd seen him in Helensburgh.' Bad health seems to have driven him south as winter approached, and this time he chose Folkestone as a base. This seems an odd choice if one accepts the traditional story. He had colleagues, a home and a lab in Hastings, yet he chose to continue his work in a town some 40 miles away. The move makes sense, however, if there were facets of his work which he wanted to shield from most of his colleagues. Folkestone was far enough away to do so, yet close enough to Hastings to allow visits from people at his old base, perhaps from J. J. Denton and Mephy, who were most likely to be party to his plans. He certainly does not seem to have mentioned his Hastings connection to his new friends in Folkestone.

Several local newspaper items contradict most versions of the Baird story. In the *Folkestone Herald* in February 1961 a diarist known as the Reamer described seeing Baird at work in the Arcade at Hastings 'with a large plywood disc having small electric bulbs round the edge and hundreds of fourpenny electric batteries. Even then Baird transmitted a picture of his hand onto a screen in the room.'[17] This item drew forth other reminiscences, this time from Mr P.A.Bennett of Folkestone, who had been a director of T. C. Gilbert & Co. Ltd, an electrical contract firm in the town which was also involved in wireless. Mr Bennett believed that Baird had started his first experiments in the firm's premises at Guildhall Street. He stated that Baird had come from Scotland after a breakdown and mistakenly gave the date as 1924, when Baird was actually in Hastings. Mr Bennett said that Baird lodged in West Terrace where, as usual, his landlady eventually objected to his cluttering up his bedroom with experimental equipment.

T.C.Gilbert were recommended to him when he subsequently looked for accommodation. Mr Bennett added: 'He stayed here perhaps two or three months, and during that period was in touch with someone in the Tunbridge Wells area who was experimenting with a light cell, a component which Baird would have found useful. When he left Folkestone I felt certain he went into that area and, in retrospect, it seems that he went to Hastings some time after that.'

Baird was welcomed at Gilbert's, where he was given a bench in the workshop and other facilities including the use of some Western Electric audio frequency amplifiers. Mr Bennett says that at this point Baird used ordinary carbon-filament electric light bulbs and the then new neon lamps which gave a very coarse- grained screen with little definition.[18] By a fitting coincidence the shop has now been taken over by Radio Rentals, the firm that acquired the Baird company. They were unaware of the connection but when they read Mr Bennett's story they erected a plaque on the premises. Unveiled in the summer of 1961 by the inventor's widow, it states that he conducted some of his earliest experiments there, giving the controversial date of 1924.[19]

The time was fast approaching when Baird would step into the public eye. Already *Chambers' Journal*, in its July-November issue 1923 had published an article entitled 'Seeing by Wireless'. It explained how it had fallen to a clever young inventor, a Mr. J.L. Baird, to show how persons, views and even moving scenes could be instantaneously visualized by special wireless instruments. It added prophetically: 'At present, the apparatus is complex and expensive, but no doubt as time passes it will be simplified and cheapened, so that we may shortly be able to sit at home in comfort and watch a thrilling run at an international football match, or the finish of the Derby.' Baird would accomplish the latter just eight years later!

Public interest was now aroused. By 1924 there were nearly 700,000 people tuning into B B C Radio, many of them enthusiastic builders of their own sets. The *Radio Times* was already a regular feature in many homes and it was in this publication on 26 April that William Le Queux broke the news that Baird had surpassed the efforts of Jenkins in America, and his own earlier experiments, by successfully transmitting images between two totally different machines.

Synchronism was being achieved with perfect accuracy.

The pace was hotting up. Baird was now making frequent visits to London, paving the way for his move to the capital. He had in the meantime got to know W. C. Fox, a respected Press Association reporter, who was to prove a loyal and long-suffering ally. Fox helped to publicize early progress and eventually became so caught up in the Baird whirlwind that he actually joined the company for a couple of hectic years. On 9 April 1924 he reported through the Press Association, on a special experiment 'Cinematography by Wireless'. 'The invention of a young Englishman, a wireless device whereby a cinematograph programme may be received by a valve set in a similar manner to musical pieces, was tested last night. The tests were carried out from a South Coast town and wireless amateurs listening in to the Paris "Radiola" and other Continental stations may have "heard" the picture transmission, although they were unable to see anything.' The transmission was characterized by a curious high-pitched whistle with a hint of regular and very rapid interruptions. Baird was flexing his muscles, testing his transmission powers. The PA report ended: 'With the necessary apparatus the signals could have been converted into pictures.'

On 30 April 1924, the *Hasting Times* reported that Baird was in process of forming a company to promote vision by wireless, to be known as Television Ltd. 'It is proposed to proceed immediately with the construction of a finished commercial machine for use in cinemas and other places of entertainment, reproducing topical scenes as they occur.' In his prospectus Baird was already showing signs of an enthusiasm for television in the cinema, coupled with work on TV for the home. This would continue until his death. The article said that in the meantime the company's business premises would be at 2 Queen's Arcade, Hastings, where Baird's laboratory had been for some time. Various accounts have given Baird's number in the Arcade as 2, 4, 6 and 8. He himself suggested that, whatever the number, he first rented the premises in 1924, but contemporaries have placed him there as early as 1923.

'Here I spent many happy hours,' he wrote, adding however that he 'came as near to death as I am ever likely to come and survive.' The plant had mushroomed into a positive tangle of wires, batteries, bulbs and whirling discs. He had bought several hundred flash lamp batteries to realize his dream of a 2,000 volt power supply by joining sufficient dry batteries end to end. The work was completed and he was connecting the batteries to some part of the network of wires when his attention wandered. In July 1924 a local paper reported:

> *Mr J. L. Baird, who claims to be the inventor of television (seeing by wireless) met with an accident whilst carrying out experiments in his workshop in Queen's Avenue on Thursday. A loud explosion was heard and Mr Baird was found lying helpless on the floor. He had apparently been at work upon the machine when a short-circuit occurred. He was hurled across the room by the force of the shock and was dazed. The voltage carried by the wires was 1200. Mr Baird's hands were badly burned and he was much shaken. The apparatus was damaged*[20]

Mr Leighton, the photographer and owner of the premises, was one of the first on the scene and found him in agony but comparatively calm. He took Baird to a local chemist to have his hands treated and bandaged. Baird was sufficiently recovered a fortnight later to be indignant about the report of the accident. The reporter's efforts to play safe on the question of television had not escaped him. Baird wrote, 'My attention has been drawn to a paragraph in your issue of July 26th ult. in which it is stated that I have invented a machine by which "I claim to see by wireless." The statement is both misleading and damaging.'[21] He then gave references to professional journals who had reported

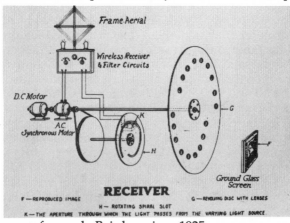

Diagram of an early Baird receiver. 1925

his progress and closed: 'The word "claims" is therefore entirely out of place and gives the wrong impression.' He was encountering from the start the attitude which regarded the lone, commercial pioneer as some form of upstart or adventurer to be treated with caution, an opinion which would mistakenly gain ground in some quarters through the swash-buckling attitude adopted by some of those who would later undertake the promotion of his invention.

The incident seems to have aroused unpleasantness with one of the local landlords (not Mr Leighton) - Baird was considered a threat to his property. He felt, anyway, that the time was ripe for a move to London. Will Day facilitated this in August 1924 by finding him a laboratory at 22 Frith Street, Soho, which Baird would occupy until February 1926. Baird now stood poised before a far more complex challenge than any which he had encountered so far. The happy days of secluded experiments were over. It would henceforth take all his determination, courage and imagination to face the added slings and arrows of an outraged scientific establishment which found it hard to accept that practical radio vision was surfacing so unexpectedly from a totally unknown source.

His stay at Hastings had seen much groundwork accomplished on straight television. He was swift to discern, however, that this new instrument could be adapted for purposes other than entertainment, purposes which could revolutionize warfare and navigation and affect the destiny of mankind. There were others in high places who also desired television for these very reasons and whose scientists were struggling to achieve any form of electrical vision. These people had begun to make a discreet surveillance of his work, though they little realized just how far he was advancing along and beyond their line of thought. They would doubtless have been intrigued by the 'box of tricks' hauled up West Hill early in 1923. It certainly puzzled Norman Loxdale, who recalled: 'That piece of equipment I remember in particular. It was like a parabola, a reflector with a lot of associated equipment, also a converter. It ran off a 12 or 16 volt car-type battery. I had only seen it twice. John told me that some day he wanted me to help him work on this.' That day arrived when Baird asked if some of Norman's scout friends would help him carry equipment to the top of West Hill. He remembers it very well.

It was a Friday evening, growing dark. The sun was going down, though the sky was absolutely clear and it was bitterly cold. We were told to stop on top of the Lady's Path, one of the highest spots on the West Hill. We set the equipment up. All of a sudden he remembered he had forgotten something. He told me to stay there. Meanwhile, my other three colleagues went back with the trek cart, leaving me alone up there. John eventually came back. He took the reflector, which had a form of spike in the middle with a knob on it, and first pointed it towards East Hill. At the same time, he was looking into an opaque glass plate, not quite square, set into a case. Lines were being made on it. He was looking under the sort of cloth used in cameras at the time. This he had over his head. I grew curious and took up one of the corners of the cloth. He swung from under and said: 'You must never do this. I might have been taking a picture.'

He then moved the reflector towards the sea and then up towards the sky and he said to me: 'Come along and have a look at this.' It wasn't fluorescing. All I saw was a brownish picture, not quite a picture. Something was moving on the screen, like a wave, yet not quite a wave. John remained there until it was quite dark. There was no cathode ray tube. The screen was made in some other way, iron filings, ferrous oxide or something. I had expected something lighter and more fluorescing on the screen. Anyway, it was growing really dark and he said: 'That's enough for today.'

The mystery increased as Baird simply waved him off and remained alone on the windswept hill with the mystery machine. He shouted down to Norman: 'I'll see you at the Arcade.' Norman Loxdale never discovered who helped Baird back with the equipment; it is likely that Baird had someone posted on a hill nearby who later joined him. Mr Loxdale says:

I've often thought of that scene and I think he was getting reflections from the sea, from the sky, and perhaps from the East Hill opposite. I'm pretty certain J.L.B. was obtaining signals back from the sky, from what is known as the Appleton Layer. He was improvising some form of what we now know as radar. I don't know if he ever published what I saw on the Hill. He was quite pleased with the results. He was never one to articulate much. He was pleased a few times but otherwise he was pretty calm whether things worked or not. He left in 1923 for quite a time and I never saw that piece of equipment again. When he eventually left Hastings he gave me the offer of joining him at work in London, but I felt I was too young and was in the middle of school. I didn't see Baird again until the early thirties when he showed me some of the equipment he was then making in the Crystal Palace.

It seems that Baird was already giving his invention a broad base so that it could evolve to meet many needs. A year or so later, on 28 November 1924, a secret file was opened at the Air Ministry in Kingsway, London: its title was 'Experiments in connection with the use of television in aircraft'. If one believes traditional historical accounts, the date seems amazing - not 1934 or 1935, when television was really starting, but a decade earlier. One of the file's main contributors was a certain Major, later Lt Col Lefroy, an intelligence officer. When approached in 1926 for information for the file, he revealed: 'I have been making abstracts of published accounts of Mr J.L.Baird's work in connection with television since April, 1924. I have also discussed the matter with persons who have seen his apparatus and witnessed his demonstrations.'[22] The file noted a newspaper article of November 1924, on the possible wartime use of television in aircraft for reconnaisance, written by Dr W. H. Eccles, President of the Radio Society of Great Britain and the future (1928) President of the Institution of Electrical Engineers.[23] Those biscuit tins and bullseye lenses from a back room in a holiday resort were beginning to cause rumblings in the corridors of power.

NOTES
1   Baird, autobiographical notes, *Sermons, Soap and Television*, ch. 4, p. 1.
2   V. R. Mills, *Hastings and St Leonards Observer*, 4 November 1978.
3   'Inventor Injured', *Hastings and St Leonards Observer*, 26 July 1924.
4   'Wireless Invention at Hastings', *Hastings and St Leonards Observer*, 19 January 1924.
5   Baird, 'The Baird Television System', *Amateur Wireless and Electrics*, 10 May 1924. Baird, 'An Account of Some Experiments in Television', *Wireless World and Radio Review*, 14, 7 May 1924, p. 153.
6   Baird, 'Seeing by Wireless', *Chambers Journal*, November 1923, p. 776.
7   V. R. Mills, 'Invention of Television', letter to *Electronics and Power*, May 1976, p. 310.
8   R. Deacon, 'A History of the British Secret Service', Muller, 1978, p.

129. N. St Barbe-Sladen, *The Real Le Queux, The Official Biography of William Le Queux*, Nicholson and Watson, 1938.

9   W. Le Queux, 'The Wireless Spy Menace', Wireless, 19 September 1925, p. 17.

10   List of Experimental Transmitting Stations Licensed in the United Kingdom', *Wireless World and Radio Review*, 1 July 1922, pp. 418-25.

11   R. F. Tiltman, *Baird of Television*, Seeley Service, 1933, photograph opposite p. 64.

12   *Hastings and St Leonards Observer*, 12 April 1924, p. 8.

13   'Television', *Hastings and St Leonards Observer*, 3 May 1924, p. 3.

14   W. Le Queux, 'Television - A Fact', *Radio Times*, 25 April 1924.

15   *Baird of Television*, p. 64.

16   Baird, *Sermons, Soap and Television*.

17   The Reamer,'Talk of the Town,Folkestone Herald, 11 February 1961.

18   P. A. Bennett, 'When J. L. Baird Experimented in Folkstone', *Folkestone Herald*, 25 February 1961.

19   'Pioneer of Television Research, Memorial to J.L.Baird,' *Folkestone Herald*, 3 June 1961.

20   'Inventor Injured'. *Hastings and St Leonards Observer*, 26 July 1924.

21   Baird,'Seeing By Wireless,*Hastings and St Leonards Observer*,9August 1924.

22   'The Use of Television in Aircraft', opened on 28 November 1924, Secret Air Ministry File, Air 2/S24132, Public Record Office, Kew.

23   'Aeroplane with Eyes', *Daily Express*, 18 November 1924.

7

World Beater

In April 1925 a radio enthusiast called Bob Kennedy, on leave from India, was honeymooning with his bride, Ret, in London. Kennedy, an electrical engineer from Dundee, worked in jute mills in the subcontinent but had built a reputation as an amateur expert on radio - in fact he held licence No. 2 in India, pipped only by the Marconi Company itself. He had recently distinguished himself by informing the authorities that a ship whose signals no one else had tracked, was sinking in the Red Sea. The young electrician was fascinated when he learned that a fellow Scot, John Logie Baird, was to give the first public demonstration of television at Selfridge's in Oxford Street. No complete pictures were promised, merely outlines, but even this step in radio vision would be a marvel. What Bob Kennedy and his wife witnessed at Selfridge's confirms the mystery that underlies Baird's experiments, and gave Kennedy a tale which bewildered fellow radio hams in the years ahead.

As the couple stared at the outlines of a grinning mask - just two gashes for the eyes, one for the mouth - the screen went blank. Then a picture, not a still but the live, moving head of a man appeared. The features were recognizably those of His Royal Highness the Prince of Wales, the future King Edward VIII and Duke of Windsor: this was ten months before Baird gave the first public demonstrations of true television pictures, in January 1926. seconds later the image vanished and the screen again showed only outlines, which Baird at that point claimed was all he had achieved. He would later use a portrait of the Prince of Wales for an intermission filler between television programmes. The Prince was a radio ham also, and Patron of the London Wireless Society. He befriended the inventor and was to prove a useful ally in the 1930s in Baird's eventual struggle against what he suspected was a backdoor American takeover of British television.

All the traditional accounts, including Baird's own, name William Taynton, an office boy, as the first individual to be televised. But the Kennedy story suggests that the Prince of Wales might be a contender. However, a Falkirk radio engineer and businessman, Mr John Hart, one of Baird's band of secret helpers, always claimed that he was the first; new evidence from the West Indies, mentioned earlier, makes it likely that someone from the Caribbean could have held the honour; while the doorman of a London club said for years that he was the one. The plot thickened in 1951 when, at the unveiling of a plaque to Baird at 22 Frith Street, his Soho laboratory, a Mr J.E.Hamelford showed the assembled company a frayed letter, written and signed by Baird on his company's letterhead, saying that Hamelford was the first person to be televised.[1] Witnesses state that the signature on Hamelford's letter was definitely Baird's. One certain fact emerges: the details that Baird made public were far from representing the whole story. It had been thought that at this early period he had worked with just one or two machines. In fact, he probably used many and had already achieved true television pictures. He liked to work well in advance of public demonstrations; he would announce certain objectives by a specific date and then almost miraculously deliver the goods. The groundwork would have been done months before. By 1925, though desperately short of funds, he was working intensely to launch television at 22 Frith Street, the premises organized by Will Day.

The trail of his hidden machines is now fairly cold, but recently one of them turned up in Falkirk, the Scottish town which had so many associations with his ancestors, thus confirming the previously unsuspected existence of units other than those Baird allowed to be publicised. The existence of the Falkirk transmitter,[2] as it has now been called, poses several questions, and leads one to take another look at the South Kensington Science Museum apparatus, presented by Baird in early September 1926 and still there.[3] That machine has long been believed to be the original one used for the world's first demonstrations to be described later, of instantaneous, living, moving pictures by wire and wireless. This is an oversimplification, perhaps, as even a quick glance at contemporary technical articles and interviews reveals a staggering variety of models and, incidentally, indicates with hindsight just how devious Baird was forced to be in safeguarding his work.

The Falkirk transmitter dates from the same period as the unit in South Kensington, approximately 1925-6. For half a century it languished in the Falkirk Museum until a new curator, Mr Jack Sanderson, made a fresh inventory. He paid special attention to a machine with discs and lenses which lay unheeded in a cellar. The unit was known to have come from the father of television, J. L. Baird. It had been loaned to schools and children had tinkered with it. Mr Sanderson sensed its importance and got in touch with Strathclyde University; the unit was subsequently valued at many thousands of pounds and taken for renovation to the Royal Scottish Museum, in Edinburgh.

It had been assumed that the unit was a Baird receiver, of which several are still in existence. The Falkirk Museum archives reveal that, like the Science Museum version, their unit also had claims to be the original television transmitting section as used by Baird in experiments which led him from outlines to true television. Half of it was missing, but what remained indicated that the unit was capable of beaming pictures across the Atlantic and beyond, and had the elements of a three-dimensional and colour television system as well. Baird's first public demonstration of transatlantic, colour and 3D television did not take place until 1928. He was clearly running ahead of himself again with the Falkirk unit. The first indication that he was experimenting with 3D television appeared in an article published in January 1926[4] and the first indication of colour television experiments in August of the same year.[5]

The Falkirk machine was taken to Scotland in September 1926, within days of the other one arriving at South Kensington. An unlikely explanation of its provenance appeared in the *Falkirk Herald*.[6] This article mentions the enigmatic Mr Hart, who owned a Falkirk radio shop, and who apparently had been in London for the National Radio Exhibition at Olympia. He called at Baird's premises, and after a congenial chat he was inexplicably handed the machine, which had been in use in the laboratory until just a couple of days before. Mr Hart was told he could exhibit it in his shop, on condition that it was eventually transferred to the museum.'[7] It does not seem plausible that Baird would lightly divest himself of a working machine at such a crucial period. When Mr Hart's widow was interviewed in Scotland recently, she revealed that her husband had been no stranger to Baird, but had cooperated with the inventor for many years. Mr Hart had been no ordinary shopkeeper either. As early as 1925 he protected his premises from burglars with a radio beam that set off an alarm if crossed. He would spend late nights working on a system of coils and then hurry south for a rendezvous with Baird. Once again, reality differed from the public version.

The Falkirk machine was probably used in transmissions between Scotland and London, not publicized at the time but now known to have taken place. The Falkirk Museum archives clearly point to its use at a date later than the presentation to Mr Hart; they mention it as 'the transmission portion of apparatus used by Mr J.L. Baird in the experiments which led to the transmission of human faces from Glasgow to London on January 27th, 1927', a previously unknown event. Baird is known to have conducted transmissions to London from several provincial cities, including Belfast and Leeds, in preparation for his proposed national television service. The Falkirk transmitter was almost certainly no mere exhibition piece during its first year in Scotland. In 1928 Mr Hart staged a radio exhibition in Falkirk. Baird, was photographed with the transmitter. Also in the photograph was a dummy quite unlike any seen in the published work of Baird and presumably used in his secret experiments in Scotland.

The Falkirk machine included several intriguing features, the most notable being the use of image interlacing. Two spirals of eight lenses are arranged on a disc in such a manner that the two 8-line images interlace together, to give a 16-line image. Baird needed only to place red-orange filters over one set of lenses and blue-green filters across the other and he had a form of colour television, plus the beginnings of stereoscopic vision, one spiral giving a left eye view. The other spiral a right eye view. Today the principle of image or picture interlacing, which helps to prevent image flicker to the observer, is one of the most important aspects of modern television, yet it has never been attributed to Baird. British electronic television presents twenty-five completed images per second or fifty half images per second, in other words fifty half images are interlinked to give twenty-five complete images per second. Modern television interlacing normally consists of scanning lines one, three, five and so on, and then swiftly retracing and scanning lines two, four, six and so on. The two half images are then imposed almost simultaneously, accommodating the eye and eliminating flicker by preventing the observer from responding to a definite pattern of scanning. If interlacing is not used then a much larger number of television images per second is required to prevent flicker. The television camera output signal frequency would increase, thus requiring a higher-frequency transmitter carrier beam, resulting in a reduced range for the television picture.

Baird would utilize an interlacing system for colour television from 1926, calling it his staggered scanning disc. He developed an interlacing scanning disc which had three sets of holes, each in spiral formation. The first spiral scanned image lines one, four, seven, ten, thirteen and so on. The second spiral scanned lines two, five, eight, eleven, fourteen and so on, while the third spiral scanned lines three, six, nine, twelve, etc. He based the system on the three colour system of photography: the three additive colours, red, green and blue, when appropriately combined, supplied all the other colours. He finished with images having an inter-laced line structure of alternate lines of red, green and blue, repeated across the screen. In 1933 Baird was publishing the fact that he knew that such interlacing discs would reduce image flicker.[8]

The idea of interlacing images certainly predates Baird's personal use of the idea from 1925 onwards. There are many methods of interlacing, all patentable. Research uncovered two paper patents: S.L.Hart, GB15,270 (1915), and W.S.Stephenson and G.W.Walton, GB218,766 (1924), of the General Radio Co. London. W. S. Stephenson, a Canadian millionaire and First World War hero, gave Baird a close run to be first home with working television. Stephenson was also to play an important role in the Second World War: under his code name Intrepid and assisted by Ian Fleming, author of the James Bond books, he set up collaboration in the USA between the British Secret Service and the 0 S S (later the C IA), just established under William Donovan. Stephenson was dabbling with secret signalling from 1924, when he purchased a German 'Enigma' system and apparently worked on radar with R. Watson-Watt in 1934 (the year before Watt is supposed to have invented radar).[9]

It should be noted that by sending out the images one part at a time, that is red image first, blue image second, and so on, the video output frequency of the camera is minimized; the carrier frequency can be correspondingly reduced, and the range of the images thus increased. Baird was to be the world master of interlacing; in the Second World War he would interlace 200-line images three times over, to give 600-1ine images, displaying both 3D and colour on a screen 2 feet by 6 inches by 2 feet.[10] By early 1942 he would interlace *five* times over for 500-1ine 3D-colour images.[11]

In March 1938 *Electronics* (USA) reported interlacing four times over by Du Mont for flicker-free all-electronic television images. By using 4 to 1, and not the normal 2 to 1, interlacing as used in the Marconi-EMI 1936 cameras, Du Mont thus reduced the camera output frequency, halved the transmitter carrier band width required and greatly increased the range of the transmitter signals. Multiple interlacing correctly used can be a most useful asset in television. The television historian J.H.Udelson states that RCA first employed interlacing at Camden, New Jersey, in 1934, but revealed that another American researcher, Ulysses A. Sanabria, had used a system of interlacing as early as 1929.[12] However, a glance at Sanabria's 1929 patent shows it to be identical to Baird's earlier three-spiral colour discs.

It is now clear, however, that interlacing can be dated earlier still, to the very birth of television. In a 1938 lecture Baird stated that the equipment used at Selfridge's was interlaced. He added: 'It is interesting to note that this device produced a form of interlaced scanning, and we are now employing modifications of this in some of our latest experiments.[13] Noticeably, the South Kensington machine had two non-interlaced spirals of eight lenses per spiral, which only gave an 8-line picture. It would seem, however, that the Falkirk transmitter was, at the least, in the direct line of machines which provided the first pictures, but Baird's virtuosity and fecundity with ideas make it now virtually impossible to say with certainty what were the exact specifications of the machines used in his first successful public demonstrations. W.C.Fox, Baird's Press Association friend, has stated to the authors that Baird had the Kensington unit specially made up in 1926 for presentation to the Science Museum. The unit was never a working model and is definitely not Baird's original equipment. Mr Fox was present at the January 1926 demonstrations and saw the almost completely boxed in transmitter. He could see no sign of a wobble in the line of the rotating lenses, such as would occur if a single lens spiral, or a pair of lens spirals, was being used. Was Baird using a circle of lenses? Baird's patents of September 1925 reveal that he proposed using a circle of lenses at the transmitter, the images being subdivided by a second rotating spiral slotted disc before reaching the photocell. Such an arrangement is indicated in an illustrated article of September 1926.[14] However, *The Scotsman* of 2 September that year clearly states that the Kensington unit was the original unit and had been used up to January 1926.[15] Quite obviously Baird was using deception on a grand scale. The situation is further complicated by the gift to Glasgow University in 1927 of a third model, which has subsequently vanished, and the 1930 donation by Baird to the Science Museum of the single spiralled 30-hole receiver supposedly used by him for the January 1926 demonstrations. However Baird's colleague, J.H.Barton-Chapple, has stated that he was asked by Baird in 1930, to make up this receiver disc for presentation to the museum. It is *not* the original receiver.

He had started in 1923 with discs pierced by small holes which let in too little light for the photoelectric cell then in use. He responded with lensed discs in 1924, the lenses concentrating the light onto the cell. In order to prevent flicker he had to increase the speed of these lensed discs which, because of their weight, sometimes unbalanced and even flew off, as described earlier. Interlacing helped to solve this problem by keeping the image flicker and disc speed to a minimum. Ideas came and went. Between 1924 and 1926 he used single and double spiralled discs, discs without spirals, lensed and unlensed discs. At one point he even had a disc 9 feet in diameter, containing around fifty lenses in spiral formation. However, in the spring of 1928 he started selling a machine which used small aluminium discs with spirals of small holes, not lenses. He had improved the sensitivity of his photoelectric cell and returned to his original idea. So in 1924 Baird, with his spiral holed disc arrangement, was once again ahead - by three and a half years - of such a system being patented.

The recurring trouble with lensed discs and his eventual use of infra-red in experiments for seeing in the dark led Baird to another crucial invention which, after some adaptation, subsequently revolutionized medical investigation and telecommunications, and gave birth to a brand-new industry. Baird invented fibre optics, a fact not widely known. Even those who attribute the idea to him consider it a paper patent, never applied. [16] But Baird's fibre optics British patent 285738 of 1926 can be seen in use in several publications, mainly in the USA in 1926 and 1927.[17] Today images or information are sent along thin rods of glass quartz or other transparent material. Baird replaced lenses with a honeycomb of hollow metal rods, packing them closely together.

Individual parts of the object image were passed axially down different tubes to reach a photocell, being scanned by two small slotted, unlensed, rotating discs. The action of the rotating discs was to scan the tube ends, allowing only the image in one tube to reach the photocell at any time. When the rods or tubes were arranged parallel with each other the resultant image was of the same linear dimensions as the object image. He could gain magnification or diminution of the image by slightly diverging or converging the diameters of the rods. Fibre optics was also Baird's ingenious way of cutting the costs of his infra-red work: the rays would have demanded expensive lenses made of special glass, but at a stroke he dispensed with the requirement for these lenses, because the hollow rods provided no obstacle to the passage of the infra-red. The stationary fibre optics tube bundle had dissected the image without the use of rotating lensed discs and transmitted infra-red images without expensive infra-red optics - a clever combination.

By 1924, Baird was set to stake his claim to television, but he needed publicity and funds. A visit to the *Daily Express* in Fleet Street had an amusing if futile result. A burly reporter was sent to interview him in the reception room and listened to his tale, but nothing subsequently appeared. Years later Baird learned from the reporter that he had been told there was a madman downstairs claiming to see by wireless, and had been instructed to watch him carefully as he might have a razor hidden. Such was the novelty of the idea that Baird was attempting to present to the public.

The lengths to which Baird would go to disguise his work are apparent from an account which appeared in a Dundee evening newspaper in 1958. The journalist involved recounted an early visit, probably in 1926, during which he and a friend were televised. He described the machine as having two discs connected to each other by string, knotted through each hole - an impossible contraption. Nevertheless they were successfully televised to onlookers in another room, presumably captured by a genuine machine operating unheeded close by.

Baird received a cool reception when he called at Marconi House, having learned that the general manager, a Mr Gray, had once been a neighbour of his parents in Helensburgh. The interview was short and to the point. He was told that Marconi were not interested in the slightest. Baird left in high dudgeon. It was therefore a pleasant surprise when Mr Gordon Selfridge, owner of the large London department store of that name and looking for an attraction for his birthday week celebrations, thought that television would be a startling novelty and offered him £20 a week for a three-week demonstration in the store. This was launched on the stage of the Palm Court in Selfridge's, and afterwards, from 1 April to 22 April, was to be seen in the electrical department on the first floor. Long queues formed, mostly consisting of ordinary shoppers, but a few scientists also turned up. By peering through a long funnel arrangement they could see the outlines of shapes. The work proved no sinecure for Baird, who found himself busy chatting with customers and dashing to head off old ladies who seemed to have a penchant for tampering with wiring which could have connected 3,000 volts, blowing them prematurely to kingdom come.

Mr P. R. Bird, assistant technical editor of *Popular Wireless and Wireless Review*, gave his impression of the scene in a May 1925 article.[18] He found the inventor almost invisible behind his invention, which was spread out over half a dozen tables and overflowed a floor space about the size of an ordinary room. An artificial wall had been erected across the middle. It was about a foot thick, with a transmitter on one side and the receiver on the other, all boxed in. There were accumulators, arc lamps, switches, batteries, neon tubes, transformers and, he noted whimsically, a biscuit tin (Rich Mixed). He also noticed several small electric motors which bore a strong family resemblance to electric fans from which the blades had been detached. He deduced that despite financial difficulties the inventor was not deterred and his resourcefulness was unbounded. Mr Bird saw the grotesque outline of a mask and was impressed, commenting: 'Baird passed his hand over one of the eyes and made it wink. For all its coy behaviour and winking ways there was a faint, disturbing sense of power about it.'

He ended by saying that he would never forget the grinning gargoyle - the first face he had ever seen by wireless. Other professional magazines duly commented. They were generally impressed but felt that, though Baird had overcome many practical difficulties, there were many more to be tackled before ideal television could be accomplished.

Selfridge's themselves were aware of the machine's importance, and an advertisement made the prescient observation: 'The picture is flickering and defective and at present only simple pictures can be sent successfully; but Edison's first phonograph announced that "Mary had a little lamb" in a way that only hearers who were "in the secret" could understand - and yet from that first result has developed the gramophone of today.'[19]

Newspapers throughout the country carried stories of the demonstrations. Baird could feel reasonably pleased, especially as he surveyed the opposition. Many scientists were still insisting that television could not be accomplished on the principle he was using. Dr E.E.Fournier D'Albe, inventor of the optophone, a device for helping the blind read print, and assisted by Harry Grindell Matthews, had embarked on a complicated system to send every picture element on a different wavelength.[20] A.A.Campbell-Swinton, whose ideas on television were thoroughly sound, had abandoned his work, Baird later commented: 'Fortunately for me'. In the U SA C. F. Jenkins, a worthy rival, was using a pair of circular, specially shaped prismatic discs. Baird said of him: 'He was baulked chiefly, I think, by the insensitivity of the short coils, and showed only shadows.'

Baird's fortunes and mode of living were now on the verge of transformation. On arrival in London he had moved into a room in Ealing where he cooked his own food on a gasring. Above him on the wall was a framed poem:

> Short was the traveller's stay.
> She came but as a guest.
> She tasted life then fled away,
> To everlasting rest.
>
> Elizabeth Brown, passed away,
aged three months.

Further along was a picture of the dead infant in her cot. To lighten the atmosphere the landlord had supplied a few books, including *Jokes and Teasers from Various Columns*. That

Baird sustained his will and seldom flagged in spirit is something of a mystery, considering his surroundings and lifestyle since his return from the Caribbean four years before.

A glimpse of the better life came after the Selfridge's demonstrations, when on 1 May his old schoolfriend Jack Buchanan, now a musical star of the West End and Broadway, threw a party for him at Romano's, a fashionable restaurant of the day. There, in an elegant room under stained glass windows, Buchanan, immaculate as ever with sleek hair and white cuffs showing, cut a marked contrast to the jumble of wires and tin presented to the press.[21] It is unlikely that the machine on show was the best Baird had, or even, for that matter, the one used at Selfridge's, though it strongly resembled it. He was busy doctoring accounts of his experiments at this juncture, so that though general principles could be ascertained, any attempts to follow them up would lead imitators into blind alleys. It was not in character for him to unveil the intimacies of his latest machine to a band of press photographers. His smokescreen tactics were involved when he described a Selfridge's-type machine in *Wireless World* of January 1925, in which he set out to convince readers that he was less advanced than he was. A diagram and words indicate the use of a large, easily unbalanced, single spiralled, lensed disc transmitter. A photograph, however, shows a double spiral of lenses at the transmitter and a small-holed single spiral receiver disc. If the single spiral of lenses had been copied this would have have led to a low-grade picture on account of the necessarily low rotational speed to prevent vibration and consequent image blur. Flicker would also increase as the disc speed fell.[22]

Meanwhile, the quest to improve his light cell continued. Intriguingly, in its Radio Notes the *Illustrated London News* of 9 May commented that he was using a cell more sensitive than the well-known selenium cell. Selenium was sensitive, but had a problem of timelag. With his new photoelectric cell Baird could show the difference between light and total darkness by the use of very powerful lights. His struggle all along had been to improve the cell to respond to the infinitesimally small intensity of light reflected back by a human face. 'Light-light', wrote Baird. 'I soon reached a limit in this direction.' One of his methods had been to build larger discs with bigger lenses, but this had led to the old danger of the equipment unbalancing and ripping apart, with lenses crashing dangerously around the lab.

At one- stage this obsession led him to the macabre use of a human eye. It was considered by some scientists of the time that the light sensitivity of the human eye stemmed from a visual purple fluid found in the retina. Baird decided to experiment in the hope that by artifice he might rival nature. He called at Charing Cross Ophthalmic Hospital and somehow or other managed to charm the chief surgeon into cooperating. He had to wait a long time, as unimpaired eyes are not usually removed, but eventually one was supplied and Baird gingerly accepted it, wrapped in cotton wool. Much later, on 11 February 1928, following his successful transmission across the Atlantic, the *New York Times* carried the story of how Baird claimed that the eye of a London boy had helped him to 'see' across the ocean. The report said that the boy's eye was part of an experimental machine with which Baird made his tests for long-distance television, and told of how he had hurried to the lab by taxi and within minutes had the eye in the machine. He had turned the current on and the waves carrying television were broadcast from his aerial: 'The essential image for television passed through the eye within half an hour of the operation . . .'

This could have happened, but it is unlikely that the eye helped his experiments. Baird loved a good story and this one has the ingredients and style of his old schooldays' favourite, H. G. Wells.

He also had a deadpan sense of humour. A more probable version is given in his own biographical sketch, in which he says he tried to dissect the eye with a razor. This proved too much for him and he ended by throwing it into a nearby canal.

If abundant productivity is one of the hallmarks of genius, then Baird could certainly add that quality to his other claims. His free-ranging mind was already dancing with the myriad possibilities of radiovision and he was simultaneously experimenting in several fields of the new technology. The main factor in his primacy with true pictures lies, though, in a secret he always guarded - in the constitution of his photoelectric cell. He had trouble with its weak response at first, but by 1927 he had made a breakthrough.

A thorough survey by W. Kaempffert[23] of the inventor's work to date appeared in the *New York Times* in March 1927.

The essence of Baird's invention is not his system of chopping up images optically and reassembling them again at the receiving station; not his system of synchronizing the speeds of motors separated by miles; not his method of flooding a form to be televised with invisible infrared, but his photo-electric cell. Highly sensitive cells have been developed in Europe and America but none of them is able to produce impulses as powerful as that of Baird. *No one has been able to wring Baird's secret from him. He will explain everything about his television apparatus - everything but the cell* [authors' italics].

The article also noted that the British government had requested Baird not to disclose any details of his apparatus.

Kaempffert pointed out that Baird's first crude apparatus in the Science Museum in South Kensington was there minus the cell. He referred to an article in Nature of 13 January 1927 which strongly chided Baird. Rather fatuously it said: 'The policy of withholding publication of an essential item does not commend itself to modern inventors. It savours too much of medieval practice, and usually defeats its own object of securing the inventor the fruits of his invention.' Intriguingly, Kaempffert's article described Baird's current apparatus in both diagrams and words, as having sixteen lenses arranged in two spirals, eight lenses per spiral. The two spirals produced two series of adjacent strips (that is 1 6-line interlaced images) . The unit described is thus identical to the 1926 Falkirk Museum transmitter.

With niggardly regard to a fellow countryman, *Nature*, while casting doubts on Baird, went on to praise others who, in reality, were lagging behind. It said: 'There are at least three pioneers in the field who seem to be on the verge of a complete solution to the television problem. Belin in France, and Alexanderson and Jenkins in America, all are approaching the problem by way of transmission of photographs, which they accomplish in great perfection.'

This is an interesting example of the ill-informed criticism which Baird was to encounter so often in his own country. It is a strange fact that he was always more honestly evaluated and acclaimed abroad, a fact noted in *Electronic Engineering* years later, in 1942. While praising Baird on a 3D colour demonstration to the press, it said:

If Mr Baird wishes to obtain more recognition of his pioneer work in television, work which has occupied his life for nearly

*twenty years, he might try growing a beard and calling himself
Professor Bairdsky. He doesn't seem to be getting much encour-
agement in this country as he is. There have been from time to
time people who decry Mr Baird's work, but they cannot
gainsay the fact that he is our television pioneer, and as such
deserves our admiration and better official recognition.*[24]

Baird would have been foolish to have followed *Nature's*
recommendations. In a reply to that magazine on 29 January
1927, he pointed out that his inventions were the property of
a limited company. Disclosure of technical details likely to
assist competing interests would therefore be a grave breach
of trust to the share-holders. But he went on to give an even
more important reason for silence, one that would play an
increasingly more persuasive role in his life. He said: 'I may
further add that we have demonstrated the invention to
government experts, *and have received a letter from the
Government requesting us to withhold publication of technical
details*. [Authors' italics.[25] The simple, happy-go-lucky days
of invention were over. He was beginning to wade into very
deep water.

As we have shown, it is difficult to date many incidents
because Baird postdated them to fit the official version. He
had been ill after the strain of conducting the Selfridge's
demonstrations, but after a few weeks' convalescence he
was forging doggedly ahead. The time was now ripe to
reveal his true pictures, and he always gave the date of his
first breakthrough with real pictures as the first week of
October 1925. He also said that he had returned to using the
selenium cell, improving its timelag performance by means
of a new transformer unit. In view of the hidden incidents
which have since come to light, these statements must be
viewed with some scepticism. At this period he was using a
dummy, a Pinocchio-type head on a stick, and according to
Baird one Friday everything functioned properly: 'The
image of the dummy's head formed itself on the screen with
what appeared to me an almost unbelievable clarity. I had
got it. I could scarcely believe my eyes and felt myself
shaking with excitement.' Mr Cross, a solicitor, had an office
on the first floor at Frith Street. Baird wrote:

*I ran down the little flight of stairs to Mr Cross's office and
seized by the arm his office boy, William Taynton, hauled him
upstairs, and put him in front of the transmitter. I then went to*

the receiver, only to find the screen a blank. William did not like lights and whirring noises and had withdrawn out of range. I gave him 2s. 6d. and pushed his head into position. This time he came through and on the screen I saw the flickering but clearly recognisable image of William's face - the first face to be seen on television - and he had to be bribed with 2s. 6d. for the privilege of this distinction.[26] The original apparatus and the dummy's head are now of course supposedly in the Science Museum at South Kensington.

Captain Hutchinson was back on the scene by late 1925 and became Baird's business manager. For once Hutchinson, the extrovert, was in favour of caution. He advised that they should tread warily over the announcement of successful images lest other wireless firms with richer resources be encouraged to take up the challenge, using Baird's previous work as a guide. Baird disagreed. He wanted to show his results, to demonstrate to the world that he was the first. He was nervous, however, and wrote: 'Television had been achieved. I was definitely able to transmit the living image and it was the first time it had been done. But how to convince the sceptical, hidebound, select and exclusive scientific world? Would they admit that a wretched nonentity working with soap boxes in a garret, had done something which many had stated was impossible?'

A compromise was reached. No large auditorium would be hired, no fanfares. Instead he and Hutchinson decided on a select number of guests, with a representative from *The Times* present to witness and lend respectability to one of the biggest scientific breakthroughs of the century - in the 'garret' in Soho. Reports of the dating of Baird's early television have often been at variance. There were several minor showings of his first pictures in the days preceding the official demonstration, as can be seen from the newspaper reports of the time.[27] The date selected for the official launching was Tuesday 26 January 1926. In his autobiographical sketch Baird himself got the date wrong, giving Friday 27 January - a mistake repeated by his friend and biographer, Sydney Moseley. Baird would repeatedly use the same wrong date for many years afterwards, a quite remarkable mistake for what must have been one of the most important days of his life. He and Hutchinson had invited several scientists including a number who were members of the Royal Institution. Hutchinson was never

Baird on the big day - preparing equipment for the first public demo 26 January 1926 at Frith Street, Soho.

Baird in his studio with ventriloquist's dummy 'Stookie Bill', July 1926.

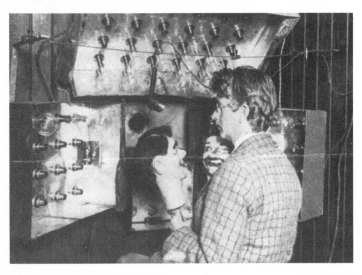

slow to capitalize on the publicity potential of a situation, and press reports of the demonstration were to highlight and dwell upon the presence of members of this august body, in some cases giving the impression that this had been an official event sanctioned by the Institution. Some members subsequently felt their names had been used to add weight and backing to Baird's work, and they made their objections known. While there was some validity to this criticism, it smacked of the carping which Baird himself had nervously anticipated from a scientific establishment whose work he had pre-empted. Of the 40 guests who turned up only a few were members of the Royal Institution. Several were probably from the Davy Faraday Research Laboratory, whose work was the subject of a current lecture at the Institution. At least two women scientists were present, as well as Sir William Bragg, Fullerton Professor of Chemistry, at Trinity College, Cambridge. Many wore full evening dress and were obviously not prepared for the surroundings and what eventually transpired.

As usual, the faithful Press Association man W. C. Fox had been rooted out from the comfort of his home and talked into the double role of doorman and security guard. He recalls that the front door was open to the street and the steps to Baird's premises on the second floor were cold and draughty. He says: 'I could hear their footsteps echoing as they climbed, and their mutterings. Inside they had to find their way over a litter of cables and other equipment.' He was instructed to send them up in batches of five or six because of the cramped accommodation. While some entered, others stood shivering, waiting their turn. Most allowed themselves to be televised, little guessing the real risk they took. Baird himself described the scene: 'In one room was a large whirling disc, a most dangerous device, had they known it, liable to burst at any minute and hop around the room with showers of broken glass.'

One scientific greybeard was being transmitted when his beard got caught up in a rotating wheel and several tufts were yanked out. He proved to be a good sport, however, waving the incident aside and insisting on continuing the experiment. The images that appeared were flickering but recognizable, and most of those present realized that they were witnessing the birth of something very important indeed. The discomfort of the premises was soon forgotten in the excited chatter afterwards. Outside, Mr Fox was

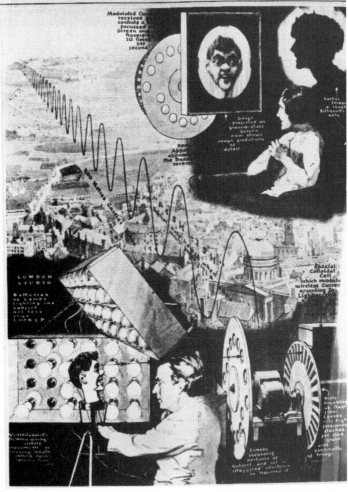

How Mr. Baird's Wonderful System of "Television" Transmits Its Wireless Pictures

The Sphere magazine illustrates Bairds system.

amused by snatches of conversation. He recalls: 'One man remarked that this chap Baird was a twister trying to get their pennies from them. Another, however, Mr Sanger Shepherd, had done work on telegraphing still photographs, and therefore knew the significance of it all. He simply said: "Well, he's got it right. It's only a matter of Lsd to carry on with developments." 'The game was now afoot with a vengeance. From that day on Baird was destined to be a public figure who would almost single-handedly force the birth of a television service in Britain, and accelerate the process in Europe and America. The little-known figure who spent his days in a spartan workshop, and his nights in seedy lodgings, would now find himself in the pantheon of giants in the frenetic twenties decade. His name would soon appear as often as Pickford and Fairbanks, and with even bigger headlines on both sides of the Atlantic. It was an era of scientific tension with apparently boundless possibilities. Lindbergh was set to cross the Atlantic. Talking pictures were round the corner. And Baird was there, in the forefront, with an invention that to the man in the street sounded like an impossibility. Yet just thirty years later it would be regarded as almost an essential part of every home, its very familiarity smothering the name and reputation of the man who started it all.

It was also the age of Cadillacs and champagne, and for a time Baird was subjected to the blandishments of the bright life, the transatlantic liners, and the ballyhoo of Broadway and Fleet Street. It is a testimony to the firmness of spirit of this warm-hearted man that he did not succumb. His health and physique could not stand up to the nights of heavy drinking or socializing, a fact which acted as a natural brake, but, this apart, he was always to spurn the easy path, the way to quick riches. The boardroom table, the chairmanship of the mammoth company were his for the taking, but the future would find him always back in those austere workrooms, pushing ahead with the same obsessiveness as Kipling's explorer: 'Something lost behind the ranges, waiting for you - GO.'

Today it is difficult to imagine just how big a figure he cut in the interwar years. However, any temptation to bask in the glory of it all was always tempered by the considerable opposition that he encountered in his own country. Perversely, a Britain that lauded lone pioneers of sea, air and mountain, tended to resist the idea when it came to science.

For many Baird was always the eccentric entrepreneur. But perhaps, with hindsight, his contemporaries cannot be blamed completely, for so much of his story, so many of his achievements, remained under a cloud of secrecy.

Following the TV demonstration, *The Times* was for once slow off the mark. Its report did not appear until two days later, Thursday 28 January.[28] The article related how pictures had been transmitted first in the one room, and then from another room to a portable receiver. For the purposes of the demonstration the head of a ventriloquist's doll was manipulated, though the human face was also reproduced. It commented: 'The image transmitted was faint and often blurred, but substantiated a claim that through the "Televisor", as Mr Baird has named his apparatus, it is possible to transmit and reproduce instantly the details of movement and such things as the play of expression on the face.' It was also reported that application had been made to the Postmaster General for an experimental broadcasting licence. Trials of the system might shortly be made from a building in St Martin's Lane. Somehow or other, presumably through W.C.Fox, the *Daily Chronicle* had reported the world's first public demonstration the day before, on the 27th, and said it saw no reason why the Derby might not be viewed in Australia.[29] This was true. Baird saw no barrier to long-distance television. It was not beyond the capabilities of his machine even at this early date. If wireless could span the oceans, so too could television. But Baird himself was the first to admit that the quality of the picture was at this stage the most important factor, and that was the present challenge. However, from the beginning, publicity was in danger of outstripping achievement. The public, having been given a taste of television, expected even more, and it appeared that Captain Hutchinson was in euphoric mood in his eagerness to consolidate their position, and was outlining as 'round the corner' developments that would take another three or four years. Just three weeks before the so called Royal Institution demonstration, in January 1926, Hutchinson was reported in the *Daily Express* as saying, 'We have applied to the Government for a licence to broadcast vision to and from London, Manchester and Belfast, and will shortly be in a position to send pictures of actual human faces from stations erected there.'[30] Such claims were to damage the credibility of the Baird Company in those early days, and added to the growing problems between the

Four of the first photos from a television screen. Left to right dummy 'Stookie Bill', Miss King, secretary, and two magazine covers, one of the Prince of Wales.

Baird and Hutchinson fix the aerial on roof of the Baird studio at Long Acre, London.

inventor and his old friend. Hutchinson would increasingly try to guide the destiny of the new invention, an attitude which Baird resented, and the situation was further complicated by the claims of old friendship. W. C. Fox remembers:

> *I believe they had both been colleagues in the early days in Glasgow. They continued to get up to all sorts of adventure. Sometimes they were like a couple of apprentices on a night out. They drank a mixture of champagne and stout, Black Velvet, it was called. I was rather alarmed by this and I pointed out they were fast becoming important public figures and this sort of thing might do them harm. They were surprised. I don't think it had really occurred to them.*

However, Baird and Hutchinson were now in the grip of events. They moved to more spacious premises, Motograph House in Upper St Martin's Lane, near Leicester Square, in February 1926. A contemporary photograph shows Baird with Hutchinson, erecting an aerial on what was to be the world's first television broadcasting station. Hutchinson wears a suit and highly polished shoes; Baird a yellow plaid sports jacket, which was to be a familiar item of apparel in so many pictures of the period. On his feet are carpet slippers.

Having demonstrated his invention, in the laboratory, Baird was now eager to transmit over a distance. He approached Mr Kirke, chief research engineer of the BBC, who was interested an proved helpful. Arrangements were made to send television pictures from Motograph House to the BBC by telephone line. Mr Kirke then returned them by wireless from the BBC to the laboratory, where Baird picked them up. He found the pictures virtually unaltered and commented: 'It is interesting to record that the BBC actually transmitted television in 1926, although unofficially I was bound to silence and did not mention the matter at the time. It amused me to hear people say that while I could send television in the laboratory, it could not be sent over the BBC.[31]

Transmission came to an abrupt halt, however, Baird said that someone 'up above' at the BBC - Kirke would not say who - had ordered them to cease. One can surmise that Kirke's reticence indicated the intervention of no less a figure than the Governor, Sir John Reith. His earlier acquaintance with Reith at college in Glasgow was a stumbling block to Baird, who seemed to be more inhibited in his dealings with the BBC than would have been the case had its head been a stranger. Certainly, the appearance of television on the scene posed problems for the radio men. Though a national monopoly, the BBC itself was only four years old, and it would be almost a year before the company became a public corporation, the British Broadcasting Corporation, with Reith taking the new title of Director General. Strictly speaking, therefore, the Baird Company was older than the newly formed Corporation. Observed from that vantage point, the Baird Company's pugnacious attitude to the BBC when refused facilities seems more understandable. The BBC's problem was how to react to and deal with a completely new and potentially more complex medium. Several leading technicians and officials explained their caution, saying that the technical quality would have to be improved before television was acceptable. This seems reasonable but, as Sydney Moseley pointed out in his biography of Baird, these same people were willing to leap at the rather dull and unrewarding exercise of sending wired still pictures into people's homes. The Fultograph sold for £22 and printed a picture 4 inches by 5 inches.

A section of Bairds 'electrical eye', the forerunner of fibre-optics.

Nevertheless, the BBC allowed experiments with it as late as October 1928, while still opposing Baird.

Baird himself certainly hoped that television might escape the all-embracing grip of the BBC, though he probably realized it was a vain ambition. He had his allies within the Corporation, however, and a revealing account of an attempt to ease his path with the Corporation is given by Anne Gladstone Murray, whose father, Bill Gladstone Murray, was right-hand man to Reith from 1924. The effort went slightly awry, partly due to the familiar plaid jacket that Baird favoured. Anne Gladstone Murray recalls that her father always encouraged Baird and kept the 'black box' television receiver under the stairs at their home in St John's Wood. Mr Gladstone Murray decided to throw a party for BBC chiefs to meet Baird, and many of them turned up in dinner jackets. Baird was late. Some guests were passing cynical comments when he finally arrived, slightly dishevelled, wearing his old tweed jacket and odd socks. Always his own man, he must have been a trial at times to those who tried, for his own good, to persuade him at least to pay lip service to London society. However he had not forgotten those dark days in the Glasgow engineering shops, and tended to find the lifestyle of those in high places with whom he had to deal too soft and wasteful. He persisted in donning a cloth cap to demonstrate his solidarity with those who he felt really had to work for a living.

His relationship with the Post Office was somewhat easier. After considerable negotiation involving Hutchinson and himself, the Post Office issued licence 2 TV in 1926. A full account of the intricacies and correspondence leading to the granting of this licence can be found in an excellent booklet. [32]

The following year, on 27 April 1927, the Baird Television Development Company was floated. Hutchinson had interested Ian Anderson, a partner in a firm of issuing stockbrokers, Vowler and Co., following a private demonstration at Long Acre. The elderly Mr Vowler was suspicious about embarking on a wild adventure, but his younger colleague pointed out that Baird had the monopoly of this amazing invention. It was agreed, and £100,000 .was raised, £33,000 of this by Baird and Hutchinson, and £5,000 invested by the ever-reliable Inglis cousins. Underwriting facilities completed, Baird and Hutchinson were jubilant, and retired to the Engineers' Club to celebrate.

Next day a thunderbolt hit them. Literally overnight their monopoly was dramatically shattered. On 28 April the newspapers revealed that the Bell Telephone Company had come from out of nowhere, it seemed, with a television demonstration over distance, 200 miles from Washington to New York, using a thousand technicians in support. This news badly shook the underwriters and the shareholders in the new company, who were furious and felt that they had somehow been misled. 'Television at last,' shouted one headline. Baird was angry. Much later he wrote:

> *I write perhaps somewhat bitterly and egotistically about this matter even after the lapse of years,and at an age when such things should not matter. I feel again the anger against the jealous malice which would willingly, against all justice and evidence, have brushed my work aside and distorted the facts by every mean trick of omission, innuendo and misrepresentation. The detractors did not find it easy to crush me. I kept fighting and shouting, sometimes (I am afraid) paying little attention to dignity and reticence in the publicity methods employed. Nevertheless, the fact remained that I was demonstrating television and no one else was.* [33]

He was still facing scepticism in his own country. At one demonstration he returned to find a distinguished old scientist crawling about under the apparatus. The man explained, in embarrassment, that it was his duty to satisfy himself that no trickery was involved. Baird even found himself accused of hiding a boy in a box behind the receiver. When repeated demonstrations refuted such ridiculous suspicions, his critics fell back on the last resort: 'Anyone could have done it.'

Baird would soon reply to the American achievement in such a way that it drew the unstinted praise of the American press. But first he outstripped the Americans by demonstrating television between London and Glasgow, a distance of 435 miles - twice as far as the United States' effort, and using just two technicians. On 24 May 1927 the images of Wally (the office boy) and Bill (the dummy) were sent over a telephone trunk line from Motograph House to a semi-darkened room on the fourth floor of Glasgow's Central Hotel.[34] Among those present was E. Taylor Jones, Professor of Natural Philosophy at the University of Glasgow. He found the pictures at times unsteady, but at

Baird in Glasgow in connection with the long-distance
London transmission accompanied by civic dignitaries

others remarkably steady and clear. The operator at the
Glasgow end gave instructions by 'phone, and the office boy
in London waved his head as instructed. The Glasgow
operation was run by Ben Clapp, a wireless enthusiast who
had an amateur transmitter in Coulsdon, Surrey. He had
joined Baird's company and was to prove an invaluable
assistant in the years ahead. Alongside Baird he must rate as
one of the great television pioneers working on it from its
inception. He already had a high reputation for some of the
earliest trans-atlantic sound broadcasts. During the First
World War he had a colourful career, at one point manning a
balloon attached to a warship, spotting U-boats, and, at
another, campaigning against the Germans in East Africa.
Baird trusted him implicitly and chose him as one of his
main representatives when he tried to launch television in
Australia.

Honour was now more than satisfied, but Baird was not.
He was determined not to let matters rest. Soon he was
secretly preparing for an even bigger coup, pictures across
the Atlantic. The headquarters were Mr Clapp's villa on the
Surrey downs. A vertical aerial wire 35 feet long was erected
and operated on a wavelength of 45 metres. In August 1927
Mr Clapp took ship to the USA and joined forces with
another radio amateur, a Mr Hart who had a transmitter at

Hartsdale near New York.

Back in Britain, operating after midnight, Baird and Denton practised sending signals by telephone line to Surrey, from where they were flashed across the Atlantic. Many radio hams heard these signals, like the drone of a giant bee, and wondered what was causing them. At the end of 1927 the Baird Company moved to larger premises at 133 Long Acre, in Covent Garden, and the experiments continued from there. Then, on 18 January 1928, Hutchinson sailed from Southampton with an improved receiver. A first attempt to send pictures rather than just sound signals failed on 7 February. The intending subject of the camera, actress Elissa Landi, was disappointed and made do with champagne and sandwiches in the middle of the night. On the following evening, the 8th, at midnight London time, 7 p.m. in New York, Baird gathered with Mr Fox from the PA, Mr Howe of Associated Press, Howe's wife and one or two privileged guests. Bill, the doll, was scanned and his image signals sent by telephone line to Surrey. The station had a power of only 2kw; its call letters were 2 KZ. From there the image signals, together with a synchronizing frequency, were sent 3,500 miles across the Atlantic. In Hartsdale Ben Clapp waited anxiously with Hutchinson, Mr Hart and a Reuter's press representative. The signals arrived, and soon the doll's features were tuned in successfully on the receiver. Mr Hart jubilantly signaled from his station, 2 CVJ, on his short wave transmitter to Baird's receiver at Purley, near London, using morse. Baird himself was then televised for about half an hour, followed by Mr Fox and Mrs Howe.

It was a triumph. For days the newspapers were full of it, headlining it from New York to Nova Scotia. On 11 February the *New York Times* said: 'Baird was the first to achieve television at all, over any distance. Now he must be credited with having been the first to disembody the human form optically and electrically, flash it piecemeal across the ocean and then reassemble it for American eyes. His success deserves to rank with Marconi's sending of the letter 'S' across the Atlantic . . .' Unstinting in its admiration, one paper noted that Baird's achievement was all the more remarkable as he had matched his inventive wits against the pooled ability and vast resources of the great Corporation physicists and engineers, thus far with dramatic success. *The New York Herald Tribune* hailed Baird as an experimenter of the classic type and compared him with Lindbergh. They noted that the American experiment over 200 miles between New York and Washington was said to have involved more than a thousand engineers and laboratory men, and commented: 'Only a dozen worked with Baird.' In fact, the number involved was eight. The experiment confirmed a statement that Baird had continually made - that distance spanned was merely a question of power, and did not depend on developments of the television apparatus itself.

On Sunday 13 September 1931 the *New York Times* printed a table called 'Outstanding Inventions of the Past Eighty Years'. Among such names as the Wright Brothers, Marconi and other such giants just one name appeared under the heading of 'television': J. L. Baird, in 1926. Yet few Americans today have heard of Baird or his achievements. Baird reinforced his superiority when his little team of helpers returned home from America on the liner Berengaria. Clapp and Hutchinson cooperated with the radio staff of the vessel to receive pictures in mid-Atlantic. Baird, with his flair for publicity, traced Miss Dora Selvy, fiancee of the liner's chief radio operator, Stanley Brown, who had no idea she was involved. Other gold-braided

The Berengaria transmission. Mrs Clapp seated, husband Ben directly behind her, Captain Hutchinson, far left.

officers watched as first the back of her head appeared, clearly enough to make Brown start with surprise as he recognized her characteristically bobbed hair. He was dumbstruck when she turned round and he looked into her eyes, spanning more than 1,000 miles of ocean.

Shares in the company now rushed upwards. Baird had formed his first company, Television Ltd, in 1925. This became the holding company for Baird Television Ltd 1927, and in June 1928 a third company was formed, Baird International Ltd, with an authorized capital of £700,000. Baird and Hutchinson were joint managing directors, paid £3,000 a year each. They also received another £1,500 as managing directors of Baird Television Ltd. The shareholders realized what a precious asset the inventor was, and Baird's life was insured for the then astronomical sum of £150,000.

Prosperity brought some of the good things in life. He now travelled by hired Daimler and lived in a comfortable villa high up on the beauty spot of Box Hill in Surrey. Here his friend Mephy, now grey-bearded and long-haired like an Old Testament prophet, organized his domestic life. Baird was now forty and the affair with his first love continued, made more awkward by the increasing publicity surrounding him. Success also brought other problems. He found himself increasingly involved in boardroom meetings, which he regarded as similar to attending church. He would lapse into dreams of wheels and pulleys, jerking awake as some point was made. Then he would drift back to 'further permutations' and combinations of wire and mirror drums and lamps. He was particularly irritated by the chairman of one of his companies, Sir Edward Manville, also chairman of Daimler. Sir Edward, a man of robust girth, was an engineer and would frequently interrupt Baird in the laboratory with his own ideas. When he moved to Long Acre the harassed inventor characteristically solved this problem by making the door to his laboratory so narrow that Sir Edward could tackle it only with danger to his trouser buttons.

Baird achieved many more world firsts. By June 1928 he had moved television from the laboratory into the open air. He was now able to dispense with artificial light and use only that necessary for a normal photograph. Hot on the heels of this, on 3 July he demonstrated television in colour to the press and a party of scientists. He showed in their real colours delphiniums and carnations, and red strawberries in a white basket. A man appeared tying a red and blue handkerchief round his head. *Radio News* for October 1928 reported all these events in one article and said that 'the vivid reality of the colourings was most remarkable.'[35]

Baird achieved colour by using three interlaced spirals in his transmitter: one fitted with a green filter, another red, and a third blue. A similar disc at the receiving end reconstituted the picture in colour, all the green lines first, followed by all the red and then all the blue. It was remarkable for the time, but again Baird was only showing something he had probably achieved years before. An illustrated article in *The Sphere* of 28 August 1926, two years before, stated: 'Mr Baird has now transmitted by wireless a moving image, showing gradations of light and shade and even a little colour- red and blue.' The apparatus illustrated was a double spiral unit, eight lenses per spiral and similar to both the Falkirk and Kensington Science Museum units in general appearance. But only the Falkirk unit had the necessary interlacing to lay down consecutive image lines of different colours, as depicted in Baird's patents of the period.

Then there was the world's first video recording. The sound made by his image signals had always fascinated

Daylight television achieved. Baird on roof of Long Acre with Jack Buchanan, left.

him. He could tell a cabbage, or a face, or whether a subject was moving or still, by its distinctive sound. This led to his recording the signals and to British patent No. 289,104, applied for in October 1926, showing how the recording was made with a needle cutting into a wax disc, responding to signals from the microphone. A second patent, No. 292,632, applied for on 26 January 1927, provided for magnetic discs. Baird was again before his time. He planned to market his recordings, the forerunner of home videos. He termed the invention Phonovision and, half a century later, a few of these discs still survive, can still be played and still give a recognizable picture.

As if this was not enough, Baird rocked the public and the technical journals by giving on 10 August 1928, before an audience of scientists and the press, a demonstration of television in three dimensions. He also showed stereoscopic television and colour combined. His receiving screen displayed two images separated by approximately half an inch. One of these corresponded to the objects as seen by the right eye, the other to those as seen by the left. These images were viewed through a stereoscopic viewing device consisting of two prisms which blended the images into one. However, *Radio News* for November 1928 noted that the stereoscopic device was really unnecessary. One could make the images blend without it. Professor Cheshire, lately President of the British Optical Society, said that the picture of a man sitting at the transmitter was 'in perfect relief' and he declared that 'the experiments promised considerable development and importance in their practical application'.[36]

Soon after a Baird demonstration to a British Association meeting in Leeds in 1927, the Television Society was founded, with Lord Haldane as its first President. Interest was increasing. Introduced by Lord Angus Kennedy, Baird joined the Caledonian Club and soon found himself giving an official demonstration to the Prince of Wales. Baird's membership of the Club was an indication he had arrived in society, and through it he made many influential contacts. He was still sniped at, however. *Popular Wireless* continued to cast doubts on his system, and in March 1928, issued a £1,000 challenge to Baird to give them a superior television transmission. But they made conditions which he could not possibly fulfil at that time. A new friend came to the rescue, Sydney Moseley, a financial journalist of considerable flair and panache who witnessed a Baird demonstration and wrote favourably in *Popular Wireless*. From then on Moseley was to become Baird's self-appointed champion, deeply involved in negotiations on his behalf with the B B C.

There were basic problems. Baird had to improve his normal televisor. The picture was $3^1/2$ inches by 2 inches, though this could be doubled by the use of a lens. He also needed to find his company a proper station to make public trials; he was finding the wavelengths allotted him by the Post Office unsatisfactory, and complaints had been coming from the armed forces, saying that it interfered with their signals. Formal application to the BBC made little headway at first; Baird found stiff opposition from Captain Peter Eckersley, the chief engineer of the B B C. Eckersley persisted in blocking the Baird Company, claiming that the system was not developed enough for the B B C to sacrifice vital wavelengths.

Post Office engineers were impressed, however, and the Post-master General was dismayed by the BBC's generally negative attitude to television. Eventually a panel of independent judges was appointed, including the Postmaster General, selected Members of Parliament, Reith himself and Vice Admiral Sir Charles Carpendale from the BBC, advised by their top engineers. They were to witness a Baird demonstration through 2LO. The event took place on 5 March 1929. Receivers were placed at BBC headquarters in Savoy Hill and at the GPO in St Martin's le Grand. Baird nervously watched the transmission at the GPO with his friend, Sir Ambrose Fleming. Among the artists appearing was Jack Buchanan, and even Captain Eckersley made a brief appearance. Afterwards the Postmaster General called it 'a note-worthy scientific achievement', and agreed to a B B C station being made available to Baird outside normal broadcasting hours.

Baird was overjoyed. The B B C, however, delayed and came up with narrow-minded suggestions and almost suffocating conditions; the arguments went on and on. While it is understandable that the Corporation should not know how to deal with this new technology which complicated their existence, there seems to have been a strong antipathy to the Baird Company with its challenging ways, its cockiness and its threats to go it alone. Some evidence exists for believing that Reith himself was annoyed that Baird had tied himself up with City interests and failed

The inventor pictured with one of his discs at an early TV
demonstration in Glasgow.

to get in touch with him at the very start, even though Baird had in fact approached the B B C without success. The amazing absence of any reference to Baird in the published writings of Reith, only paralleled by the same omission by radar's Sir Robert Watson-Watt, could well be an indication of just how problematical their relationship was. Reith would have to regard Baird's proposed national television service as a competitor to the B B C. Baird stated that he 'frankly regarded the BBC as a rival'. Such attitudes probably account for Reith's coldness towards Baird and the omissions in his published diaries.[37]

A strange story was unearthed by Mr Somerset Sullivan, a former education officer with the RAF, whose hobby of literary detection brought him in 1948 in contact with George Bernard Shaw. It was a G. B.S. custom in old age to walk around Marylebone, St Pancras and Bloomsbury, areas of London which he had known well in the past. On one of these strolls, he told Sullivan, on a wartime summer's evening he encountered Reith standing outside the ruined Presbyterian church in Regent Square,whose minister had been instrumental in introducing him to broadcasting. Reith seemed to be in some distress. At first, Shaw thought he was drunk, but soon realized that he was suffering emotional stress. G. B. S. tried to calm him, and claimed that, in the conversation that ensued, Reith made what amounted to an open confession of jealousy and instant dislike for John Logie Baird. It was clear that, if television had come from any other source, he might have accepted it, but never from Baird.

Reith was convinced that he should have been appointed Governor General of Canada or Australia, and that he, not Beaverbrook, should have been made Minister of Aircraft Production. That he had not received those posts he somehow connected with his involvement with and attitude to Baird and the birth of television.

Following their conversation, Shaw had Reith delivered home by taxi. He remained shocked, however, by the encounter and by Reith's assertions. Mr Sullivan says: 'He was very sorry for Baird but the damage had been done. However, I feel certain that had he been a younger man, he would have taken up the case one way or another.' The story grows in credibility when one realises that Reith was in a state of wild depression at the time, and that he himself stated in an unpublished diary entry that his wife and his secretary had warned him about his state of mind.

G. B.S. and Baird had met in the early thirties, when both appeared in a film, *Signposts to Success*, Baird representing invention and Shaw drama. Shaw had long been interested in television. His play *Back to Methuselah* described a scene supposed to take place in the year 2170. The head of the British government holds conferences with his ministers, who are several hundred miles away. He has at his desk a switchboard and in the background of the room is a silver screen. When he selects the proper key at the switchboard a life-sized image of the person with whom he is speaking is flashed on the screen at the same time that he hears the voice.[38]

The Baird Company's negotiations with the B B C were long and often acrimonious. Questions were even raised in the House of Commons.[39] But Baird was not prepared to stand around and do nothing. In the early 1950s Mr Martin Curley,a Wembley borough councillor, tripped over a weed-covered giant slab of concrete in the grounds of Kingsbury Manor, once a private residence and by that time an old people's home. Puzzled, he consulted a gardener who indicated another slab 35 yards away. Mr Curley, chairman of the newly-formed Wembley History Society, investigated and found he had literally stumbled onto a clandestine Baird operation of the past. In 1928 Baird moved some of his team to Kingsbury Manor. There in a coachhouse and stables he set up a transmitting station under the command of H.J. Barton-Chapple. a brilliant young engineer. A steel-structured building was planned, but first the two great concrete slabs were laid, and into them were set two 80-foot-high television aerials made of wood. So secret was the venture that Baird himself rarely visited the site, which was set well back from the main road, hidden from prying eyes. All the staff were sworn to secrecy. Years later Barton-Chapple wrote: "The pall of secrecy had perforce to be drawn over the experimental work being conducted at Kingsbury Manor." He added: "Everything Baird did, every line of research he followed, would have been of tremendous interest to competitor scientists. Locals who saw the aerials thought they had something to do with wireless."

Baird now had his eyes on Europe and was conducting negotiations with the Dutch, the French and the Germans. His Long Acre studio had become a mecca for important visitors, who included British government ministers, scientists, and also naval, air and military representatives from as far afield as Russia and Japan. German interest was intense and Dr Bredow, Radio Commissioner of the German Postal Ministry, called on Baird and invited him to Germany. Baird accepted and set off on what was to be, arguably, the world's first pirate television enterprise.

Thought on these lines may well have been inspired through a previously unchronicled association with a flamboyant individual, Leonard Frank Plugge, a former Royal Flying Corps captain. While a scientist with the Air Ministry, Plugge conducted a fashion transmission by radio from the Eiffel Tower to London. His sponsor, as in the case of Baird, was Selfridge's; it happened in 1925, the same year which saw the first Baird public demonstration of outlines. The exercise gave Plugge the idea of commercial pirate broadcasting from the continent, and in 1930 he acquired a small French radio station, Radio Normandy, and was soon challenging Reith from the port of Fécamp, home of Benedictine liqueur. A *Who's Who* entry prepared by himself shortly before his death in 1981 stated clearly that he had worked with John Logie Baird on the first television set. Plugge was to play a busy role in the Second World War, and Baird's diary for the war years shows that they had regular meetings. They were similar characters. Plugge invented two-way car telephones, the ancestor of CB. It is unlikely that the idea was not mooted of television joining radio as a pirate of the airwaves. Evidence exists that in 1928 Oliver George Hutchinson and the Earl of Dysart were also involved in continental pirate radio broadcasting into Britain, to rival the BBC.[40]

Baird arrived in Berlin in 1929 and stayed at the Adlon Hotel with Hutchinson, Moseley and a team of helpers who had brought a truckload of equipment. There were meetings with the Reich Postmaster, and instruments were set up in the Reichrundfunk, the German Broadcasting House. Baird found himself a flat in Lindenstrasse and was soon preparing for the first Eurovision signals. Back at Kingsbury Manor a special receiver had been constructed and in July 1929, after seven months' work, transmission started. Baird's colleague Barton-Chapple wrote: "My heart pounded as we waited for our colleagues in Berlin to come through. A week elapsed before any success was achieved. And then one night we heard the familiar whirring sound through the ether. Our men in Berlin were coming through. And, upon my soul, so was the image on the screen. It was blurred at first, then it became a crude face, the face of a gnome with a pointed beard and peaked hat." This was a new acquisition that Baird had bought in Berlin, a doll he nicknamed Albrecht. They had made it at last, with standard equipment. Barton-Chapple's little team cheered and hugged each other with joy.

More signals followed and the effects were far-reaching. Some have suggested that Baird was in Berlin with Reith's blessing, but this is unlikely. Werner Nestle who, through Baird, became one of Germany's first TV engineers, commented in a German television magazine: "The BBC then said - What, an English firm broadcasting in Germany ! And at once they invited Baird to see them." And Barton-Chapple, who should have known if anyone did, believed that the Kingsbury Manor episode was, apart from a valuable breakthrough, the first step to persuading the BBC to grant them facilities; or, if that failed, to setting up a rival station on the continent. Whatever the cause, the BBC certainly reacted swiftly. From the end of September 1929 vision only was granted to Baird for five hours a week outside broadcasting hours, with dual transmission from Station 2LO commencing the following March. The plans for the erection of a permanent transmitting and receiving station at Kingsbury were scrapped. The house had already accomplished its task. On 30 July 1953 David Gammans MP, Assistant Postmaster General, unveiled a plaque to commemorate the site of the masts, which had been removed in 1940.

Much of Baird's life was, like the Kingsbury Manor sequence, hidden. He was to be associated with the Crystal Palace in the thirties and to work mysteriously during the Second World War in one of the towers that remained after the fire of 1936. But few people realized until recently that he had operated out of the Crystal palace as early as 1926. Mr A.W. Nicholson, a former engineer manager at Plessey, recalls Baird in a workshop on top of the tower at the same time that he was supposed to be struggling in Frith Street, Soho.

Running parallel with normal television, Baird was also deeply immersed in another aspect, vision by infra-red, which enabled him to see in the dark, a system he called Noctovision. The glare of sizzling hot lamps for normal lighting had led him to try ultra-violet, which proved uncomfortable to the eyes, so he then turned to infra-red. At first he achieved this by covering ordinary light bulbs with thin ebonite, which blocked the normal subject illuminating light, but allowed vision through infra-red. Baird was now able to televise people in a completely dark room. He exhibited the system to members of the Royal Institution in December 1926, and to the British Association. Though he abandoned the idea of using the unit for normal television he had other plans and these were connected with that other part of his life that has remained a secret until now.

An indication of this other interest appeared in headlines in several national newspapers during April 1927. One article stated: "Red Rays Startle the West End, Inventor Tries It on Nelson's Column, Fog Piercing Test".[41] People had seen a weird red glare in the sky at night above the West End and had grown anxious. A fire alarm was given, but the fire engines were halted in time. The newspapers explained that television's inventor, John Logie Baird, had caused the glare while training a searchlight on Nelson's Column, and at the time had been in the process of fitting an infra-red filter over the searchlight. They reported that he could now see through a smoke pall in his laboratory and was waiting for a real peasouper fog in London.

Just three weeks earlier, on 19 February, a press Association news item written by Mr Fox had contained an odd item of information. It said: "On a suitable night we shall have an aeroplane flying overhead and pick it up by this apparatus" It added that the British, American, German and French governments had sent representatives to inspect the apparatus. This is the first indication that, in addition to his efforts to perfect television, Baird was already doing something with an entirely different application. He was well advanced on the path that he would follow until the end of his life. Unlike his television, it would remain largely unknown to the public, reference to it petering out almost entirely in the 1930s. A development of his Noctovision, in which the infra-red was replaced by reflected radio waves, would appear in the Second World War under the name of radar, though others were to claim the credit for its conception.

NOTES
1   *Journal of the Royal Television Society,* October-December 1951, p.287.

2   P. Waddell, "John Logie Baird and the Falkirk Transmitter", *Wireless World,* January 1976, pp. 43-46.

3   "Scots Inventor of Television Apparatus", illustrated article, *Glasgow Herald,* 4 September 1926.

4   Living Face by Wireless", *The Morning Post,* 25 January 1926, p.12g (3D images).

5   "Living Pictures by Wireless", *The Morning Post,* 10 August 1926 (colour images).
      "Sending Pictures through the Air", *The Sphere,* 28 August 1926 (colour images)

6   "Televisor for Falkirk, Inventor's Gift to father's birthplace, Seeing by Wireless", *Falkirk Herald,* 1 September 1926.

7   Advertisement "Seeing by Wireless", 18 September 1926 *Falkirk Herald.* Unit still on display at J. Hart's radio shop, Falkirk.

8   A. Collins, *Experimental Television,* Pitman, 1933, pp.63.

9   William Stevenson, *A Man Called Intrepid, The Secret War* 1939-45, Sphere, 1976.

10   Baird, "Baird Colour Television, Development Proceeds in Spite of War", *Wireless World,* February 1941, p.43. "J.L. Baird's New Colour Television System", *Electronics, TV and Short Wave World,* February 1941, pp. 69-70.

11   "Stereoscopic TV", *Electronic Engineering,* February 1942, pp. 620-21.

12   J.H. Udelson, *The Great TV Race,* University of Alabama Press, 1982.

13   Baird, *"Television, a General Survey",* World Radio Convention, Sydney Australia, April 1938.

14   "Television, a New Radio Miracle. the Transmission of Pictures', Illustrated London news, 11 September 1926, p.145.

15   "Gift for Museum, First Television Apparatus", *The Scotsman,* September 1926, p.9d.

16   N.S. Kapany, *Fibre Optics,* Academic Press, 1967, p.1

17   Videtur, "Television by Invisible Rays", *Popular Wireless,* 12 February 1927, p.1417.
      A. Dinsdale, "Seeing in Total Darkness". *Wireless Magazine,* April 1927, pp. 200-202. "The invisible Searchlight, Seeing in the Dark by Black Light, Infra Red Rays and Their Uses in War"
      Illustrated London News, 25 December 1926, p.1271. H. De A. Donisthorpe, "Some Notes on television", *Radio (USA),* August 1926, fig. 2.

18   P.R. Bird, "Wireless Television, a Preview of the Baird System", *Popular Wireless Review,* 23 May 1925, pp. 622-3.

19   R.F. Tiltman, *Baird of Television,* Seeley Service, 1933. Selfridge's produced and advertisement (reproduced on pp. 74-75 of that book) in connection with Baird's demonstations in the store during April 1925.

20   "A new Wireless Wonder, Pictures While You wait", *The Graphic,* 26 January 1924.

21   "Actor sees by Television", *Daily Sketch,* 2 May 1925.

22   Baird, "Television, Description of the Baird System by Inventor", *Wireless World,* 15, 21 January 1925.

23   W. Kaempffert, "How Baird Sees Through Space by Radio", *New York Times,* 6 March 1927.

24   "Pioneering", editorial, *Electronic Engineering,* February 1942, p.619..

25   Baird, *"Television'*, letter, Nature, 29 January 1927.

26   *Sermons, Soap and Television*, ch. 4, p. 2.
27   "Broadcast Pictures of the Derby", Daily Express, 8 January 1926.
      "Television", Manchester Guardian, 9 January 1926.
28   "The Televisor, Successful Test of New Apparatus", The times, 28
      January 1926. Illustration.
      "Seeing Through Walls by Televisor", The Times, 2 February 1926.
29   "Living scenes Broadcast", Daily Chronicle, 27 January 1926.
30   "Broadcast Pictures of the Derby", *Daily Express*, 8 January 1926.
31   *Sermons, Soap and Television*, ch. 5, p. 8.
32   M. Exwood, *Fifty Years of Television*, booklet published by Institute of
      Electronic and RadioEngineers, 1976.
33   *Sermons, Soap and Television*, ch. 5, p. 2.
34   "Television marvels - Glasgow Looks in on London", *Glasgow Herald*,
      27 May 1927.
35   R.F. Tiltman, "Television in Natural Colours Demonstrated", *Radio
      News* (USA), 10 October 1928, pp. 320, 374.
36   R.F. Tiltman, "How Stereoscopic Television Is Shown", *Radio News
      (USA)*, 10 November 1928, pp. 418-19.
37   'Television Rival to BBC "Still" Pictures', *Evening Standard*, 10
      September 1928.
38   E.F.W. Alexanderson, "Radio Photography and Television", *GEC
      Review*, 30, February 1927, pp. 78-84.
39   See R.W. Burns, *"The History of British Television, with Special Reference
      to John Logie Baird"*, Ph.D. Leicester University, 1976.
40   "Red Rays Startle the West End, Inventor Tries It on Nelson's Column,
      Fog Piercing Test", *Daily Chronicle*, 9 April 1927.

8
The Big Apple

When the liner Aquitania sailed from Southampton for New York in September 1931 her passengers included John Logie Baird, on a mission to find a wavelength and launch his television system in the United States. Already the Baird TV Company had made forays into Europe, forging links with varying success in Germany, The Netherlands, France and Denmark. They had even sent representatives to Australia and South Africa. But America, with her vast resource of potential television viewers, was by far the best proposition.

Baird had always received favourable press coverage in the United States, and American backers had helped finance his transatlantic experiment. Rich entrepreneurs such as Benjamin Sangor and Charles Izenstark, a radio pioneer from 1915, had attended an international conference on the commercial development of the Baird system throughout the world as far back as 1928, cutting a dash with their gold-topped canes, straw boaters and big cigars.[1] A Baird Television and Development Corporation with offices in New York had been formed to explore the possibilities of television, not just in the USA but also in Canada and Mexico. Progress was slow, however, despite a television boom that started in 1928 and lasted five years, with more than eighteen television stations operating throughout America, including one owned by Baird's rival, C.F. Jenkins. The American situation had become a subject of contention in the Baird Company, particularly after Hutchinson, on a month long visit to America, managed to achieve nothing more that a hefty expenses bill. This led to acrimony among the board members and the eventual resignation of Baird's associate from apprentice days, who had shared so many of the joys and heartbreaks of those pioneering years. It was now decided to send Baird himself, to move daringly among their transatlantic competitors and investigate the affairs of the American company.

By a quirk of fate the Aquitania was a liner which he had helped to build in grim, windswept conditions on the Clyde while an apprentice on his college studies. Another coincidence was the presence on board of his boyhood idol, H. G. Wells. Baird had taken with him in a secretarial capacity W.H. Knight, a friend of Moseley, and it was Knight who engineered a meeting between the author and the inventor whom he had unknowingly inspired.

The two met on the boat deck. Baird was delighted, but faintly surprised at the subject and quality of their conversation. In his own words:

> *Mr Wells proved to be a substantially built man, of medium height, with a cap pulled over his eyes, utterly void of any affection or any effort at effect: a great anti-climax after the magnificent Sir Oliver Lodge and the overpowering Sir John Reith. No formal facade here, only a poor, vulgar creature like myself. We had a short chat about youth camps. I said these organizations appeared to ignore sex. "Oh well," he said, "every Jack has his Jill", and that is all I remember of the conversation with my demi-god.*[2]

Knight captured the occasion with his camera.

The voyage afforded Baird the opportunity to sit back and rest after two hectic years of achievement and problems. The first programmes officially involving the BBC had started at his Long Acre studio on 30 September 1929, travelling by landline to Savoy Hill and then to the transmitter on top of Selfridge's. By March 1930 the second of the BBC's twin transmitters at Brookmans park was ready for service, vision and sound were now went out simultaneously. Among the few people able to watch was the Prime Minister, Ramsay MacDonald. A Televisor had been installed at 10 Downing Street, and MacDonald wrote to Baird of the most wonderful miracle being performed under his eye: "You have put something in my room which will never let me forget how strange is this world and how unknown.[3] Broadcasts took place mainly late at night, outside normal radio hours. Baird found himself wandering from his austere laboratories into the exotic atmosphere of the Long Acre studio. There, in a confined space, young ladies floated about in tights, and red-nosed comedians applied make-up amid a chaos of pianists and violinists rehearsing.

He remained bitter that his company not only had to

meet the cost of these transmissions but also had to pay the BBC for the use of their transmitters. This was in contrast to the German Post Office in Berlin, which had paid the company for using the apparatus. Baird felt he was having to fund the BBC to introduce them to television; not a businesslike proposition. In 1930 he had launched another of his dreams, large-screen television to public audiences, at the London Coliseum. He had developed one of his early patents and devised a screen comprising, 2,100 flash lamp bulbs covering an area 6 feet by 3 feet. He wired these up and, as the subject was scanned up and down, the corresponding bulbs in various shades lit up to supply a picture. The venture ran from 28 July and was a resounding triumph: "House full" notices had to be put up. The *Daily Mail* commented on the 29th: "With a dramatic success which convinced the most sceptical, television established itself at the London Coliseum yesterday.[4] *The Sunday Express* simply said: "Television has come." Celebrities thronged to the Long Acre studio to be televised. At the Coliseum large screen, there were politicians and statesmen; Frederick Montague, Under Secretary of State for Air; and Rt Hon. George Lansbury; Oswald Mosley, future leader of the British Fascist Party, then a Labour MP; Lord Baden Powell, founder of the Scout Movement; "Bombardier" Billy Wells, the boxer; and many others. The new medium already had tremendous pulling power. The large screen created interest throughout Europe and Baird was soon at the Scala Theatre in Berlin, the Olympia Cinema in Paris and the Rodoekvarn cinema in Stockholm. Scientists, as well as the lay public were impressed by a string of twenty-six performances that went without a hitch. By 1932 the large screen at the Arena Theatre in Copenhagen would be picking up television broadcasts from London, 700 miles away, including performances by the popular Danish actor, Carl Brisson.

Baird had achieved a closed circuit outside broadcast of his friend Jack Buchanan in June 1928, but he waited until 8 May 1931 before making the first-ever scheduled outdoor transmission. All pictures had previously been obtained using powerful indoor lighting; now viewers saw the bustling scene at Long Acre directly from a van parked on the kerb outside the studio. This led to one of his greatest achievements, the televising of the 1931 Derby, a feat which he had promised the public five years before. Following months of preparation he loaded his large mobile van and parked opposite the grandstand, with his mirror-drum receiving apparatus pointed at the finish. Post Office lines were laid under the stands and travelled direct to Long Acre, from where they were passed to Brookmans Park. An ingenious mirror device fitted on the outside of the televising caravan pointed away from the course, allowing the camera to receive reflected pictures of the crowd. The BBC had allowed only a minute voltage, which contributed to interference and flicker. Those watching back in London held their breath as they saw the winner, Cameronian, flash past the post and heard the frenzied cries of the crowd. Baird had confounded his disbelieving critics yet again, and the race was seen as far away as Berlin.[5]

Baird built on this triumph a year later when he transmitted the 1932 Derby to an excited audience at the Metropole Theatre, Victoria.[6] He increased the screen size by using three telephone lines from Epsom and sending three pictures side by side, which were joined into one large picture 7 feet high and 9 feet wide. People packed the passages, and outside a disappointed crowd clamoured for entry. The horses were seen parading past the grandstand and then again at the finish, as April the Fifth passed the post followed by Dastur and Miracle. The audience stood and cheered as the inventor was ushered onto the platform. Ben Clapp affectionately recalled that Baird was so anxious at the start of the transmission that he said 'Phew', when the horses came into view, 'and only by placing my chair beneath him was he prevented from sitting on the stage'.

An eye witness on the roof of the caravan had reported the race to the audience and, although the BBC had again limited the power available, they were not informed that the buccaneering Baird technicians had increased the permitted voltage ten times over, without causing any problems to the public supply. Ben Clapp had grown used to challenges involving electrical supplies. When Baird used the Clapp household's facilities in Surrey, the public lighting in the street outside used to dim and flicker during his transmissions.

On 14 July 1930 Baird televised the first B B C play, Pirandello's *The Man with a Flower in His Mouth*, produced by Lance Sieveking. An audience of dignitaries viewed it on a large screen inside a great canvas tent on the roof at Long Acre. It was a success, though Baird feared that the tent might blow away in the fierce gale which raged that day. One of the visitors was Marconi himself, who found it 'all very interesting'.[7] He tripped as he made his departure, and was saved from falling by Moseley. Baird was not over-impressed by Marconi as a scientist, but admired his courage and his pioneering zeal, and observed that 'a man who could continue to maintain an attitude of dignified reserve in the arms of old Mr Moseley borders on the superhuman.' By 1931 Baird had also experimented with television phones, and produced a portable TV receiver that could be taken on a picnic by car.

There were general problems, however. Ultrashort waves were not yet in use and Baird was still restricted to medium waves. The choice of a 30-line transmission at $12^1/_2$ images per second was the result of the waveband restrictions imposed upon him by the B B C. The metal Televisor receivers made by the Plessey Company were selling, but the revenue they produced was a drop in the ocean in relation to the finance needed for the battle ahead, with electronic rivals gathering on the horizon. To help out, Baird voluntarily halved his own salary.

He was now middle-aged and very much a public figure. It was time to marry and have a family, a prospect complicated by his long-standing affair with the mistress of his youth. As always he embarked on the project in a practical, if unorthodox, manner. With the aid of Mephy he organized what were advertised as auditions for lady pianists at his studio - in fact he was taking first sightings for a wife. As the ladies tackled Chopin and Liszt, Baird watched from behind a curtain. His gaze lingered on a beautiful young woman with raven black hair. Twenty-four-year-old Margaret Albu had been born in Johannesburg in 1907; her mother was an Anglican from Yorkshire, her father a liberal and unorthodox Jew. Margaret's grandfather had been a rabbi, and the family was related to the composer Mendelssohn. Her father was a manager at De Beers' diamond mine at Kimberley, and his three sisters had travelled the world singing with the Carl Rosa Opera Company. Convent-educated, Margaret became a fluent linguist and an accomplished pianist, and in 1925 was sent to London to continue her music studies. She and her mother visited Selfridge's that year and witnessed the first Baird demonstratlons, although she does not recall seeing him. She embarked on a career as a concert pianist and by

1930 was invited to broadcast from Savoy Hill.

The Baird audition had a momentous sequel for the musical aspirant from South Africa. She was telephoned by a girlfriend who asked if she would accompany her on a visit to 'a man who lived on top of Box Hill'. The man proved to be Baird and at this encounter he took the opportunity of asking her to dinner. There was nineteen years between them, but she found the blue-eyed man with the courteous manner a person she considered loyal and without guile in personal relationships. After a few further meetings they decided to marry in the near future.

Baird could feel, therefore, that his life had reached another watershed as he steamed past the Statue of Liberty aboard the *Aquitania*. He could hardly have been prepared, however, for the greeting that awaited him at New York harbour. On the quayside a body of Highland pipers endeavoured to march and play with elan. It transpired that an over-zealous publicity agent had arranged a real Scottish welcome and hired the comic opera pipers from the Ziegfeld Follies. A horrified Baird found that he was expected to join them in a cavalcade to the royal suite of the Waldorf Astoria, with an escort of motorcycle police. He swiftly gave them the slip and arrived at the Waldorf unobtrusively in a taxi. Minutes later, the Highlanders from Czechoslovakia, louisiana and Hollywood followed, and it was an expensive matter pacifying them with drinks. Baird was dazed. Even the bathroom was like a palace, with a vast black marble bath set in the floor. He found the suite crammed with pressmen and photographers, flash bulbs popping. They stayed on and on, drinking impressive amounts of liquor. Said Baird: 'At two in the morning the last of them had reeled out or been carried out, and I returned to my gilded bedroom.'[8] Many diverse individuals arrived to talk to him over the next few days and usually drank themselves senseless. The last straw came when a couple of businessmen burst in with girlfriends and 'spare dames' for Baird. He asked Knight to bid them a diplomatic farewell!

Meanwhile, the flamboyant Mayor Walker had invited him to a banquet at City Hall, an occasion on which he did not escape the police motorcycle escort. He found his old friends, the Ziegfeld Highlanders, marching up and down attempting to play 'The Barren Rocks of Aden'. In his welcoming speech Mayor Walker continually referred to him as an Englishman rather than as a Scotsman, and said:

'We have with us here today a man who has given us his world famous invention of' - here he hesitated for a minute, and his secretary said in a stage whisper: television.'

Baird spent the next week meeting a collection of millionaires who, though willing to talk, were difficult to bring to any decision. However, real business started with Donald Flamm, a pioneer broadcaster and president of WMCA in New York, who in 1983 was still president and chairman of two radio stations in Westport, Connecticut. It was Flamm who had invited Baird to America and offered to help him set up his system using the radio network based on WMCA. Baird duly proceeded to Washington and, after he had given evidence to the Federal Radio Commission, a permit was granted to WMCA. It was revoked on Baird's return to London, however, following an appeal by the giant Radio Corporation of America, on the grounds that no foreign-controlled company could be allowed to broadcast in the USA. Baird was not to forget their opposition and would fight them when he discovered that they were trying to gain a backdoor foothold in Britain through Marconi-EMI.

Donald Flamm, an anglophile and still a loyal admirer of Baird, remains scornful of British neglect of the inventor, and on each anniversary of the first public demonstration of Baird's television (26 January) he reminds listeners of his achievement. He says that if Baird had come to America his life story would have been the subject of a film, in the same fashion as his countryman Bell was honoured years ago in a classic, often-shown picture: *The Story of Alexander Graham Bell.*

Baird eventually grew tired and unwell in the heat of New York. He telephoned Margaret Albu, reminding her that a call cost £1 a minute, and asked her to join him. She arrived in less than a fortnight on the *Olympia,* but found difficulty in disembarking on account of a law concerning women travelling alone and the white slave traffic. An irate Baird came aboard and browbeat the officials, threatening them with Mayor Walker; his fiancee was then allowed to land and saved an uncomfortable spell in the custody of the immigration authorities on Ellis Island. After some discussion they decided to desert the city for Coney Island with its fresh sea breezes. They found it logical to marry at once, though they had informed neither the company nor their families. The ever-resourceful Knight arranged a special licence and a municipal judge, Murray Hearn,

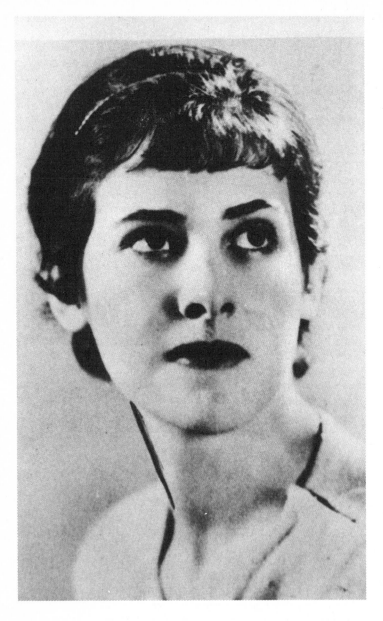

Margaret Baird at the time of her marriage in New York.

agreed to travel to Coney Island. He had a burial on 12 November and so the wedding was celebrated on the 13th at the Half Moon Hotel, neither party being superstitious. Baird was ill with influenza and was dressed in carpet slippers when the judge arrived. Mrs Baird recalls that he was so nervous that he kept sidling away during the ceremony. She says: 'At one point I think poor Knight was standing closer to me than Logie and thought he was being married in error.'

They spent their wedding day in the hotel, where Baird tried to write a letter to his old love. Mrs Baird says: 'The situation had become hopeless but he was kind and loyal and did not want to hurt her. However, he just could not find the words and the room was strewn with discarded bits of paper. Eventually, I wrote it for him. This proved futile, as she read about the wedding in a newspaper the same day while in a London restaurant, and fainted on the spot.'

Baird recovered from his illness and two days later was well enough to enjoy a reception arranged by Donald Flamm at the Half Moon Hotel. Soon afterwards the American adventure was over. The couple arrived back in Britain in midwinter, and Baird faced the delicate task of explaining his new circumstances to his old friend of bachelor days who had eased so many of his social duties. Though amiable, Baird had always been a deeply private individual, allowing few people to know the extent of his work and the depth of his feelings. With Mephy he could talk poetry and metaphysics and be plain John Baird from Helensburgh. Back at Box Hill, Mephy handed the keys over to the new Mrs Baird and moved to Dorking. He caught flu, however, and was fetched back to Box Hill by Margaret and nursed to health. Afterwards, the man who had witnessed all the birth pangs of television from Hastings onwards bought a little herbalist's shop in Ryde on the Isle of Wight

With the revoking of the broadcasting licence in America, the Baird office in New York was closed. By 1933 most television stations in the United States, except experimental ones, had shut down. The boom was over for the time being. Electronic television was incapable at that point of supplying a service, and mechanical television, though satisfactory, had, by the limitations of its programmes at that stage, failed to sell enough receivers to attract advertising revenue.

A similar problem had arisen in Britain as early as 1930.

Baird shares fell on the capital market. In June 1930 the Baird Television Development Company and Baird International Television Ltd amalgamated to form Baird Television Ltd. Soon afterwards the parent company, Television Ltd, went into voluntary liquidation. This company held one million deferred shares in the public company, a controlling interest. Baird therefore allotted to his personal financial wizard, Sydney Moseley, the task of securing these shares from the liquidators and guiding their destiny. This Moseley accomplished in an epic episode of financial juggling, the controlling interest eventually being bought by Isidore Ostrer, managing director of the Gaumont-British film company, a fact announced in January 1932.

When Baird visited Germany in 1929 he had helped to form a new company Fernseh AG, to develop television. His own com- pany supplied the television, the Zeiss Company the television optics, the Loewe Radio Company the wireless sections, and the Bosch Company contributed the electric motors. For some years Baird engineers were permanently in Berlin, and he enjoyed his trips there until the advent of Adolf Hitler. He appreciated the clear air of

JLB in Europe. The inventor meets journalists in Austria, 1930.

the German capital and the comfort and luxury of the German hotels, which surpassed those in Britain and America. One of his leading technical assistants, C.L.Richards, recalled Baird's preoccupation with foot comfort, which raised eyebrows in the plush Adlon Hotel in Berlin. He said: 'As he sat at a table, I saw Baird pulling at his shoes. Then I noticed waiters gliding past with caviare and wine, faltering and staring in our direction. I looked down and there were Baird's stockinged feet stretched out. He seemed blissfully unaware of the effect he had created.'

Baird had befriended Major Church, a Labour M P whom he considered a born fighter and a man of brilliant intellect, and it was Church who introduced him to many of the leading figures in Germany, most of them anti-Nazis. Through Church he became friends with Bruening, the German Chancellor, whom he visited many times. One of their last meetings occurred after Hitler's rise to power. They dined at the villa of a friend at a time when Bruening's life was in extreme danger. Baird also worked with and befriended Baron Manfred von Ardenne, the great German television pioneer. Captured by the Russians at the close of the Second World War, von Ardenne returned to Germany years later and devoted the rest of his life to research at a cancer clinic in Dresden.

In 1931 Baird stayed at the Kaiserhof Hotel. Adolf Hitler, two years away from grabbing the reins of power, sat in the lounge with his entourage, close to the tousle-headed inventor whose ideas would eventually play a prime role in his defeat. Baird found him the exact opposite of the dreaming, studious Bruening. He was surrounded by a dozen cronies, no doubt including Goebbels and Goering, but Baird did not recognize them. Hitler, though, could not pass unnoticed. Baird wrote:

He sat at the head of the table and his eyes, with a strange fixed look, stared in front of him from under a shock of black hair. He sat erect, silent and unmoving, except occasionally when some member of his party whispered respectfully to him, when he would bow or shake his head. The gathering regarded him as a god. I gaped, fascinated by the scene. The maitre 'hotel approached and warned me discreetly to look elsewhere. Nazis in brown shirts came to Hitler's table, gave the Nazi salute, took instructions and departed briskly. It was the first time I had seen all this. I was told it was a lot of nonsense and would soon fade away! The man was simply a Fanatic, followed by a few out-of- works and others of no importance.[9]

On Baird's next visit to Berlin Hitler was not in the Kaiserhof Hotel but in the Chancellery. Nazi officials were on guard at every stand at the radio exhibition Baird was attending. Bruening had been forced to flee. A grim reign of terror had taken over. Smiles had vanished in Liberal quarters and people now looked hostile. Those opposed to Hitler - and Baird found many - were terrified.

The strutting, marching Nazis got on his nerves and he took the first train back to London, heaving a sigh of relief as it steamed out of the Friedrichstrasse Station.

Hitler's rise to power affected Fernseh. The Fuehrer ordered that, as a British concern, the Baird Company interest must cease. David Loewe, the head of Loewe Radio, was a Jew and had been expelled from Germany; the Nazis now wanted to take over the Loewe interest and gain control. Fortunately for the Baird Company, the amazing Major Church managed to negotiate a deal which resulted in a substantial payment for the Baird share. He also arranged an affiliation which gave the Baird Company all Fernseh rights in the British Empire. When one follows the subsequent story of Baird's secret involvement with the British government and the armed forces, it is a fair assumption that there was more to the German connection than has ever been realized. His contacts with leading Jewish scientists and anti-Nazi politicians placed him in an excellent position to evaluate German technical progress and act as a scientific spy.

In Britain his relations with the BBC had improved slightly following his Derby screening triumph. Noel Ashbridge, the chief engineer, even reported in October 1931, after a visit to Long Acre, that the picture he saw was 'easily the best television I have seen so far and might be compared, I think, with a cinematographic close-up of fifteen to twenty years ago'.[10] Even Reith mellowed and supported a plan to grant Baird an annual subsidy of £10,000 but this was rejected by the Postmaster General, Sir Kingsley Wood.

In May 1932 the B B C felt it was now time to set up a studio of their own and learn about television production. Broadcasting House had just opened, taking over from Savoy Hill, and housed their first television studio. Douglas

Birkinshaw, a BBC engineer, became the first Corporation television appointee, and he was joined by D.R.Campbell and Thornton Bridgewater from the Baird Company, who both helped to instal Baird equipment in the new premises.

The same year saw Baird studying the possibilities of ultra shortwave transmission. Medium waves, the ordinary waves used by the BBC, permitted no more than a certain amount of detail which limited him to 30 lines. The advantage was their ability to carry signals hundreds of miles. Ultrashort waves, on the other hand, allowed much more detail but had a range of about 40 miles, which would necessitate a relay of transmitters if pictures had to go further. Nevertheless Baird was encouraged to investigate ultrashort waves, following a talk with his friend Professor E.V. (later Sir Edward) Appleton. On 29 April 1932 he gave a demonstration from his ultra shortwave transmitter at Long Acre, the images being received by the 30-line receiver on the roof of Selfridge's - one of the first public demonstrations of ultra short-wave television in the world. The Dutch company of Philips, in Eindhoven, had arranged the first ever public demonstration of ultra shortwave television from the tower of the Carlton Hotel in 1930.

January 1932 had seen the Bairds move from Box Hill to Hampstead, and in September their first child was born, a daughter, Diana. Soon afterwards Baird's father died. They moved again in 1933 to 3 Crescent Road, Sydenham, taking with them a nanny for Diana. Mrs Baird first learned of their new home when her husband turned up one day and informed her that they had a new house and that he hoped she would like it. Margaret found herself mistress of a large Georgian residence with windows out of reach, and seemingly acres of bare rooms, but she soon transformed it, buying the largest pieces of furniture she could find to fill the spaces. The grounds, too, were extensive, dominated by four giant beech trees which Baird quaintly named Bach, Beethoven, Brahms and Baird.

The house had obviously been chosen for its proximity to the Crystal Palace, the huge cast-iron and glass edifice built in Hyde Park in the heyday of Queen Victoria to house the Great Exhibition and subsequently moved to this part of south London. Part of the Palace was rented in 1933 by the Baird Company, and there is some evidence that Baird himself may already have been occupying part of the Palace for work which he preferred to keep from his general

The inventor as public figure - 1932.

associates. He used the South Tower for his ultra short-wave experiments, and by 1934 was televising 180-1ine images from the tower to a cathode ray tube screen, giving images 10 inches by 8. This tower would still be associated with him during the Second World War, at a time when he was supposed to have abandoned it.

Relationships within the company had been tempestuous since Ostrer had taken charge. Baird resented the feeling that he was an employee. Moseley had departed with very adequate compensation after a series of clashes, usually in support of Baird. For some time Baird had wanted a link-up with Marconi, in order to give his company a broader and sounder base to continue its pioneering work on television, but approaches and negotiations were discontinued, and a possible tie-up with GEC was also quashed. Baird regarded these actions as catastrophic and grew increasingly estranged from the company. Eventually he withdrew more and more to his private lab with its own research staff, where he forged ahead with new ideas for colour and three-dimensional television.

Rivals were now appearing and the whole television scene was becoming so important and complex, with the possibility of high definition, that in May 1934 the Postmaster General set up a special committee to investigate. The Selsdon Committee, headed by Lord Selsdon, the former Sir William Mitchell-Thompson, induded the BBC's chief engineer, Noel Ashbridge, and the Controller, Admiral Carpendale. They submitted their report on 4 January 1935. While recommending that the time was ripe to launch a high definition television service run by the BBC in one station based in London, they could not decide which system should be used. The favourites were Baird, with a 240-1ine system, and the company then known as Marconi-EMI (interestingly this was changed later to EMI-Marconi). Electrical and Musical Instruments Ltd had been formed through an amalgamation of the Gramophone Company (HMV) and the Columbia Graphophone Company. The work of EMI was on all-electronic lines, and in 1935 they were courageously offering an electronic system, interlaced once for 405 lines.

Baird was fiercely opposed to Marconi-EMI, not just as rivals, but also because he suspected a possible American takeover, something he was determined to oppose. He detected the long arm of his old enemies, the Radio Corporation of America, who were also tied up with the great Telefunken Company in Germany. As early as 1932 there was disquiet in British radio and television circles over the growing interest of RCA in British television developments. The head of publicity for the British Radio Manufacturers' Association, Mr Garry Allighan, wrote in 1932 of 'the RCA and other branches of this large electrical trust which has thrown its octopus arms around the entertainment of the whole world'. The article mentioned millions of sets ready to be imported into Britain so that viewers could receive American programmes. It commented that negotiations were going on with the BBC, which were either very innocent or very sinister. Allighan had attended a lunch in honour of Samuel Rothavel, known as Roxy, the entertainment king of America, who was accompanied by various executives from RCA. Allighan claimed that the chief engineer of the National Broadcasting Company of America had told him they were intending to broadcast American programmes through the B B C. [11]

RCA was known to independents in the industry as the Radio Trust, because of its patents pools and trade agreements linking it with General Electric, Westinghouse,

United Fruit and ATT. There was also a surprising link between two of the main figures in RCA and the key man with EMI in Britain. David Sarnoff, President of RCA, and Vladimir Zworykin, the brilliant inventor who developed the Iconoscope electronic camera used by RCA, were both immigrants from Russia; so was Isaac Shoenberg, the perspicacious head of research with EMI. Sarnoff had become a national hero in America at the age of seventeen when, as a radio operator working in the Wanamaker Building in New York, he picked up radio messages from the SS Olympic on 14April 1912 that the 'unsinkable' Titanic had struck an iceberg and was, in fact, sinking. Sarnoff stuck to his post for seventy-two hours, the only link with the tragedy which was unfolding in the Atlantic. That same year Zworykin had taken his electrical engineering degree at the St Petersburg Institute of Technology where he had studied with the early television pioneer, Boris Rosing, aiding him in experiments. Shoenberg had also studied at the St Petersburg Institute, and joined the Russian Marconi Company before going to England in 1914.

There was a noticeable similarity between the Marconi-EMI Emitron camera and Zworykin's invention, the Iconoscope, a charge-storage style of transmitting tube, though the British company continually claimed that theirs was a purely home-based development. Embarrassingly, however, David Sarnoff said virtually the opposite in a statement in New York when he returned from a European tour on 25 September 1937. He commented: 'The system employed is known abroad as the Marconi-EMI Television System, which is fundamentally based on the RCA Television System first developed in the RCA laboratories in the United States. Under an exchange of patent licences this British company may use RCA patents in England and, in turn, its American licencees may use British patents in the United States.'[12] In October 1937 there was a swift rebuttal from Shoenberg, who hastened to point out that the system had been developed entirely in Britain without any cooperation from R C A. [13]

That Baird viewed the suspected inroads from America with considerable concern is evident from the flurry of correspondence on the subject, with Moseley writing to Stanley Baldwin and Ramsay MacDonald at Westminster, and Baird himself writing to the Prince of Wales. This letter, sent in February 1935, possibly never reached the Prince, but was intercepted by his secretary and passed to the chief engineer at the BBC, where it eventually vanished into B B C files. [14]

After the Selsdon Committee had made its report, it was decided to hold trials to choose between the Baird and the Marconi-EMI systems. Preparations were soon under way at Alexandra Palace. Despite the committee's recommendation that 30-1ine transmissions should continue until a high definition service was available they were closed down in September 1935, causing an outcry in some circles. When talk of stopping these transmissions had first arisen in 1934 a flood of letters was received by *Wireless World* from viewers as far afield as Scotland and the north of England. People felt justifiably chagrined that the broadcasts should be stopped for a high definition system that would not reach them, and would serve only those living in the London area. This view was backed editorially by *Wireless World* in March 1934 and by the Royal Television Society, who both urged the B B C to continue with 30 lines.[15] The Royal Television Society's President, Sir Ambrose Fleming, mounted a blistering attack on the BBC, dubbing it 'the perfect autocracy', and an 'uncontrolled monopoly'. He criticised the ridiculous night-time hours allocated to television and called for a better use of the new medium. He declared that television was being held back by the overcautious and unenterprising spirit of the B B C. [16]

This enthusiasm for 30-1ine mechanical scanning may seem odd to generations used to the hundreds of lines necessary for good viewing on electronic television. In fact, the two systems made entirely different demands and it is quite wrong to judge them on paper by simply counting the number of lines used. Low definition mechanical television could give a better definition of a single head than high definition, if there were many figures in the high definition picture. In general, mechanical scanned television needed fewer lines than electronic systems to give good images, which was the result of the higher contrast in the television image points. Fewer image points or lines meant a greatly increased range and a larger audience. As early as December 1928 Dr Alfred Gradenwitz, a leading German scientific writer, remarked on the unusual clarity of Baird's 30-1ine pictures and 'an outstanding wealth of detail enabling, for instance, an outline of finger nails, the smoke of cigarettes and even the lines on their faces to be seen'. He said that the

Baird system was unquestionably in advance of anything on the Continent. [17]

In an article in *Television* in November 1928 Sydney Moseley attacked armchair critics of Baird's 30-1ine system. He said: 'Men like Campbell- Swinton (who will live to regret the attitude he has taken up) have not been near the Baird laboratories in Long Acre.'[18] The prophecy was fulfilled just over one year later when Campbell Swinton had the grace to change his opinion, and in a letter to *The Times* on 16 December 1929 praised the quality of the image in a demonstration given to him by Baird.[19] Campbell-Swinton died two months later, and never saw his vision of electronic television become reality.

Impressive praise came from the veteran American radio pioneer, Lee De Forest, in 1934, when he wrote to the President of the National Radio Institution in America: 'Four nights a week they broadcast one hour of genuine artistic entertainment. Baird is limited by British regulations to 9,000 kHz side bands. Imagine getting a good picture out of that! Yet Baird does it - by the use of a 30-1ine picture and $12^{1}/_{2}$ pictures per second. Considering the handicaps the results are amazing.'[20] Since the Second World War critics of Baird have maintained that the 30-1ine system used between 1930 and 1935 was a useless one foisted on the public by Baird, but the published facts indicate the reverse. A large public wanted the system to be retained after September 1935. It should also be remembered that Baird was limited to 30 lines, $12^{1}/_{2}$ images per second, by the BBC band width allocated between 1930 and 1935.

The great TV duel between the Baird Company and Marconi- EMI has often been seen too simply as a clearcut matter of up-and-coming superior electronic systems dealing a death blow to the outdated mechanical system. The facts were more complex. Baird knew the limitations of the electronic systems then available. Modern judgements are too frequently based on the assumption that prewar electronic television was basically as accomplished as it is today, but this was not so. It had severe limitations which hampered prewar British television, while high resolution mechanical scanning with cathode ray tube receivers continued to develop on the Continent, giving a more comprehensive service. Baird himself had no direct technical involvement with the equipment used in the contest. It was based on his work, but while he planned a colour service for the future, his system was worked on and adapted by Captain A. G. D. West, former chief research engineer for the BBC, now a loyal colleague of Baird. EMI offered equipment based on their Emitron camera, an all-electronic system of 405 lines interlaced, at 25 images per second. The Baird Company's system was mechanical television of 240 lines sequentially scanned, at 25 images per second. The Baird pictures were acknowledged by all who saw them, including EMI, as excellent. Baird used two systems: one, the flying spot camera, scanned with a fast-moving spot of light and necessitated the subject being in a dark room; the other was an intermediate film camera, which recorded both pictures and sound. The film was fed into a tank containing chemicals for developing, fixing and washing. The processed film, wet or dry, was then scanned by a flying spot Nipkow disc transmitter, the images being observed on a cathode ray tube receiver. Amazingly, the delay between filming and conversion into a television signal was a mere forty-five seconds. By the Second World War Baird would use a superior cathode ray tube flying spot transmitter to scan subjects and film, a development of Manfred von Ardenne's 1929 German system.

Baird also used an electronic camera. In 1934 he allied himself with an American television pioneer, remarkably similar in character to himself. Philo Farnsworth, born in 1906 in an isolated farmhouse in Utah, had conceived ideas of sending pictures without wires at the astounding age of fourteen. His father had taught him to read the constellations in the sky by means of bamboo poles and string. The brilliant young Farnsworth was demonstrating an all-electronic form of television by the time he was twenty-one, when he transmitted the picture of a dollar sign. His efforts, like those of Baird in the West Indies, were sometimes misconstrued. While working behind closed doors in Los Angeles he aroused suspicion and his premises were raided by the police, who thought - this was the time of Prohibition - that he was running an illicit still.

Like Baird, the young American was an opponent of RCA, for whom he posed a major problem. He held so many master patents that between 1930 and 1939 RCA spent more than 2 million dollars in legal wrangles, and another 7 million in developing television equipment, in attempts to overcome Farnsworth's patents. A final settlement was made in 1941, enabling Farnsworth to retire to a farm in

Maine at the age of thirty-four. By 1939 Farnsworth had successfully coupled his image dissector camera to an improved image intensifier tube, giving a combination far more sensitive than any RCA television camera.[21] This was probably the reason for the RCA climbdown, the first time this had happened to them. Like Baird, Farnsworth was for years afterwards deliberately ignored and almost forgotten. But his blocking of RCA's progress at home made outlets into other countries a very promising prospect for that company, a situation of which Baird was only too well aware.

Baird borrowed Farnsworth's image dissector camera under licence, and used it in the scanning of his film. The unit was worked into his own system so that, by February 1935, the press witnessed the transmission of talking pictures from one room to another at the Crystal Palace, involving an electronic camera giving pictures with a definition of 700 lines, 295 more than EMI.[22] In 1934 Baird told the Selsdon Committee that he could go to 700 lines, but such definition would drastically limit the range and audience without a string of expensive booster stations.

It has been suggested, in retrospect, that no public trial was needed, that Baird was only allowed to compete because he had captured the public imagination and had the backing of many sections of the press. That was not the view at the time. The competition was real and many were impressed by the quality of the Baird pictures. A March 1935 article found that Baird's 180-line television images were 'bright and clear, with considerable detail, while at no time did they "hunt" or go out of synchronism'. The editor added: 'Undoubtedly, the whole demonstration was a striking tribute to the enormous progress made by the Baird Company, and showed quite clearly that the transmission of high-definition television pictures over a large area was already an accomplished fact.'[23]

The trial was in the hands of the BBC, who brought their engineers into Alexandra Palace, a greater part of which they had taken on a twenty-one-year lease. The numerous problems were not helped by the engineers having to face the mutual suspicions of the two companies regarding the leaking of information or plans and techniques. The target date was set for 2 November 1936. But the impetus towards an opening was boosted by the request for a few days' television in August at the Radio Show at Olympia. Despite the difficulties involved, both companies worked at break-neck speed and supplied a wide range of programmes, including one which Baird televised from aboard a KLM plane. At Alexandra Palace there were some worrying breakdowns and technical problems in the Baird camp, and sabotage was suspected.[24] The press, electronic experts and private witnesses reported that Baird's 240-1ine live images were as good as the Marconi-EMI 405-1ine images and that Baird's 200-1ine televised images from dry, pre-recorded cine film were excellent.[25]

A lull followed Radiolympia, with the service closing down until 2 November, when the opening ceremony of the high definition system took place at Alexandra Palace. Speeches were made by the Postmaster General; the Chairman of the BBC Governors, Lord Selsdon; Sir Henry Greer, Chairman of the Baird Television Company; and Alfred Clark, Chairman of EMI. One figure, though, was missing from the platform; John Logie Baird, the man who had first given television pictures to the world, was not invited, but sat in considerable anger and disgust in the body of the hall among the rank and file. It is now fashionable to say that this was an oversight, but Baird himself had no doubt that he was being snubbed by the BBC. He had forced the pace, had pushed Britain and the BBC into a position of leadership, but he was ignored. He commented: 'What the devil had they done for television? But there they sat sunning themselves in the limelight as the men responsible for this great achievement, for so they apparently wished to appear.'[26]

The Baird Company batted first after winning the toss of a coin by Lord Selsdon. Pretty Adele Dixon sang the signature tune specially written for the opening, *'Television'*, and the show was on, with EMI following half an hour later. The opening was judged a success.

The trial then started in earnest over the ensuing weeks, with each company televising on alternate weeks. But Baird suffered a cruel blow on 30 November, just four weeks after the opening ceremony. At 7.30 p.m. flames were spotted in the central section of the Crystal Palace, and by 2 a.m. the following morning the major part of the Palace was still burning, despite the efforts of firemen from all over London and the suburbs. Baird was in the middle of dinner at home in Sydenham, less than a mile away, when the telephone rang and a wildly excited voice told him the Palace was ablaze. He rushed to the window, saw a red glow in the sky, and immediately dashed out hatless and in slippers. Long before he reached the fire the road was blocked by traffic and people, but he elbowed his way through to the front. Flames roared 150 feet into the sky. Glass cracked and fell continuously. Section by section the huge skeleton of ironwork twisted and collapsed amid showers of sparks. High on a ridge, the blaze dominated the whole of south London.

Firemen were anxious in case the flames reached the South Tower, because it had been reported that it contained explosive material used by Baird for experimental purposes, but the intense heat brought the south-west wing down before flames could touch the tower. The Duke of Kent arrived and donned a fireman's thigh boots as he viewed the blaze. Mounted police cleared back thousands of onlookers. Baird just stood there, stunned. Despite his phlegmatic temperament, he was shaken. Margaret Baird recalls: 'Despite this, with his ability to live in the present, I actually believe he settled down to enjoying the spectacle once the initial shock was over. Later he told me sadly that he believed it was sabotage.'

Almost £100,000 worth of equipment was lost, including the Farnsworth camera and records that were irreplaceable. The suspicion of sabotage was justifiable, for Baird had made many enemies over the years, and some of his work at the Palace may well have had associations with fields far removed from entertainment. During this period his secret work had continued and it may well have attracted the attention of German agents. Certainly at this time Hitler was sensitive about the potential of television and its closeness to radar and other detection systems. As early as July 1935 Eugen Hadamovsky, Director General of the German Broadcasting Service, had made a plea for cooperation on television between Britain and Germany. He was impressed by the 30-1ine television and said that the British had proceeded with German thoroughness - a tribute to the Baird system.[27] However, two days later Herr Hadamovsky had to eat his words when Hitler responded by making a declaration that, in future, all television development in Germany was to be a state secret. The admiration of Germany's head of broadcasting may well have made Baird's operations a prime target at this time. In a British article of April 1935 it was admitted that Germany now held the lead in high definition television, but that Britain had not abandoned the race.[28] It is possible that even more serious issues were involved. Britain at this moment was secretly engaged in a desperate race with Nazi Germany in the development not only of television but also of its offshoot radar.

During the continuing duel at Alexandra Palace, both sides had to contend with difficulties. Camera sensitivity, especially during outside broadcasts, was a continuing problem for EMI, and their camera was proving virtually useless for film. They just could not replay recorded material. The Emitron's image storage ability caused the image to be retained from one frame of the film to the next, which caused blurring. However, their equipment was light and portable, and this, for 'live' television, impressed the BBC.

Baird's telecine film images were considered excellent, but the equipment was hard to maintain. His flying spot 'live' TV 240-1ine camera was bolted to the floor of the studio and was considered cumbersome. Baird himself, though not directly involved with the equipment, could see some of the problems and tried to alert his company, but he found that the leadership there had no grasp of the situation. West was energetic, but Baird found him a child in a situation of the sort 'which needed the craft of a Machiavelli'.

In February 1937 the Television Advisory Committee announced its decision in favour of Marconi-EMI. Baird was bitterly disappointed, especially as his vision of the future of television was one in which live broadcasting would have its place, but, as he correctly foresaw, recorded programmes would provide the bulk of material. The prewar BBC found itself with an electronic system which could not replay properly from recorded material. They were forced to correct this, augmenting their electronic service, using the flying spot technique developed for telecine by Baird, and adopting Manfred von Ardenne's cathode ray tube flying spot-style transmitter cameras. To this day they still use flying spot CRTs for film transmissions, supplied by Rank Cintel, the direct descendant of the Baird TV Company. Baird had offered them the world's best recorded TV images from film, based on long-range 200-1ine film images in 1936, but this was rejected   for the short-range EMI system suitable for live TV only.

Latter-day pundits frequently claim that the Baird prewar system was not capable of improvement, but the subsequent history of mechanical television in Europe shows the opposite. In *Electronics* of January 1938 Mr Lack of Bell Laboratories emphasized the advantage and superiority of mechanically scanned film, following demonstrations of 180-1ine images in Berlin. These appeared to have far greater details than pictures of many more lines in America.[29] The definition or resolution of the earlier German 180-line high definition television system images was also extremely good. In February 1935 *Wireless World* reported on the new public two-way television-telephone service from Leipzig to Berlin and commented, 'The quality of the picture is remarkable, every detail, including rings on the fingers, being clearly discernible.'[30] Earlier, in September 1937, the same publication had reported that Baird's old associates, Fernseh AG, fed the output from a Nipkow disc transmitter into an electron multiplier; 441-line interlaced images appeared on cathode ray tubes 25 inches in diameter and were superior to 405-line Marconi-EMI images seen in Britain.[31] Results similar to this could easily have been achieved in Britain with developed Baird equipment, but the will was not there. Technical editorials such as in *Wireless World* grasped the point, and suggested all along that Baird should have been allowed to develop his excellent equipment of 1936 for mechanically scanned television.

Much play is made today with the fact that the EMI picture was interlaced while the Baird image was not. Baird, however, had been interlacing television images since 1925, which on contemporary evidence is the earliest known use of interlacing. His company did not use interlacing in the contest for the sole reason that they found the interlaced image quality insufficient to warrant the associated complications and cost of such a feature. Baird himself would soon be interlacing to five times over, using a cathode ray tube flying spot transmitter, which in the Second World War would give him images of 500 lines, highly praised by the technical press of the day.

The Marconi-EMI System, on the other hand, had to be interlaced once, to give 405 lines. More image lines and elements were needed with this type of electronic system in order to offset the poorer contrast in the image points and provide image quality comparable with that of the Baird system. Unfortunately the higher output signal frequencies from the EMI cameras greatly reduced the range of their programmes, as mentioned earlier, and it would take many expensive regional stations after the Second World War before the London programmes could be relayed to the rest of Britain.

Pat Hawker, of the Independent Broadcasting Authority Engineering Information Service, has written in an article that the Baird 240-1ine sequential scanned system of 1936 was at that time capable of providing pictures as good as those of 405 lines by the Marconi- E M I system. He added: 'What defeated Baird was that he had no effective electronic camera.'[32] However Farnsworth's image dissector camera, as used by Baird, was to be vastly improved by the addition of an effective image-intensifier tube, so much so that by 1939 RCA had admitted defeat and licensed Farnsworth's television patents, as we have seen. Thus, if Baird had been allowed to develop his mechanical and electronic systems, Britain would have had a natural direct progression to a national colour television service, instead of the black and white system recommended in 1945.

The launching of the contest between Baird and Marconi-EMI has been heralded by the BBC as the world's first regular high definition public service of television programmes, a claim that has always been hotly contested, with some justification, by the Germans and others. No less a person that Douglas C. Birkinshaw, the first ever research engineer in television appointed by the BBC, has written that if the words 'high definition' are omitted then the Germans were first, with a service on 22 March 1935 operating in Berlin using 180 lines.[33] This appears to be quibbling. In a definitive article in 1933 E. W. Engstrom stated that: 180 lines are sufficient for high definition - the minimum acceptable, but still high definition.[34]

A BBC publication, *World Radio*, reported in March 1935: 'Herr Eugen Hadamovsky, Director General of the German Broadcasting Service, opened the world's first high definition television service on Friday, March 22nd.'[35] *The Times* of 23 March also reported: 'The world's first regular high-definition television programme was opened in Berlin tonight (22 March).'[36] The Olympic Games, held in Berlin in August 1936, were broadcast successfully to 150,000 people by the German Post Office, which used mirror drum cameras similar to Baird's earlier equipment. Sweden also had a regular, high definition mechanically scanned service

ring the
Ministers
organic"
tish India
all negotia-

which was elected in 1930, expires in
November.

which the
1g are those
Court and
e the Com-
conclusions,
ubmitted to
ndon.

E

misunder-
which fol-
)ay meeting
1e Ministers
el Hoare's
)mmons go
sions. It is
1, which has
;iety to the
redrafted.
ve not yet
is expected

BERLIN TELEVISION

BROADCAST THREE TIMES A WEEK

FROM OUR OWN CORRESPONDENT

BERLIN, MARCH 22

The world's first regular high-definition
television programme service was opened
in Berlin to-night. The Director-General
of German Broadcasting, Herr Hadamovsky, addressed a gathering of representatives from the Ministry of Propaganda, the German Post Office, and the
leading television firms, who had assembled, together with German and foreign
Press representatives, at the Berlin Broadcasting House. In the address opening
the service Herr Hadamovsky emphasized
the fact that it was his aim to imprint the
image of the Führer in the hearts of the

(240 lines) from Stockholm in December 1935.

Baird was now totally out of the B B C after his years of
pioneer work. But he found little sympathy from his fellow
directors, Greer and Clayton, who were mainly interested in
selling receivers. Baird, the researcher, spent an increasing
amount of time in his own laboratory and eventually
created another big screen projector, capable of supplying
colour. This was installed, with Ostrer's consent, at the
Dominion Cinema. In February 1937 Ostrer had been
disappointed at the choice of Marconi-EMI television
cameras in Alexandra Palace and was hinting at
withdrawing his support from the Baird Television
Company. Baird met him at a television exhibition in the
Science Museum and turned on all his old power that he
had used to raise money and recruit enthusiasts for his
projects. Ostrer was converted and left the exhibition fired
with the idea of launching television in cinemas.

The first priority was a front man, a fighter; and so
Sydney Moseley was again drawn into the fold, much to the
dismay of the other directors who preferred to stick to
familiar paths. A new company was formed, Cinema
Television, which would virtually control Baird Television.

The plan was ambitious, to embrace the whole cinema industry, televising live scenes and even sending out films by television to cinemas throughout the country. Baird was down but not out. The phoenix was rising.

Baird had always planned and hoped for an independent television service, an ambition that was never ignored by the B B C, who always considered him an opponent. That both should have operated from 'palaces' was symbolically fitting. From the Crystal Palace Baird had posed a threat to the state monopoly, and his new cinema activity was a clear sign that he regarded the battle as far from over. If he could not televise programmes into people's homes, he would reach the public through the cinema. Despite their reverses at Alexandra Palace, Baird Television zealously worked on. Baird Company receivers sold well and big screens were installed in several Gaumont cinemas. The Boon-Danahar boxing match and other topical events drew large crowds. Baird demonstrated his particular enthusiasm, colour, on the large screen at the Dominion, persisting correctly in his conviction that the future was with colour, not monochrome.

Early in 1938 he was invited by the Australian government to address a World Radio convention, and on 22 February he sailed with his wife from Marseilles aboard the *Strathaird*. They now had two children, for a son, Malcolm, had been born on 2 July 1935. The voyage was leisurely and Baird relaxed. They stopped at Bombay and, thanks to a syndicate which had acquired Baird Television rights in India, he became the guest of HRH the Maharajah of Kutch at the Taj Mahal Hotel. 'What a meal' enthused Baird. All other banquets he had experienced paled before it. He ate heartily, enjoyed an exotic evening, and paid for it with his internal organs twanging all the way to Perth. In Australia he encountered an enthusiastic welcome, especially in Sydney, and Baird responded with zeal. He fell in love with the country and its freedom from the flaunting of wealth and of class-conscious- ness. He found it the happiest, healthiest and most commonsense community he had ever visited. There was something else that he admired, too: in addition to the Australian Broadcasting Commission, there were private stations with advertising. This was in line with Baird's thinking. He was against monopoly in the world of television and entertainment.

Baird's spirits seemed to fall as he returned to Europe. Perhaps, through contacts in the secret double life he was

William Taynton, reputedly the first person to be televised
when a boy, examines a range of Baird 'Cathovisors' at
Radio Olympia 1939. The largest was 26" in diameter, then
the biggest in the world

leading, he could surmise just what the future had in store
for the West. For a time he stayed at Minehead in Somerset.
Moseley, too, scented war in the wind. Margaret Baird
suggested heading for Africa with the children, but Baird
was immoveable, and they stayed on.

The Radio Show took place as usual in August 1939.
Baird had a first-class exhibit, including a 26 inch cathode
ray tube television receiver, probably the biggest available at
the time. William Taynton, the former office boy, now a full-
grown man, was pictured with a selection of cathode ray
tube receivers at Olympia.[37] He looked serious, respectful.
The rebellious lad who once had to be paid half-a-crown to
sit in front of a television camera now looked thoughtful, as
though he understood that he had played a part in history.

Ominous threats of war continued to pile one upon the
other, until on Friday 1 September Birkinshaw, engineer in
charge at Alexandra Palace, was told to cease transmission
by noon. It had happened at last. The world was at war for
the second time in just twenty-one years. The last item to be
televised was a Mickey Mouse cartoon, the last words: 'Ah
tink ah go home.' The war came at a crucial time in the
fortunes of Baird Television. If the conflict had not erupted

they would have swung dramatically upwards. They had spent £1,500,000 on developing television equipment and had just started to reap the benefits. Their large cinema screen project was so popular that they had received orders for fifty-five large screen systems priced at £2,750 each. Six were already operating in London. War meant the cancellation of all this. By August 1940 the company, almost bankrupt, had a receiver appointed.

But by this time John Logie Baird had much more on his mind. Now the nation, in fact the world, desperately needed those secret ideas, systems and plans of his, so far hidden from the public, but developing since his days in Hastings. A hint of them had appeared when he sailed for Australia in 1938. The Daily Telegraph of 25 February reported that Baird was taking his magic eye equipment, with which a bomber pilot could see his target from 50 to 100 miles away.[38]

Margaret Baird knew nothing of this project. As far as she was concerned it was a straightforward business trip abroad. But with Baird things were seldom as they seemed.

NOTES
1   'The Baird System in America - The Men Who Intend to
    Commercialise it', *Television*, July 1928, pp. 20-1
2   *Sermons, Soap and Television*, ch. 8, p. 6.
3   R.F.Tiltman,*Baird of Television*,SeeleyService, 1933,p. 153.
4   Television in a Theatre', *Daily Mail*, 29 June 1930.
5   'Race Seen in Berlin', *Daily Hcrald*, 4 June 1931 .
6   'How the Derby Finish Was Seen by a Cinema audience 14 Miles
    Away', *Illustratcd London News*, 11 June 1931, pp. 966-7.
7   *Sermons, Soap and Television*, ch. 8, p. 2.
8   *Sermons, Soap and Television*, ch. 8, p. 7.
9   *Sermons. Soap and Television*, ch. 8, p. 5.
10 Asa Briggs, *The History of Broadcasting in the United Kingdom*,
    vol.2,p.559.
11 G. Allighan, ' B B C Should Support British Inventors First' *Yorkshire
    Weekly Post Illustrated*, 7 November 1932 .
12 D. Sarnoff, 'Television, Comparative Status in England and the USA',
    WirelessWorld, 15 October 1937.
13 I.Shoenberg,'Television in England',*WirelessWorld*,29 0ctober 1937 .
    Several patents on the Iconoscope camera were handed over to the
    Marconi Wireless and Telegraph Company in Britain by Zworykin
    prior to 30 July 1932. EMI's first patent on an electronic camera
    (No.406,353) was applied from 25 August that year. But was this
    likely? Zworykin had applied for a patent on his Iconoscope electron
    camera in America on 17 July 1930. However a corresponding patent,
    No. 369,832, for Zworykin was granted to the Marconi Wireless and
    Telegraph Company in Britain. Three other British patents were also
    granted for Marconi: Nos 384,094 and 407,521, dated 24 February 1932,

and No. 421,201 dated 30 July 1932. EMI's first patent on an electron camera (No. 406,353), the Emiscope or Emitron, was dated 25 August 1932. If the Emitron was a purely British invention, it is very difficult to explain the necessity of accepting patents, knowledge and backing from America. It should be remembered that, when RCA was created after the First World War, one of the companies absorbed was the Marconi Wireless and Telegraph Co. of America. In 1937 Marconi-EMI introduced their Super-Emitron, and simultaneously RCA unveiled their Super-Iconoscope. Television publications of the day were not so easily fooled. Some stated that the Emitron was merely a development of the Iconoscope, while others bluntly said that the Emitron was the Iconoscope.

14   Asa Briggs, *The History of Broadcasting in the United Kingdom*, vol. 2, *The Golden Age of Wireless'*, Oxford University Press, 1965, p. 573.

15   *Wireless World*, 2 March 1934: '30-Line Broadcasts Must Go On', editorial; 'Broadcast Television - The Case for Continuing 30-line Transmissions', pp. 146-7.'A Society in the Making, '*Television*,50th anniversary issue, 1927-1977, November- December 1977, p. 22.

16   Sir A.Fleming,'BBC Attacked by Famous Scientist', *Daily Mail*,15 March 1934.

17   F. Gradenwitz, 'Now This Is Television', *Television*, December 1928, p. 25.

18   S. Moseley, 'Sydney Moseley Reveals Some Secrets', *Television*, November 1928, pp. 19-20.

19   A. A. C. Swinton, 'On Television', letter, *The Times*, 16 December 1929, p. 8c.

20   Lee De Forest, 'A Veteran on 30-line Television', News of the Week, *Wireless World*, 11 April 1934.

21   K. McIlwain, 'Survey of Television Pick-up Devices', *Journal of Applied Physics*, 10, July 1939, pp. 432-42.

22   S. A. Moseley and H. J. Barton-Chapple, *Television Today and Tomorrow*, Pitman, 1940, p. 26. S. A. Moseley and H. McKay, *Television, A Guide for the Amateur*, OxfordUniversityPress, 1936,p. 136.

23   'Baird's Outstanding Television Demonstration', *Practical and Amateur Wireless*, 2 March 1935, pp. 871-3.

24   Asa Briggs, *The History of Broadcasting in the United Kingdom*, vol. 2, Oxford University Press, 1965, p. 597.

25   'Television - A Surprise Item', *Practical and Amateur Wireless*, 21 November 1936.L.C.Jesty,letter,*Electronics and Power*,April 1976,p.247.

26   *Sermons, Soap and Television*, ch 9, p.5.

27   'TV German Plea for British Cooperation', *The Times*, 10 July 1935, p.13g.

28   'High Definition Television in July', *Wireless World*, 19 April 1935.

29   'Reviewing the Video Art', *Electronics (USA)*, January 1938, pp. 9-11.

30   'The Television Telephone', *Wireless World*, 22 February 1935.

31   M.P. Wilder, 'Television in Europe', *Electronics (USA)*, January 1938. The Television Race between Britain and Germany', *Wireless World*, 29 October 1937, p. 418.

32   P. Hawker 'Do We Want Bigger, Better Pictures', *Television*, January - February 1983, pp. 17-19.

33   D.C. Birkenshaw, 'The Birth of Modern Television', *Television*, 50th anniversary issue, 1927-1977, November-December 1977, pp.32-7.

34   E.W. Engstrom, A Study of Television Image Characteristics', Part

1, *Proc. IRE (USA)*, 21 December 1933, pp.1631-51.

35   'Berlin Begins Television', *World Radio*, 29 March 1935.

36   'Berlin Television', *The Times*, March 23 1935, p.11d, p13d.

37   M. Hallet, *John Logie Baird and Television*, Priory Press, 1978.

38   'Television in Bombers', *Daily Telegraph*, 25 February 1938.

9

The Mystery Ray

As Winston Churchill took the helm at 10 Downing Street and Britain prepared for her finest hour, scientists and technicians were moblized and transformed into boffins at factories and secret establishments throughout the land. The staff of Baird's company proved no exception and were soon operating in several important fields including radar. Only Baird was ignored, or so the legend would have us believe. The man who had developed the world's first true television pictures and, starting with Noctovision, had broken so much new ground in object detection, was now abandoned to his own private devices and enthusiasms at a time when his country was desperately utilizing all the technological and inventive skills that could be mustered, or so it seemed.

Long after his death, Baird's family and friends were mystified by this strange neglect. Sydney Moseley was baffled at the time and remained so for the rest of his life. He could not fathom why the outstanding genius of his friend had not been harnessed to the war effort. This disturbed him so much that as early as 1939 he wrote to Captain (later Admiral) J.H. Godfrey, head of British naval intelligence from 1939 to 1942, assuming that the Admiralty had realized the potential of Noctovision, and drew attention to Baird's availability.[1] This approach received a polite acknowledgement, nothing more, and Mosely continued to believe it was madness not to have called upon his friend's prodigious inventive talents.

On the outbreak of war Baird evacuated his family to Bude in Cornwall, where they were joined by his mother-in-law and a menagerie of pets. Strangely, he stayed on in London, apparently continuing television research at his home in Sydenham, despite continuing air raids which blew out the windows and brought down the ceilings. He remained firmly planted there, despite repeated entreaties and invitations from Mosely to go to America where, he was assured, he would be welcomed with open arms. He also resisted his wife's apparently logical exhortatons to seek new and more useful pastures if the British government did not want him.

The whole scenario is unlikely, yet it was generally accepted that one of the world's most brilliant inventors was allowed to sit out the war, amiably pursuing his old activities as though little were at stake. However, recent evidence must dispel this misconception once and for all. Baird's wartime appointments diaries are in the possession of his family, and it was only recently, on examination of the cryptic and often hastily scrawled entries, that it grew clear that he had had regular meetings with some of the country's mot important military and scientific figures. Though heavily engaged in the struggle against Nazi Germany, it seems that they had a great deal of time to spare for the hermit of Sydenham.

The conclusion that Baird had a deeply clandestine involvement in the war is inescapable, and though it emerges that he was working on several quite separate top secret projects, it is radar which provides the most fertile ground for clues to his activity and influence. Only his television research was allowed publicity during the war years, yet in 1944 Baird noted in his dairy that he had taken out what he himself termed 'secret radar patents'. Radar, an American abbreviation for radiolocation and ranging, had first been revealed, with few details, by the British press in June 1941.[2] The British at first called it radiolocation, also RDF, or radio direction finding. Radio waves of a suitable wavelength were transmitted out to be re-radiated and hence reflected from aeroplanes, ships and so on. The reflected waves or echoes reached a receiver aerial, usually placed near or combined with the transmitter aerial. A receiver cathode ray tube display screen was used to study the reflections and indicate the direction, distance and height of the reflecting objects.

In the summer of 1940 the British radar system played a vital role in the Battle of Britain by locating the approaching Luftwaffe squadrons at long range, thus giving the Royal Air Force sufficient time to arrange the best possible defence formations. Later the radar radio waves, travelling at the speed of light, would aid the Americans in the Pacific, help decimate U boats in the Battle of the Atlantic, play a key role in the sinking of the Bismarck and the Scharnhorst and guide Allied bomber squadrons to their targets.

How, when and where had this magnificent system originated?

In 1943 Britain and America simultaneously released further details. A US Army-Navy statement appeared jointly with one from the British Information Service.[3] Both sides stressed radar's vital role in the war. But, despite cooperation in timing, the reports managed to engender very bad feeling between the Allies. The British made a diplomatic gaffe by suggesting that radiolocation would have rendered the Japanese attack on Pearl Harbour impossible. This was a sore point in the United States, as American-built radar had in fact been present at Pearl Harbour and Japanese planes had been plotted in, but there was a mistake in identification. The outcome might have been different if the Americans had possessed secondary radar, involving identification signals from their own planes, separating friend from foe.

The reports clashed, however on something far more basic. The Americans stated bluntly that radar was first invented in the United States during 1922 by scientists who observed that reception from radio stations was interfered with when certain objects moved into the path of the signals. In the British section of the statement, credit was attributed to Sir Robert Watson-Watt, a Scottish scientist and civil servant, and an old acquaintance of John Logie Baird. The basis of this claim was a February 1935 experiment by Watson-Watt in which radio waves were reflected from an RAF Heyford bomber. Sir Robert did not disagree with this. He was knighted for his efforts in 1941 and became the self-styled 'father of radar'. Intriguingly, years later, Sir Robert, one of a syndicate of seven scientists seeking reward from the Crown, would be denied the 'invention' of radar by his old masters, the Air Ministry. Nevertheless he would be awarded £50,000 for what was officially and carefully termed the 'initiation' of radar.

Signs of a radar row between Britain and America showed as early as October 1945. The US magazine *Fortune* stated: 'When the war ended radar was a larger industry by a considerable margin than US radio had ever been. More than a billion dollars' worth of radar systems, tubes and accessories were produced in the United States that year'.

It went on:

But there is a sequel to it. Civil strife over scientific recognition, patent rights and fiscal business threatens to break out in the industry now that the necessary cooperation has ended. Moreover, the conflict is not confined to the United States.

Jealousy between British and American radar proponents has added special bitterness to the issue. So serious a view was taken of this situation that military authorities and the State Department frowned on all mention of radar for some time after security restrictions had been relaxed.

The article said that, at the start of the war, British radar had reached a state of development that was somewhat higher than that of the United States, as the British had been working against the deadline of war.

It described how British physicists brought 'a magnetron, the most important single contribution to radar technique' to America in Autumn, 1940. This item was considered so secret that the British agent who brought it, to cover his tracks, carried it around with him for several days before delivering it to US engineers.[4]

At the outbreak of war British and American scientists could only make shrewd guesses on an official level as to the progress each had made in the radar race. By 1940 the beginnings of a secret Atlantic Alliance were being forged between Roosevelt and Churchill, with the United States supplying destroyers in return for leases on British island bases in the Caribbean. The British then made a suggestion which the Americans accepted, drawing the nations closer still. Technical secrets would be shared. To this end an exploratory British government mission was sent to the United States led by Sir Henry Tizard, Rector of the Imperial College of Science and Technology in London and Adviser to The Ministry of Aircraft Production. The United States sent a reciprocal mission to Britain, where the delegates had an eye opener. They admired Britain's development of pulsed long-range radar, anti-aircraft gun control radar and the beginnings of centimetric airborne radar, but it was not only these achievements that make a lasting impression. Where they had expected to find a country on the verge of defeat, Major General Emmons of the Army Corps and General Strong, Chief of the War Plans Division of the General Staff, were awed by the order, system and progressive refinement that they observed in the British scientific establishment.[5] They were particularly struck by the design, construction and organisation of the command posts, the corpuscles of the British defence, and by the rapidity and accuracy of radar plane detection. They were amazed at the extent and capability of the fixed long-range radar stations, started less than five years before. In August 1940, 957 Nazi planes had been shot down, 15 per cent of the attacking force, and on the famous Sunday of 15 September the Luftwaffe suffered 185 aircraft shot down out of a force of 500 raiders. Other countries might be in the radar race, but Britain had certainly committed herself wholeheartedly to the system at an extraordinary early date.

The curious fact was that the planning of the famous wall of radar stations known as Chain Home had been started in 1935, just months after Sir Robert's much vaunted experiment. Soon he was superintending their rapid erection along the vulnerable east and south coasts of Britain. If his experiment had indeed been the first step in British radar, then matters had progressed with near impossible speed. These stations were conceived and built with confidence and at astronomical cost, at a time of great unemployment and national depression. A Britain which found itself militarily unprepared to take the offensive at the outbreak of the Second World War nevertheless had complete confidence in radar, apparently invented just months before. It had committed itself to a programme whose costs would rival those of the Americans on the atom bomb. The story takes some swallowing. Whatever the truth, though Munich and appeasement were the outward order of the day, in the latter half of the 1930s Britain felt it had sufficient technical expertise to put its trust in radar, and was preparing to defend itself as early as 1935.

After the war both Allies politely acknowledged the efforts of the other in radar but neatly sidestepped the awkward question of paternity. The Americans turned a blind eye to Britain's puzzling 1935 confidence in the system. The United States' earlier claim for 1922 can be discounted, because at that date there was no suitable functional display units or screens capable of locating and observing the movement of a distant object. Any object detection system of that time could only trigger an alarm, indicating an intruder, but could not pinpoint or track the object. However, the Americans could claim to have outstripped Watson-Watt. In the USA in 1931 a certain Project 88' was transferred from the Chief of Ordnance to the Army Signal Corps Laboratory at Fort Monmouth and given the title 'Position Finding by Means of Light'. Basically it was an investigation into object location by the detection of infra-red or heat rays radiated by or reflected from an object. In 1932 and 1933 the project was extended to include reflected short radio waves.[6]

Quite apart from this American research on radar, and the British story of radar stations being built in 1935, it appears that between 1934 and 1939 the French managed to install thirty units of radar equipment along the French-German border and around Brest harbour, a fact not widely known.[7] Moreover the German navy had experimented with radar in Kiel harbour in 1934, and the pocket battleship *Graf Spee* was successfully fitted with centimetric wavelength gun-ranging radar in 1938.[8] At the beginning of the war Allied air forces had to contend with the long-range German Freya early warning radar system and the short range Würzburg radar, which helped anti-aircraft gunners. Italy and Japan also had forms of radar. At the end of the war the British government and others claimed that in 1939 they had not known if the Germans even knew about radar, let alone if they possessed a radar chain. The origins of the system, which helped to transform the world in peace and war, are ironically shrouded in mystery as dense as the fog and the smoke it helped to pierce. The facts which have survived, often in isolation, indicate a story so far untold, one of secrecy and duplicity involving a scientific struggle for radar among the nations, long before the start of the Second World War. Radar may have been a tree with many branches, but its roots must surely go back to John Logie Baird.

To understand his involvement in radar, it is necessary to look back to the beginnings of radio in the last years of the nineteenth century. It was discovered then that radio waves behave differently, depending on their wavelengths. The long waves, as used originally in signalling, can have wavelengths to several hundred metres. Such waves follow the curvature of the earth's surface and can travel thousands of miles over the horizon. The waves open out in all directions from the transmitter aerial and are thus open to interception by possible enemies, a minus feature when secret signalling is involved in wartime. On the other hand as the wavelengths decrease to the short and ultrashort waves, the waves act more like light waves and travel in straight lines. Such waves do not follow the earth's curvature. To dispatch them over the horizon, use is made of the phenomenon of radio wave reflection between the earth's surface and the charged layers of the atmosphere. The waves are initially transmitted towards the charged atmospheric layers in the atmosphere, from where they are reflected to earth, to be reflected once again to the atmospheric layers. Repeated reflections mean that such waves can travel many thousands of miles. Radio wave energy is lost at each reflection and therefore a powerful transmitter must be used to ensure that sufficient energy reaches a distant receiver. (It should be noted that America is beginning to use this old idea for 'over the horizon' radar. Radar radio waves will travel from America and Britain to be multireflected between sky and earth and reach over the horizon to distant targets. The target will reflect these waves, by multi reflection, back to the observers' receiver screen.)

It was observed that such short waves could be directed from the transmitter in any one desired direction, by means of a curved reflecting screen of wire cables placed partly around the transmitter aerial. This metal screen acted like a curved concave mirror for light waves, reflecting the waves in the direction of the mirror and transmitting a beam of waves which spread out very slowly. Marconi used such reflectors in the mid-1920s for his 'beam' wireless stations.

The radio wave beam was extremely powerful, since all the transmitter aerial energy was going out in one narrow path. Such a beam could withstand many reflections between the atmosphere and the earth and still retain sufficient energy to make receiver amplification a simple process. By using a higher carrier frequency, the shorter waves of long-range radio made it possible to carry much more information on the beam. The use of such a beam also meant increased security against detection by enemies in wartime. In order to reduce the wavelength still further to centimetric values, it was necessary to use solid metal, parabola-shaped concave mirrors placed partly around the transmitter aerial. Such an arrangement produced a beam of waves with an extremely small spread, the radio wave equivalent of an anti-aircraft searchlight beam. As early as 1898 Marconi had used such parabolic reflectors at both transmitter and receiver aerials for centimetric wave signalling. The receiver reflector focused the incoming beam onto the receiver aerial, thus significantly increasing the detected energy and greatly reducing the required amplification. The reduction of receiver amplification resulted in considerably less distortion of the received signals sent along the beam. To this day radio wave reflectors remain extremely useful units in shortwave and ultrashort-wavelength wireless.

Referring to radar, as opposed to wireless, a decrease of the transmitter wavelength resulted in the receiver screen image containing more details of the reflecting objects. Centimetric waves could accurately detect small objects, such as the conning tower of a surfaced submarine. The 1939 long-range Chain Home stations used medium waves of approximately 10 metres and no metal reflectors, the beam spreading out to floodlight a large area. Reasonable control of the spread angle could be achieved by placing several transmitters close together in a predetermined pattern. The magnetic fields interacted to send out a very powerful beam with a known spread angle. Such a system could intercept a large number of aircraft, the one beam covering an entire group of planes. No accurate assessment of the exact number of aircraft present was possible at the receiver, since each aircraft reflected only a small part of the total beam. A guess could be made, though, of the numbers of aircraft by observing the energy intensity of the reflected waves at the receiver, a large number of aircraft giving a high energy reflected signal and vice versa.

The 1939 German radar system used centimetric waves with parabolic metal reflectors at transmitter and receiver. The resulting narrow radio beam could be 'scanned' in the sky just like a searchlight. Such a system gave high accuracy in determining the direction and range of approaching British aircraft, and the narrow beam made it possible to detect more accurately individual aircraft flying in large groups. But the 1939 German system had one flaw; the maximum range was only about 80 miles, compared to the 140 miles of the medium-wave British system. When the German system was designed and built in the late 1930s centimetric pulsed wave radar transmitters, necessary to generate extremely high powers for very long range, were just not available. The British 1940 medium-wave radar transmitters used known and proved technology, could generate very large amounts of power, and made possible the very long-range detection of enemy aircraft.

Modern 'scanned' radar transmitters as carried in aircraft

can now operate down to millimetric wavelengths. The radio waves leave the aircraft and are scanned over the earth's surface in a predetermined manner by the movement of the transmitter reflector and associated aerial. The waves reflect from the earth back to the receiver, which in general uses the same reflector as the transmitter. By using millimetric wavelengths, great detail or high resolution of the ground below the aircraft can be obtained in the radar receiver images. The system is now used for aerial mapping. If centimetric waves are adopted in the same system then the receiver images have lower resolution and reveal less detail, indicating only the outlines of cities, rivers, coasts and so on.

Allied bomber squadrons were equipped with such scanned radar systems from 1943 onwards. The systems enabled aircraft to operate above cloud level, while navigating accurately to and over their designated targets. The codename for the 10 cm wavelength version was H 2 S, for the 3 cm version H2K and for the 1 cm version H2X. As will become apparent, John Logie Baird was associated with at least the H2S version. No one yet knows why the symbols H2S, H2K and H2X were chosen, though various guesses have been made. Significantly, the S radio band is 10 cm, the K radio band is 3 cm and the X radio band is 1 cm. 'H' probably stands for the H electromagnetic vibration modes associated with the rectangular waveguides used in the apparatus; one can obtain or reject an H2 mode of vibration.

In order for such scanned aerial radars to work successfully on centimetric and millimetric wavelengths, large transmitter power was essential. The radio pioneers who made this power possible go back to the Victorian world of gas light and Hansom cabs. Guglielmo Marconi transmitted 25 cm wavelength waves in 1897, while the English scientists Sir Oliver Lodge and Sir Ambrose Fleming achieved 10 cm in 1894 and 1897 respectively, and J. C. Bose of India 5 mm between 1895 and 1897.[9] All were influenced by Germany's Heinrich Hertz, who transmitted on 66 cm in 1888. Hertz noticed that metallic conductors reflected his waves, the first positive step towards modern radar. All the above-mentioned scientists used spark gap transmitters capable of generating surprisingly large amounts of power at centimetric wavelengths. Such transmitting power was not to be repeated again until 1940, with the introduction of the multi-cavity magnetron valve, claimed inaccurately afterwards by the British as a purely British invention.

Another important element of centimetric radar and wireless sprang from this period. Because of the extremely high frequencies used, the waves are not conducted along solid metal wires but are transmitted along hollow metal channels called wave guides. Lodge and Fleming were the inventors of the wave guide and used such devices for centimetric radio transmissions in the 1890s.[9] For both men, John Logie Baird's work held the utmost fascination, and the elderly and respected scientists became his close friends and colleagues from the 1920s on.

Much of the early work was pure research and, since the limited range of the centimetric waves made them initially unattractive for long-range signalling, they were eventually discarded by the early radio pioneers. A notable but apparently neglected exception to this trend was Christian Hulsmeyer, a Dusseldorf engineer. In 1904 Hulsmeyer lodged British, French, and German patents on an elementary radio reflecting device which used a spark gap transmitter. In an age when armies were still playing with coloured uniforms and lances, the device struck a chillingly modern note. Hulsmeyer was a nineteen-year-old student at Bremen in 1900 when he noticed the reflections of his transmitted centimetric radio waves from ships. From this observation he developed what he called his Telemobiloskop, which was tested on the River Elbe and demonstrated in 1904 at a shipping conference in Rotterdam. He did not have much success, as the shipping magnates at the time were deeply involved with the Marconi Company. In 1904 Hulsmeyer took out a British radio reflecting patent, No. 13,170, and later another, No. 25,608. The second patent covered object distance ranging by using geometry. The object range was calculated from a knowledge of the distance between the transmitter and the receiver and the angles of the object facing receiver and transmitter to a straight line drawn between them. Reflected waves from the object rang a warning bell on Hulsmeyer's specially equipped ship. A vital observation had been made, but the lack of a visual display and instantaneous range information meant that Hulsmeyer's device was limited in value for modern defence. However, the idea was not forgotten and an identical system appeared aboard the French liner *Normandie* in 1935, an indication that the French were thinking along radar lines.[10]

Marconi too showed an early interest in the principles that led to radar. As early as June 1922, on accepting a Medal of Honour from the Institute of Radio Engineers in America, he gave a lecture entitled 'Radio Telegraphy', in which he mentioned his observations of radio wave reflections from metallic objects several miles away. [11] He suggested that an apparatus could be built for detecting ships and other objects. Sir Oliver Lodge and Sir Ambrose Fleming were consultants at this time on the Marconi team and it is probable that they were thinking along the same lines. However, all such early ideas were baulked by the tantalizing lack of a workable, visual receiver unit to display the reflected waves instantaneously at all times.

Baird had not be been slow in grasping this fact, and may have had the idea in mind from the very start of his research into object detection. From at least 1923 he experimented with systems comparable to radar, using not only infra-red rays but also reflected radio waves for detecting distant objects. In 1926, close on the heels of his first official public demonstration of television, he took out a British patent (No. 292,185) which was quite distinct from television It was for a spark gap radio transmitter, a radar apparatus for object detection, and it had a real-time visual display with which to study the radio waves reflected from the objects.[12] This was John Logie Baird's Televisor, and early in 1927 he followed it with a second British patent (No. 297,014), an improved radar visual receiver display, which was a flat screen covered with small metal particles.[13] In this patent Baird stated that the new receiver was a development of Hertz's 1888 centimetric wave receiver, as used by the German himself to observe the reflections of centimetric waves from conducting metallic objects.

The yellowing pages of newspapers and magazines of the 1920s testify to Baird's overwhelming interest in detection systems, of whose tactical importance he was fully aware. Indeed he predicted and published the wartime uses of such equipment, declaring that the units would revolutionize warfare.

It is not surprising that Sir Oliver Lodge and Sir Ambrose Fleming were among his most fervent supporters from the mid-1920s. Both were noted radio pioneers. Sir Oliver, later Principal of Birmingham University, had invented radio tuning before Marconi. Sir Ambrose, a Fellow of St John's College, Cambridge, was a particularly close friend of Baird and became President of the Royal Television Society from 1928 until 1943; he had invented the Diode valve, which revolutionized wireless, telegraphy and telephony. Decades before, Lodge and Fleming had worked out many of the factors that, when combined, would be invaluable to radar. Quite apart from the wave guide, Lodge had also studied over thirty years previously the full effects of radio wave reflection and absorption on various objects ranging from the human body to metal, wood and glass.[14] This information had been languishing since the reign of Queen Victoria, awaiting practical application. Fleming, too, had published details on the same subject in 1922.[15]

Baird was also swift to notice the reflecting behaviour of radio waves. Joseph Bissett of Strichen in Aberdeenshire was a London journalist at the time, working for an agency which specialized in the interpretation of scientific subjects for newspapers and magazines. He recalls that Baird had excitedly informed him that his transmitted radio waves were going through people, but were reflected from all the metallic components in his laboratory. Common scientific interest explains the attractions of Baird's work for Lodge and Fleming. Baird was interested in object detection systems and the behaviour of radio waves and he provided a screen which made these waves visible. Baird, Lodge and Fleming had the very powerful spark gap transmitter and a specialist knowledge concerning the reflection effects of radio waves on the objects to be detected. It is difficult to imagine how this trio of vision, will and boundless curiosity could have avoided combining their talents. Together they possessed all the ingredients of modern radar almost ten years before it was claimed to have been invented by Watson-Watt in February 1935.

As will be seen, it was not long before the British armed forces were researching in radar themselves, invalidating the primacy claim for the Watson-Watt experiment of 1935. The Royal Navy was fully aware of the potential of radar and in 1928 applied for a secret provisional British radar patent to detect aircraft and ships,[16] and the British army were also successfully testing 50 cm radar at Woolwich in 1930 - both were striking examples of radar's hidden pre-1935 history.[17]

In the light of these developments and a study of Baird's early patents, the strange metal particle screen and parabolic metal dish with central spike glimpsed by young Norman

Loxdale at Hastings in 1923 no longer seem inexplicable. The dish and spike were the centimetric spark gap radar transmitter, eventually patented by Baird in 1926. The strange metal particle screen used by Baird at Hastings in 1923 was the radar receiver that he patented in 1927. Eye-witness accounts and a study of contemporary published material and pictures confirm that Baird consistently worked on perfecting his television apparatus long before applying for any patents or giving public exhibitions. His development of radar and other object detection systems followed a similar course. Baird's 1927 radar screen patent shows that the system operated like this: the object-reflected transmitter radio waves struck the metal particle screen and caused sparks to occur between the particles. The localized strength of the radio waves on the screen dictated the localized strength of the sparks, and hence the associated local light on the screen. The different light intensities on the screen created an image of the object being detected.

Meanwhile research leading to radar was also under way in America. Marconi's lecture in June 1922 appears to have stimulated interest there in the possibilities of radiolocation. A month or two later A. Hoyt-Taylor, chief physicist of the US Naval Research Laboratory in Washington, started experiments to detect moving objects by placing the objects between a radio transmitter beam and a radio receiver. By blocking the transmitted rays to the receiver the object created a variation in sound at the receiver, thus denoting the presence of the intruding body. This system, proposed for protecting harbour mouths, was not true reflecting radar equipment and had no ranging capability. The device could only operate by having either two ships or two aircraft, one with a radar receiver, the other with a radar transmitter. Any enemy ship or aircraft would have to pass between the two units before detection could be made at the receiver. Modern radar usually has both transmitter and receiver in one specially designed unit which can sweep the horizon, searching for and pinpointing objects. The first joint British American radar press release, *Electronics* June 1943, gave the American version, namely that their first truly reflected radar echoes were obtained in 1925.[18] They merely noted Hoyt-Taylor's 1922 method and in the summary of the press release it was stressed that no prior claim was made for Hoyt-Taylor in respect of radar.

The wording of the joint press release was cautious and

indicated that the basic principles of radar could be traced much further back. The report totally ignored French and German prewar published radar achievements and gave Britain the full credit for first applying the invention 'in the dramatic defence of Britain against the Luftwaffe in 1940 and 1941'. *Wireless World* of 1944 noted that A. Hoyt-Taylor had been awarded the U S Medal of Merit.[19] The citation read that Taylor had laboured tirelessly in a course of intensive research and experimentation which eventually resulted in the discovery and development of radar. The words are deliberately vague. Did the Americans discover radar? The authors of this book are of the opinion that they did not.

The American reference to reflected radio waves in 1925 was almost certainly based on the experiments of G. Breit and M. A. Tuve, of the Carnegie Institute at Washington, who transmitted pulses of radio waves to be reflected from the ionized layers in the upper atmosphere.[20] These layers had been drawing the attention of radio experimenters because of layer movements which were resulting in strange radio reflections and interference effects back on the ground at the receiver. In these experiments two pulses arrived almost simultaneously at the receiver, one pulse being reflected from the distant layers, the other pulse travelling direct by land from the same transmitter. The combined and rapidly changing effects of the waves at the receiver display had to be recorded on cine film. From the observed results, plus a knowledge of the distance between transmitter and receiver, it was possible to calculate by geometry the height of the reflecting layer. However a year before, in 1924, an identical system had already appeared in Britain utilizing not pulsed but continuous radio waves.[21] The unit operated in a similar manner to that of Breit and Tuve and was used by another of Baird's acquaintances, E. V. Appleton, who calculated the height of the ionized layers, one of which is now called after him. Appleton's research won him the Nobel Prize and his 1924 system is now known as a continuous wave Doppler radar, while that of Breit and Tuve is called a pulsed wave Doppler radar. Both systems are based on a well-known natural phenomenon known as the Doppler effect. The units work by measuring the frequency change of the transmitted radio waves after their reflection from a detected object. A similar frequency change is observed when the sound waves from an approaching train are heard to rise in frequency, only to fall after the train passes. In Doppler radar systems, the changing frequency of the reflected waves from the moving detected object is compared with the steady frequency coming directly by land from the transmitter, to give a beat or interference effect which is displayed on the receiver.

Neither of these early forms of Doppler was adopted for Britain's prewar Chain Home radar defence system, since if they were to use medium wavelengths they would require a very large distance between transmitter and receiver for accurate ranging. This made them unsuitable for mounting on ships and aircraft. Should the aircraft or ship being detected by such a system move in certain directions, it is possible that no frequency change effect would be noted on the receiver and the object would escape observation. Christian Hulsmeyer's 1904 radar and the identical centimetric radar system installed on the *Normandie* in 1935 demanded several items of information, including the angles of the transmitter and receiver to the object and the distance between the transmitter and receiver. These systems can thus also be discounted as the forerunners of Britain's defence radar. In 1936 the Normandie's radar was reported as being inaccurate for range.

Most modern radars consist of pulsed transmitters with the transmitter pulses being used to synchronize, strobe or trigger the cathode ray rube receiver time display, which is a visual display or screen for continuously viewing the object echoes or reflected waves. This design of equipment was the basis of Britain's long range Chain Home stations and, as will be shown, stems directly from John Logie Baird's radar equipment of the 1920s.

Details of the first radar unit to incorporate all these principles were published in Baird's British patent 292,185 of 1926, already referred to. In the invention covered by this patent Baird sent out continuous centimetric or millimetric waves from a spark gap radio transmitter, to illuminate the various objects being detected. The returning reflected echoes were ingeniously broken up into pulses by a rotating Nipkow disc before reaching the receiver aerial. The receiver-aerial pulsed electrical signals were then fed to a lamp at a second synchronously rotating Nipkow disc Baird Televisor, the echo electrical signals being built up element by element on the screen by a flashing lamp into a visible two- dimensional image of the object. The overall effect was

15th December, 1926.

S.24132/26/D.S.R.   SECRET

Dear Sir,

   With further reference to my letter of the 29th of
October, I attach for your information a copy of a letter
addressed by Messrs. Television Ltd. to Lieutenant Colonel
Lefroy of the Royal Aircraft Establishment dated the 7th
of October last in which the proposal is made for a demonstration of automatic spotting by radio transmission. As
it is not desired to duplicate in any way the work which
you have already in hand at the Admiralty Research Laboratory
I would suggest that the firm's proposal should be considered
by you and a reply sent. I would add that the Air Ministry
would be very willing to give any assistance to you that might
lie in their power in furtherance of any work of this nature.

                    Yours faithfully,

                    (Sgd.) H. E. WIMPERIS,

                    Director of Scientific Research.

The Director of Scientific Research,
Admiralty,
S.W.1.

Enclosures:
Letter dated 7.10.26.
and enclosures.

similar to sending out pulses from the transmitter and
accepting reflected pulses at the receiver. Transmitter pulses
were also sent directly by land, from the receiver aerial
Nipkow disc, to synchronize with the Televisor receiver
viewing disc.

In Baird's 1926 radar, movements of the reflecting object
meant that the transmitter echoes took different times to
reach the receiver aerial disc, which in turn meant that the
echo images assumed different positions on the Televisor
screen. Baird could estimate the range, or change of object
range, by simply counting the number of television image
lines by which the echo had moved. His units would have
been previously calibrated for range, by practical tests
against objects at known distances from his 'Noctovisor'
radar, thus enabling him to calculate the object range from
the position of the echo on the Televisor screen. By using a
spark gap transmitter, which could also be operated in a
pulsed fashion if required, he had eliminated all the later
radar problems of finding very powerful centimetric pulsed
radar transmitters. Modern pulsed radar sends transmitter
pulses directly by land to trigger a visible light blip on the
receiver cathode ray tube. The receiver tube is synchronized

by the transmitter pulses. The transmitted pulses sent to the object are almost simultaneously echoed or reflected from the detected object, but take slightly longer times to reach the CRT receiver. Thus the echo blip appears in a different position on the screen. The radar is calibrated so that the distance between the blips gives the object's range.

In effect, then, modern radar is merely a development of Baird's 1926 system. Indeed radar is only a form of television. Baird's original television camera of 1926 scanned the unlit object with a spot of light, which on reflecting to a sensor supplied signals to the Televisor receiver, in order to create an image. Modern centimetric wavelength radar replaces the light with a radio-wave beam which scans the skies reflecting from aircraft, ships or other objects, creating an image on a receiver screen. Even if one had not encountered Baird's early use of reflected radio waves for detection, one would still have to grant that radar is basically his 1926 television system. But it has also been shown that Baird had adapted to radio waves as well, though this was kept well out of public awareness, almost certainly as a result of growing pressure by the British authorities who realized just where such research was leading. Baird himself helped to disguise his activities by referring to the Noctovisor radar systems as a form of daylight television.

That the government and armed forces were vitally interested in television at such an early date is evident, although this clashes with previous accounts. Just how anxious they were to secure its use began to emerge as far back as 1923, the year that Baird started to receive major press coverage. Two startling secret files released in 1972 and previously unnoticed in the British Public Records Office at Kew reveal part of the story, with a tale of inter-service rivalry. One file, Air 2/S 24132, opened in 1924, is actually entitled 'The Use of Television in Aircraft'. It records the Air Ministry's discovery that since 1923 Admiralty researchers had been experimenting with television, struggling with little success to obtain pictures with mirror-drum transmitters and receivers. The Air Ministry then sent H. E. Wimperis, Director of Scientific Research, to inspect the navy's attempts at television and to suggest cooperation. Years later, in 1935, Wimperis was Air Ministry Chief to Robert Watson-Watt, at the time of the latter's controversial so-called first ever radar experiment, and he was to be instrumental in persuading the British government to embark upon the very expensive long-range radar chain around the British coastline. Watson-Watt, in his version of the birth of radar, portrays Wimperis as the initiator of naive inquiries about the feasibility of so-called death rays to be used on approaching aircraft, which is supposed to have led to Watson-Watt's first radar experiment. But this hardly fits the facts in the secret files which show that by 1924 Wimperis was already well-informed of the possibilities of television and its offshoots for military projects.

The Admiralty had been busily pursuing television for several purposes, but it was proving a will-o'-the-wisp. The Navy saw television as a means of guiding artillery by spotting shellbursts and they grasped its potential for the transmission of maps and secret information, not just on land and sea but from aircraft to ground and vice versa. But the idea which perhaps struck the most modern note was their plan to use television for guiding pilotless aircraft.

The Air Ministry file was not long in existence before a dossier was opened on John Logie Baird's television performances and publications. A secret letter dated 13 June 1926 from a Col Lefroy, who was involved in Air Ministry intelligence, indicated that he had kept a file on Baird since 1924 and had also interviewed people with knowledge of Baird's equipment. He took the trouble to speak to those who were opposed to Baird, as well as to his supporters, and these included Will Day, one of Baird's original business partners whom·0. G. Hutchinson had just bought out from Television Ltd in December 1925. It seems that Day was disenchanted by the struggle to establish television and expressed the opinion that Baird was not really interested in television, only in making money, a.claim which was to be proved hollow in the light of subsequent events.

On the Admiralty side, the researcher who appears in the files is a luckless Dr Beattie who persevered manfully throughout 1925, trying to make his television equipment work, until on 10 February 1926 an Admiralty letter reported that he had eventually gone to see Baird's television system in action at 22 Frith Street, Soho. This must have impressed him. On 27 June another letter revealed that Dr Beattie had now discarded his earlier equipment and adopted a Baird-style Nipkow disc television unit, a great tribute to the resourcefulness of Baird, who at this point had apparently achieved his images without government funds or assistance.

By 1925 the army too appeared in the file, with a Col. H. G. K. Wait and a Major A. C. Fuller, Royal Engineers Board, joining those with a special interest in television. Their specific project was television for top security secret signalling, to be undertaken at Woolwich. The file kept track of this venture and by 1929 reported that the system was working superbly. In the autumn of 1926 the file indicates that contact had already been established between Television Ltd, the Admiralty and the Air Ministry, with secret demonstrations to military officials of Baird's reflected infra-red Noctovisor. Baird then tried to secure a firm contract from them, but in their communications both services can be seen attempting to glean what they can through observation, so that they can develop their own television systems and thus avoid paying royalties, a move which Baird was swift to notice. When asked to leave television equipment with them for inspection he declined politely but firmly. They decided to play a waiting game and watch for developments before taking a final option.

Anyone studying the file would obtain the impression that the Admiralty ceased television research in late 1926 and the Air Ministry in late 1927, but at Woolwich the army continued until after 1930, when the file letters cease. This and other files are interesting as much for omissions as for revelations. They concentrate, for example, on Baird's normal television research, but make no allusion to his current publication on and demonstrations of the far superior reflected radio wave Noctovisor, the basis of modern radar. There is no reference to the provisional British patent for reflected radar, taken out by the Admiralty in 1928, for the detection of aircraft. Cross-reference numbers are given for files that have never been released, which could perhaps tell a much fuller and far different story. It is difficult to avoid the conclusion that this is a decoy production with a smattering of detail, meant to draw attention from the very important radio wave radars that were undoubtedly the subject of experiments in Britain at this time.

The revelation in the Air Ministry file of the army's interest in television for secret signalling had a fascinating sequel when, quite independently of the file discovery, the authors received a letter from Mr James G. Heath of

Edinburgh, now deceased. He not only remembered Baird as a lieutenant in the supplementary reserve of officers, but said he was on manoeuvres at Aldershot in 1928 and 1929, carrying out research on signalling. This information dovetails with details given in the file of the army's specific interest in signalling by television. Fourteen years earlier Baird had been found unfit for military service in the First World War. His family were totally unaware of any connection with the services, though as late as the months preceding the Second World War an army uniform had nestled among the suits in the wardrobe of his London home, remembered now, with hindsight, but which, at the time they presumed belonged to someone else.

Mr Heath distinctly recalled Baird, at the newly built Mons Barracks, conducting experiments in several forms of army field communications and news systems, using a teleprinter and cine- television transmissions. Aldershot was the only long-distance army wireless station in Britain during this period. Mr Heath was detailed to help the inventor lay field cables, while Baird operated from the rear of a six-wheeled Morris truck positioned between the barrack square and the edge of the Basingstoke Canal. They were assisted by a Sgt Archbold, who had trained in telegraphy at the GPO Engineering School at Liverpool.

Mr Heath wrote:

Sgt Archbold, a very able man, said that Baird was experimenting with an invention to send pictures through the atmosphere. To us this sounded as impossible as sending a man to the moon. My impression of him [Baird] in those days, when a soldier's two ideals were strong discipline and a smart appearance, was of a very untidy young man. His hair was long and unbrushed, and his uniform uncared for. He stood out a mile among the smart young officers of the time. He was very, very quiet and rarely spoke to anyone including the officers. It is to me a great pride in a long and eventful life; I met a genius.

This account shows Baird in the army, working with signallers on television film transmissions, at one of the most crucial and busy periods in his television career. When approached, the Army Records Centre at Hayes in Middlesex stated that they had no records of Baird, but, as will emerge, they also claimed to have no trace of another officer who, it eventually transpired, had distinguished himself in two world wars and had been an army

THE INVISIBLE SEARCHLIGHT: SEEING IN THE DARK BY "BLACK LIGHT."

'The Invisible Searchlight', hints of things to come. Christmas edition

The 'Invisible Searchlight', hints of things to come. Christmas edition of the Illustrated London News, 1926 shows Baird's concept of how troops, in this case in the North West frontier might detect an enemy at night using his Noctovisor.

commander of a British colonial territory.

The authenticity of Mr Heath's story is reinforced by his mention of another reserve officer working with Baird at Aldershot, whom he described as a Lt Morgan, connected with banking. Research by the authors had already uncovered a link between Baird and a mysterious bank clerk named Sydney George Morgan. It turned out that Morgan had quietly assisted Baird in his television experiments for many years, despite his job in a London bank. When war came, this bank employee was transformed into Wing Commander S. G. 'Jimmy' Morgan, operating with Eisenhower as chief signaller in the Mediterranean and one of the heads of Y Section, a special intelligence unit connected with Ultra, the breaking of German codes from the Enigma machine, an episode which will be dealt with later.

Baird must have been working with frenetic zeal at the period, though he managed to give an impression of calm and cheerfulness. As well as signalling and the battle to establish television commercially, the perfection of detection systems had almost become an obsession, outstripping his other interests. As previously noted, his television system of scanning an unlit object with a spot of light is analogous to scanned, centimetric radar systems such as the H2S radar mapping system used by Allied bombers. Baird's other television method of flooding the entire television scene with light is similar to the medium wave, long-range, radar floodlighting effect of Britain's famous Chain Home stations. All one need do to achieve object detection is to switch from light to radio waves or infra-red, and Baird had used both. He was quick to realize, however, that infrared had a major drawback. It failed to penetrate long distances through fog and mist, since the rays were absorbed by water particles. Despite this he appeared to persevere with infra-red for wartime object detection purposes, and it was this aspect that was published. He seldom, if ever, mentioned his development of the reflected radio wave system. Both versions were given the trade name Noctovision, which of course meant seeing by night. To the instruments themselves he gave the umbrella title of Noctovisors. That these were the subject of much eager curiosity from foreign powers is the most likely explanation of Baird's silence on the use of reflected radio waves.

In March 1928 R. Tiltman, one of his early biographers,

wrote in the British magazine *Television*: 'As soon as Noctovision was achieved it was demonstrated before military, air force and naval experts. Representatives of four governments came to inspect the apparatus and immense interest was aroused in all quarters. Even greater interest was aroused than by the original demonstration of television.'[22]

The four governments were those of Britain, France, the USA and Germany, as announced in a *Glasgow Herald* article of 1927, which talked of aircraft detection over London at night.[23] Intriguingly, these four governments were the very ones that developed radar before the Second World War. But, quite apart from these, military visitors from other countries, including the USSR and Japan, sought audience with Baird. In his book on Baird, Sydney Moseley quoted a letter from Sir Robert Watson-Watt, stating that he too had attended the earliest demonstrations of Baird's Noctovision. It is probable that he witnessed it as a British government representative. One thing is sure; Watson-Watt was well aware of Baird's earliest radar research.

Baird, however, persisted in holding back certain key

Mystery ship, the SS Perth

details of his work, which irritated and aroused the hostility of some other scientists. He attempted to counter criticisms. As early as January 1927, as mentioned in a previous context, he stated clearly in an article in *Nature* that he had received a letter from the British government requesting him to withhold publication of technical details of his equipment.[24] Publicity still flowed on his known earlier infra-red Noctovisors. In March 1927 a Dr E. Free commented querulously in an American magazine on 'the famous secrets which Mr Baird is supposed to have imparted to the British government'.[25] Free was critical of Baird's use of infra-red and suggested that its use was probably common knowledge in every physics laboratory. He got his facts twisted, however, by doubting that Baird could ever see in the dark using such a device. It was undoubtedly a case of sour grapes on the part of Dr Free, but he may well have been more than half right in his suspicion that everything was not as it seemed, that something was amiss. Despite the apparent government warning not to divulge any technical details, Baird still happily publicized his infra-red object detection work. From the perspective of later known radar development it seems likely that the real secret which the government was determined to guard was Baird's reflected radio wave system. Worldwide interest in his pioneering work could hardly be blocked, but it could be diverted, hence the publicity given to his infra-red Noctovisor instead of to his vastly superior reflected radio wave method.

At this early stage - it was just over a year since his first public demonstration of television - the two aspects of Baird's discovery, civil and military, seemed to be inextricably linked, a situation which was allowed to change quietly and gradually over the next few years, until the importance of his pioneering object detection work was forgotten. However, a newspaper article in February 1927 drew attention to the connection.[26] It described how Baird and Hutchinson, disgusted by the continual obstruction of their requests for a broadcasting licence from the Post Office, had warned the Postmaster General that a huge American concern had made a very tempting offer for the world rights to Baird's Noctovision discovery. In a section headed 'Army Option on Eyes in the Dark', it told how the Postmaster General had replied by express letter granting a licence and it continued: 'And so television was saved and the British army will have the first refusal of the *wonderful invisible searchlight'.* (Author's italics,) The article quoted Baird as stating that since his Noctovision demonstration to the Royal Institution in December 1926 he had been 'besieged by military agents from half the governments of the world. Even in Japan the invisible ray had stirred the military people to active interest.'

Baird's articles on Noctovision at this time talked of detecting aeroplanes approaching London at night, detecting submarines on the surface from aircraft, and so on. He was in fact showing how radar would be tactically used in the Second World War. Essentially he was describing radar, but again he stressed a system operating with infra-red, though he well knew the superiority of his reflected radio wave version. He termed his 'searchlight' black light, and in the 1926 Christmas edition of the *Illustrated London News* he presented a breathtakingly early vision of what was in store.[27] An artist's impression had hostile tribesmen on the North- West Frontier of India observed and tracked in the dark by solar- topeed troops who watched their movements on a screen. Close by, a small Televisor receiver screen was mounted on the sights of a machine gun. This article, incidentally, also supplied the first ever illustration of another of Baird's inventions, fibre optics, which he was applying in his television system.

Shortly after he had made his first pronouncements about infra-red detection, Baird somehow or other gained a remarkable 'shadow'. From then on he was frequently accompanied on official occasions by a colourful figure, Admiral Mark Kerr, famous as the man who, on 10 October 1917, had written the memorandum to the British cabinet that led to the creation of the Royal Air Force. Kerr already had an adventurous and varied service career behind him and was as familiar with charging Arab horsemen in the desert as he was with aeroplanes. As a youth he had served in the ill-fated campaign to save General Gordon in Khartoum and he had progressed over the years to be appointed commander in chief of the Greek navy from 1913 to 1915. He commanded the Royal Navy's Adriatic Squadron from 1916 to 1917 and was wounded and gassed. Undeterred, he became a flying pioneer, attempting to fly the Atlantic and made the longest then recorded flights over land and sea in 1919. In 1919 he was appointed Deputy Chief of Air Staff and a Major General in the RAF, which he helped to form

Baird with assistant Philip Hobson uses an infra-red
Noctovisor, September 1929.

From the start, Kerr was a firm supporter of Baird and, in the first issue of *Television* the journal of the Royal Television Society, in March 1928, he stated: 'As a naval man I am intensely interested in the development of the *television known as Noctovision* (author's italics) and the demonstration which I witnessed of the fog- penetrating powers of the apparatus have led me to believe that its development will have the most far reaching consequences in the direction of minimising the risks in navigation.'

Admiral Kerr eventually joined the Television Society as a council member, a move which could be attributed to personal interest and enthusiasm but also gave Whitehall a means of keeping an experienced but unobtrusive eye on the new technology. The admiral certainly became deeply involved in Baird's detection work, even making individual pronouncements on behalf of Baird and his company. It was Kerr who, with Baird, announced to the press in April 1927 that Noctovision would be tested at sea aboard the 2,208 ton passenger-cargo vessel the SS *Perth*, owned by the Dundee, Perth and London Shipping Company.[28] Newspapers said that the tests would start in June. If no fog was encountered, Baird would use smoke bombs. After such a fanfare the tests almost certainly did take place, but were they aboard the Perth? The newspapers, which could be expected to follow up a good story, remained strangely silent. Captain Alexander from Dundee, one of the last skippers of the line and at the time first mate of the sister ship *London*, recalled: 'It's odd, we read about Baird's equipment and the plan to put it aboard, but we never heard another word.' The skipper and officers of the *Perth* may have been asked to remain silent, but, in the strange story of Baird, it is just as likely that the *Perth* was publicized to draw attention away from the reflected radio wave object detection systems being tested elsewhere.

Joseph Bissett, the science journalist, recalls that at about this time word of Baird's use of reflected radio waves had reached him discreetly through the inventor. He was not allowed to see the unit in action but he knew that a secret unit was in operation in a disused warehouse on the Thames, from which Baird plotted the movement of ships and barges on the river. Mr Bissett met Baird many times during this period and Baird told him that the defence people were breathing down his neck. Mr Bissett also mentioned a rumour that one of the Baird machines was in a capsule slung below the ill-fated R. 101 airship when she left for India. 'A friend, also a radio man, gave me that news,' he told the authors. 'It was supposed to be for trying out as a guidance aid in the dark. Your guess is as good as mine. Possibly they were trying it out to see if it would display the terrain ahead. Nothing was mentioned about it at the time of the disaster. My friend perished with the others.'J. L. Baird was becoming silent on almost every subject. Even his close friend, journalist Bill Fox, made no mention of the R.101 scheme.

The only known article describing Baird's reflected radio wave television radar system was pointed out by Mr Bissett. It was published in August 1928 and again the system was termed a 'daylight television' method.[29] Baird was said to send out radio waves to scan the scene, instead of his usual spot of light which scanned objects in a darkened room. The writer was puzzled, however, as to whether the waves would reflect from human beings. If they did not, of course, it would invalidate its use for practical commercial television. This was a line of inquiry Baird would not have liked to be pursued. The system described was in fact intended as a scanned radar system for metal object detection and visualizing by day or night. This is borne out by Baird's little-known US patent No. 1,699,270, the equivalent of British patent No. 292,185. The American patent again concerned a reflected radio wave television system. It released no technical details, but for the first time Baird associated reflected radio waves with uses in warfare. The patent stated:

> *The method is thus extremely invaluable, in case the invention is used in a war for instance, where it is desired to view the enemy's position without detection. It has been found that the electromagnetic waves projected through a fog materially affect the capacity of the wave to penetrate the fog, the penetrative power increasing at the fourth power of the wavelength. It will thus be seen that the short wireless waves are able to penetrate fog more easily than the shorter infra-red rays, or the still shorter light waves.*

Baird's American patent for the infra-red version of the Noctovisor (1,781,799) applied for on 7 October 1927, also contained information missing from its British counterpart (patent No. 288,882, applied for on 26 October 1926). The American one referred not only to object detection but also

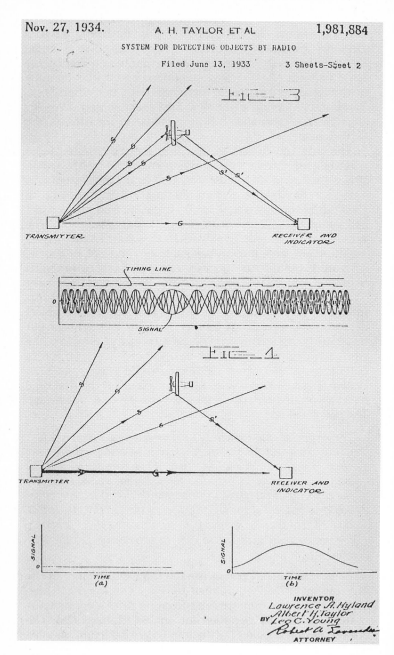

INVENTOR
Lawrence A. Hyland
Albert H. Taylor
BY Leo C. Young
Robert A. Lavender
ATTORNEY

to signalling. Infra-red beam morse signalling was not a brand-new technique at this point, as articles published between 1922 and 1924 testify, but Baird was entering the area of secret signalling with something new. Instead of the very slow morse messages then being used, he was beginning to transmit by television whole pages of information in a fraction of a second, a revolutionary innovation which will be looked at in the next chapter.

By 1930 Baird's Televisor was proving its usefulness in areas quite distinct from normal televison. In that year Britain's E. V. Appleton used the Televisor to measure the height of the ionosphere, a large ionized gas layer at the top of the earth's atmosphere.[30] Television images were transmitted upwards from the ground to reflect from the layer. The same image was also sent by land to the Televisor. The exactly similar images arrived at different times in the Televisor, just like the echo blips, and occupied different positions on the screen. By counting the television lines and hence knowing the accurate time difference between corresponding features in the two similar images, Appleton was able to estimate the height or range of the layers. Appleton was, in effect, using the radar method devised, patented and developed in 1926 by his friend Baird, the year of normal television's first public demonstration. The importance of such techniques for warfare did not go completely unnoticed. A biography of Sir Henry Tizard, who was to be highly involved from 1934 in Britain's radar programme, noted a prewar American journal's statement that reports from Britain indicated that the displacement of the second or 'ghost' reflected television image had now been correlated with the distance of an aeroplane from the television receiver. They believed that a method had been worked out whereby television receivers on England's east coast could thus serve as spotters for approaching enemy aircraft in time of war.[31]

In 1931, encouraged by Appleton's success, an English researcher called E. L. C. White used a spinning disc with holes to interrupt light shone through the holes at a photocell.[32] The resultant signals from the photocell were used to trigger a radio transmitter, which sent out one pulse of energy per hole, to echo or reflect from the ionized layers back to a cathode ray tube receiver. The same transmitter pulses were also sent by land to trigger and strobe the receiver time display, producing a timing blip on the screen, while the echoes from the layers produced a second series of blips. Knowing the timescale of the receiver display, one could estimate the time between the blips and hence estimate the distance of the reflecting object. This was the first time that a simple two-blip system was used, with pulses coming directly from the transmitter and the reflecting object. The method was suitable for the job, but all White had was one thin strip of Baird's two-dimensional reflected radar images. Instead of using two images on his receiver, like Appleton, White was using two blips. It is interesting to note from White's paper that it was Appleton who suggested to White that he should use the two-blip method.

Baird's system, however, was superior for general purposes, since the unit could also supply the outline shape of the reflecting object, enabling the viewer to distinguish enemy planes and ships from friendly ones. Appleton and White could locate an object, but their unit gave no indication of object shape. Appleton modified White's method later the same year by electronically pulsing the transmitter and not using a rotating disc, and it was this unit that most closely resembled the Chain Home radar stations of 1935 developed by Watson-Watt.[33] Whatever the changes, the fact remains that Baird's 1926 reflected radio wave system is the starting point of all modern radar, a synchronized transmitter and receiver with a visual receiver display.

Britain was not alone in research, however. The early 1930s were a period of accelerating radar activity in several countries. During 1933, American, A. Hoyt-Taylor, still at the US Naval Research Laboratory in Washington, applied for a continuous wave Doppler radar patent (granted on 27 November 1934). This was for the detection of aircraft and was similar to Appleton's 1924 apparatus already described. Hoyt-Taylor clearly stated in his patent that when the transmitter wavelengths were twice the length of a major component of the object - for example an aircraft wing or fuselage - then the radiated echoes would have maximum intensity, making object detection that much easier. The ideas in Hoyt- Taylor's US patent (1,981,884) were to have a curious echo in Britain several months later. On 26 February 1935 they formed the exact basis of Robert Watson-Watt's famous 'first ever' British radar experiment, which has always been claimed by the British as the start of radar and

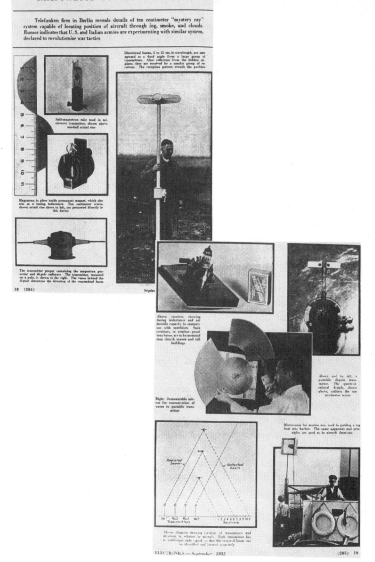

Evidence of early German radar. American magazine, Electronics, September 1935 carries a feature on German centimetric mystery ray developed by Telefunken. This leak probably caused the fury that led Hitler to declare all German television innovations a national secret.

on which Watson-Watt built his reputation as 'father of radar'.[34]

Examination of Watson-Watt's two 'secret' prewar radar patents by the authors revealed that his GB patents 593,017 and 581, 130, applied for in 1935 and 1936 respectively, and published in 1947, are 'improvement' patents, not master or original patents. In fact the wording of 593,017, on the choice of wavelengths to be used, is identical to that of Hoyt-Taylor's patent previously published in the United States. It appears from Watson-Watt's autobiography that he was ordered by his Air Ministry boss, H.E. Wimperis, to take out the radar patents, a course he found repugnant. It is possible that the Air Ministry were concerned that Hoyt-Taylor might patent his invention in Britain, and that the British would have to pay huge royalties to the Americans, as happened in the case of Penicillin. Discovered in Britain, and synthesized by Florey and Chain in Britain, the drug finished up being patented and marketed by the Americans.

The Germans had launched their radar defence programme in 1933 under the auspices of the German navy. In France, too, matters were moving fast, following radar detection of aircraft at Le Bourget airport in 1934. A Hulsmeyer-type system was placed aboard the French ship *Oregon* in 1934, and, as mentioned, a similar system was installed on the *Normandie* in 1935. From 1934 thirty radar stations were built on the French-German border and around Brest harbour. These were continuous wave Doppler systems, which were replaced by pulsed radars shortly before the outbreak of war. Professor M. Carpentier revealed these facts at a radar conference in Arlington, Virginia, in April 1975.[35] In his paper he indicated that the French were so far advanced with their pulsed centimetric radar that, under a secret 1939 exchange of information, they told the British they were using multi-cavity magnetrons for generating very powerful centimetric radar wavelengths. This information contradicts most versions of how radar developed. The multi-cavity magnetron was, arguably, one of the vital inventions of the war and the British laid sole claim to its invention at Birmingham University around March-April 1940, by J. T. Randall and H. A. H. Boot, who started their research at Birmingham in November 1939 under Professor Oliphant. GEC were also independently, but simultaneously, working on the same unit at Wembley.

Both operations were sponsored by the British Admiralty Signals Research Establishment.

On 8 May 1940 the French government handed over to the British Admiralty working multi-cavity magnetrons for 16 cm wavelength radar, developed by the French scientists Guttone and Beline for the French radar chain. These units had oxide-coated cathodes, absolutely essential for their long-term successful operation at high frequency and high power. The British adopted the French style of design. The fact that the French were therefore first with multi-cavity magnetrons for centimetric pulsed radar went virtually unnoticed until the little-known paper by Carpentier was found by the authors of this book. A complete confirmation of the story was found in another paper by E. C. S.Megaw, who in 1940 was working with the Admiralty Signals Establishment and GEC on multi-cavity magnetron development. [36] Watson-Watt admitted in his autobiography that Guttone had written to him about the French multi-cavity magnetrons. The multi-cavity magnetron transmitters were essential for the 10 cm radar mapping system, code name H2S, used by Allied bombers to recognize their ground targets from above cloud level. As will emerge, H2 S had more than a passing similarity to Baird's 1926 radar apparatus.

The prewar radar situation was complex. We have already taken with a pinch of salt the story that before the war Britain and the USA were unaware of German radar. In September 1935 a startling, fully illustrated article appeared in the American magazine *Electronics* under the heading 'Microwaves to Detect Aircraft'. [37] The article stated that Telefunken in Germany were using a 10 cm 'mystery ray', capable of locating the position of aircraft through smoke, fog and cloud. The article added that the US and Italian armies were working on similar systems. The German apparatus used a magnetron valve to generate 5-15 cm waves. After the war details were published of a prewar magnetron-powered 10 cm American radar system designed by RCA and Westinghouse and dated late 1934. The American system was identical in general details with the German one, which could be explained by RCA's technical information exchange on television with Telefunken at this period.

Magazine articles can take months to publish and it could well have been the knowledge that the Telefunken leak, if it was a leak, on centimetric radar was already in the pipeline that sparked off Hitler's abrupt decrees in July 1935 making television and related techniques a German state secret. The plain fact was that in a peacetime world, with interchange of information among civilian individuals and firms, ideas were leaking out here and there. For example, from 1933 to 1940 no mention of radar was made in the magazine *Telefunken-Zeitung*. This was checked by a colleague of the authors, Gerhardt Goebbel, a television pioneer of Darmstadt in West Germany, who examined all the back issues. Yet Telefunken had taken out British radar patents in 1935 (Nos 457,737 and 465,022). Professor W. Runge, eventual head of Telefunken radar, confirms that he knew about other German radar developments in 1934 and 1935. A. Hoyt-Taylor's 1934 American patent also broadcast to anyone interested that the Americans were detecting aircraft by radar. All this changed after 1935 as the international scene grew more tense and complicated and no one was certain who eventually would be friend or foe. In his autobiography[38] Watson-Watt dismissed the 1935 Telefunken radar article, in *Electronics*, which proves of course that he knew of the existence of prewar German radar.

Developments were under way in the Netherlands too, and when Philips of Eindhoven made reasonably powerful magnetron transmitters they were purchased in 1934 by the German navy and used for radar echoes from German battleships. A Dutch radar expert, J. L. W. C. von Weiler, had to flee to Britain in 1940, where he continued his work in the Admiralty Signals Establishment at Portsmouth. It was this establishment that in 1928 applied for a secret provisional patent (No. 6433), in the names of J.S.C. Salmond and L. S. B. Alder, for a system to detect aircraft and ships, though the patent was never completed.[39] John Logie Baird's reflected radio wave Noctovisor, had been fully patented (GB No. 292,185) and published in 1928, which would have blocked the patent of the British navy. Puzzlingly, Baird later allowed his two radar patents (Nos 292,185 and 297,014) to lapse. It could have been that the British authorities wanted no more attention drawn to the subject. Certainly the authors could find no other prewar British radar patents or articles. The brother of Sydney George Morgan, mentioned previously, has stated that he is certain that his brother published a 1920s' article on aircraft detection at Croydon airport. Mr Morgan also confirmed that Sydney had worked with J. L.

Baird for many years before the Second World War.

These divergent facts seem never before to have been collated and analyzed to give an overall picture of radar in the 1930s. Instead it has been assumed that radar was a total secret among the nations of the world. Though the name 'radar' obviously would not have appeared at that time, an intelligent reader of *The Times* up to about 1938 would certainly have been aware of the drift of events and the interest being shown by several countries in detection systems.

One of the more traceable radar projects in Britain was that of Butement and Pollard in 1930, at the Army Signals Establishment, Woolwich.[40] They had built a 5O cm pulsed radar unit with a rotating beam which swept the horizon and obtained reflections from objects at distances up to 100 yards. The War Office and Admiralty appear to have lost interest in their work, which was seemingly abandoned, though both men later went to work with Watson-Watt on the development of centimetric gun-ranging radar. After the Second World War Butement became superintendent of the Woomera rocket range in Australia and Pollard became chief superintendent of the Royal Radar Establishment at Malvern.

By 1934 Baird was busily trying to establish his television interests internationally, although even then he seems to have been heavily involved in his detection projects, as indicated by an isolated but fascinating sighting of him at the time. In November that year a small group of students from the Gateway Technical School in Leicester heard that the television pioneer John Logie Baird had called next door at Leicester Technical College to carry out repairs on some pieces of equipment. They hurried to the college and, in a basement room, caught a glimpse of something which, according to accepted radar history, should not have existed, but with which everyone is familiar today. Baird, accompanied by a lecturer from the mechanical engineering department, was leaning over an apparatus with a horizontal screen approximately 18 inches by 9 inches, a cathode ray tube display unit on which appeared bright blips. The moving blips were tramcars rounding the dock tower in Leicester and moving into the High Street about a mile away. To the left of the screen was the stationary blip used for triggering and strobing the display. Every so often interference flared on the screen, and Baird explained that this was caused by spark discharges on the tram cables. One of the pupils Albert Marvin, later a lecturer at Strathclyde University and now retired, never forgot the incident. He said: 'There were three or four of us and we realized we had witnessed something unusual, unlike anything we had seen before. The others were killed in the war, so I am probably the only living eye witness to what certainly seemed to be some form of radar.'

Questioned by the boys, Baird was secretive, but did reveal that he called the apparatus 'Novascan', and that it worked with both infra-red and long to short radio waves. He also said he had been using the system for several years. Mr Marvin also recalls that Baird let slip that he had come that day from a radio station whose call sign was 5 GB. Research by the authors disclosed that this was the call sign of nearby BBC Daventry, the location of Robert Watson-Watt's so-called first ever British radar experiment, destined to take place in February the following year. This story about Baird is not so strange when one uncovers British patent No. 441,235, backdated to August 1934 and formally applied for on 17 January 1935 by the Baird Television Company in conjunction, mysteriously, with a certain Anatole Tola Stoyanowsky, described as a Russian national living in the Rue d'Aguesseau, Paris. It was for an infra-red guidance system for bombers. Transform the infra- red into radio waves, as was Baird's custom, and one has what looks like H2S, the airborne radar mapping guidance system used by Allied bombers in the Second World War, and the most advanced radar unit actually used in that period. Radar undoubtedly existed before 1935, and there was knowledge of how it could tactically affect warfare. A stunningly pro- phetic article appeared in the November 1928 issue of *Television*, written by a Mr Shaw Desmond.[41] The work was fictitious, but Mr Desmond's scientist hero is a thinly disguised John Logie Baird, with whom he had obviously talked. Baird appears as a Professor Ian McWhirter, a youngish, good-looking Scot with a shock of reddish hair and wearing glasses. McWhirter's invention is described as an 'improved' version of the real Baird's Noctovisor, - the trade name was used - which could see by day or night. In the article pilotless radio-controlled aircraft swoop on London from Northland, a country in northwest Europe, whose capital is a city of cupolas and spires, presumably Moscow, and in those pre-Nazi days the only likely enemy.

The story recounts how aerial manoeuvres over London in August 1928 had shown that it was not possible to defend the city from a determined air attack. In desperation the Prime Minister turns to McWhirter with his magic eye apparatus. The Scot swings into action and from an aerial control centre in Whitehall the new Noctovisor is used to guide the British fighter squadrons to the correct height south of London, to pounce down on and exterminate the enemy planes, 200 of them being dispatched and just a few limping home. In fact, on the busiest day of the Battle of Britain 185 enemy planes were destroyed. The article says that McWhirter had indeed given England her eyes, saving the capital and Empire. This feature story blended fiction with some very real facts and provided a blueprint for the future Battle of Britain. It is important for its awareness of some form of vital detection system, vague in detail but definitely associated with Baird. It was also correct about the British public's growing understanding of and apprehension about air power and its threat to civilians.

Some years later, early in 1935, prompted by previously expressed concern about possible bomber attacks on London, Sir Philip Cunliffe-Lister, Secretary of State for the Colonies, but shortly to become Air Minister as Lord Swinton, was asked by Prime Minister, Ramsay MacDonald, to investigate possible methods of blocking any holes in British air defence. Swinton formed a committee in the spring of 1935, the Air Defence Research Sub-Committee of the Committee of Imperial Defence. An Air Ministry team had already been formed to look into the same problem and had taken shape in December 1934, holdings its first meeting on 28 January 1935 under the chairmanship of H. Tizard, Rector of Imperial College. Tizard was also to be present on the Swinton group and his Scientific Survey of Air Defence Committee would eventually be answerable to Swinton's. Interestingly, the 1934 Air Minister was Lord Londonderry, later to play an ambiguous role as a member of 'The Link', the organisaton formed to promote British friendship with the Nazis.

Tizard's committee had been suggested by none other than H.E. Wimperis, Director of Scientific Research at the Air Ministry, the man who, since 1924, had been so well informed about Baird and who was fully aware of Baird's Noctovisor radar systems. According to legend and official published literature, the birth of British radar stemmed from a visit that Wimperis made to Watson-Watt, the superintendent of Radio Research at the National Physical Laboratory in London, in the first fortnight of 1935. Wimperis is supposed to have asked Watson-Watt's opinion of death rays for bringing down aircraft. Sensational surmises about such rays abounded. An article in a technical publication of September 1934 suggested that most nations would soon possess the secret of this weapon that was capable of annihilating 400 aircraft.[42] Marconi was at that time in Italy demonstrating a form of centimetric radar to Mussolini.[43] It was rumoured that the rays were stopping the ignition systems of car engines.[44] When asked about his microwave experiments being used to cut out the ignition systems of aircraft, Marconi replied: 'I have nothing to say'[45] Once again, people were getting close to the real thing, but they were confusing centimetric radar with death rays. Reports of Marconi's Italian activities had been seeping back to the Marconi Company in Britain, but these leaks were plugged when Mussolini started to replace all British Marconi personnel in Italy with Italians. The secret radar struggle was speeding up.

The death ray stories owed much to the activities of Harry Grindell Matthews, a likeable but suspect figure who for a time had the ear of the British services, on whom he tried to press his death ray concept.[46] Grindell Matthews had virtually dined out on the idea since 1922. His attempts to sell death ray schemes to the British took a nosedive when suspicious security agents went so far as to break into his home and thoroughly investigate his background. Not one to be put down lightly, Grindell Matthews popped up again in Nazi Germany in about 1936, where he almost tricked Goebells into buying a machine for projecting images of the Fuehrer onto the clouds.

The death ray as a concept of war was a universal red herring, a fact of which Wimperis must have been well aware. By the end of January 1935 Watson-Watt is supposed to have dismissed the death rays as impractical and suggested instead that there was a chance of detecting aircraft at long range by reflected radio waves.[47] With the knowledge that we now have of what had gone before this suggestion is almost laughable. Watson--Watt, a talented and well-informed scientist and civil servant, takes a couple of weeks to consider a problem posed by his overall chief, Wimperis, and comes up with a solution that had already preoccupied that figure and his department for more than a decade. Whatever the truth of the matter, it offered a good cover story for the offical start of British radar. Any experiment by Watson-Watt at that time would indeed be kept secret but, should it be discovered by the agents of other nations, it would convey a very mistaken impression of the progress made, or capable of being made, on British radar.

Tizard's committee had meanwhile come to the conclusion that Britain needed at least twenty minutes' warning of approaching enemy aircraft, and reflected radio waves looked like meeting the demand. Watson-Watt conducted his famous first radar experiment from BBC Daventry on 26 February 1935, reflecting the radio waves of the borrowed B B C transmitter, from the prearranged flight of a metal-skinned RAF Heyford bomber. The experiment details were an exact copy of that illustrated in Hoyt-Taylor's American patent of three months before.

In June 1935 Watson-Watt utilised a system very similar to Appleton's 1931 synchronised pulsed radar, which in turn resembled Baird's 1926 system, and this became the basis of the Chain Home stations around the British coast. Baird, of course, had been using his Noctovisors to detect aeroplanes above London from 1927 onwards, and it was the infra-red version which had scared people in the capital when it released red rays in the direction of Trafalgar Square. Appleton joined Tizard's committee in October 1936 and was less than amused to find his apparatus being used for British defence radar and Watson-Watt taking all the credit.

Another sure sign that radar was not new to the British was a report made by A.P. Rowe, secretary of Tizard's committee on air defence, to Air Commodore Cunningham at a meeting of the Tizard Committee on 16 April 1935, the record of which is kept in the Air Ministry file (AIR 2/1579) at the Public Record Office. This stated that anti-aircraft gun radar would take five years to develop. How could this fact possibly be known when according to Watson-Watt the very first radar had only been demonstrated just six weeks before? Rowe's estimate was absolutely accurate, and the first radar-controlled anti-aircraft guns appeared around London in October 1940.[48] In *Three Steps to Victory* Watson-Watt stated that on 26 February 1935 at his first demonstration of radar, he had told Rowe that anti-aircraft gun radar would take five years to develop. Watson-Watt himself also admitted in his autobiography that he knew about the earlier radar research in the Royal Navy around 1928 and also about the British army centimetric radar research at Woolwich in 1930 and 1931 under Butement and Pollard, but he was dismissive. He criticised the navy for being too interested in using millimetric waves (almost certainly for visualising at night with Baird's Noctovisor), and he believed that if Britain had pursued only centimetric, short-range radar, essential for gun-ranging radar, it might have lost the war. He felt that he had saved the country by concentrating on medium wave, long-range radar to detect approaching enemey bombers. How correct he was is a question of degree, but Watson-Watt most certainly did not invent radar, and he was to be denied credit for the invention by the RAF patent controller when he gave evidence at a royal commission on inventions in 1951. Sir Robert, as mentioned earlier, was one of a syndicate of seven scientists who had worked on radiolocation and were making a claim to the Crown for financial reward. Undeterred by opposition, he proceeded to make a series of long and complicated speeches dismissing all earlier attempts at radar. Never one to hid his light under a bushel, he said he felt that he and his group were due a lamp sum of £657,000. This was calculated on his suggestion that all subjects of the United Kindgom would probably not grudge paying threepence a head for themselves and their dependents as a token of gratitude. After a hearing lasting four days they were awarded £87,950, of which Sir Robert took the major share of £52,000.

Sir Robert had been in the right job at the right time, a radio expert and civil servant needed by a British government to supervise the spending of vast sums of government money in secrecy, and to build up the vital radar defence chain, a task to which he brought undoubted enthusiasm and organisational ability. But the title, 'father of radar'was an accolade due to someone else. At the time of the Royal Commission John Logie Baird had been dead for five years and no one spoke on his behalf.

In 1935 the technological overlap between television and radar was beginning to show officially, partly through the actions of the German government. On 10 July of that year the *Glasgow Herald* carried a plea from Herr Hadamovsky, Director General of German Broadcasting, for collaboration with the British on the development of television.[49] Two days later this was flatly stamped upon by Hitler, who signed a decree, published on 6 August, declaring that all aspects of German television were to be placed under the control of the Air Minister, Goering, who at that time had the rank of general. A *Times* report of 10 August expressed the opinion that the importance of televsision for the security of aircraft and for national defence was one of the reasons for the German Air Ministry control.[50] However the author of this report believed that the emphasis was on television for guarding aircraft in the field, as would be shown at the forthcoming German radio exhibition, where the troops of the new German air arm would display radio and television equipment. Predictably, *The Times* had to report on 17 August that the demonstration of the new electric eye had not been permitted by the German Air Ministry.[51] Hitler went even further when on 11 October he announced that television publications too were now subject to Goering's approval. Official British Air Ministry files noted what was happening. The German radar article in Electronics (USA) of September 1935 may have been the reason for the restriction on German television publications.

There is evidence that the British were thinking along the same lines. The *New Scientist* carried a reference, on 19 June 1980 to the reported reaction of the prewar Air Minister Lord Swinton, when someone expressed admiration of Britain having started the first public television service in 1936, far in advance of everyone else.

'Swinton said apparently there was more to the event than that. The service was not started for entertainment or to be first with TV broadcasting. It was started so that British manufacturers could get familiar with the techniques of making cathode ray tubes on a large scale; without that experience they would not have been able to keep the radar sets coming for the Battle of Britain'. A recent publication also states that the British television system was a coverup for the secret radar programme.[52] The same source states that most BBC personnel went into intelligence or radar during the Second World War.

The British kept a particularly tight grip on their radar secrets, but the Germans were certainly well aware that such British secrets existed. Confirmation of this fact were the events which arose from a technical exchange of information arranged between the British Air Ministry, the British Secret Service and the Luftwaffe in 1936 and 1937. The story is unfolded in two books by F.W. Winterbotham[53] and Ladislas Farago.[54] Winterbotham was the leading British officer involved in the deal. The writers discovered that both Winterbotham and Farago got their dates well wrong. The correct dates had to be traced by reading newspapers of the day. *The Times* of 29 June 1936 reported that the German Secretary of State for Air, Erhard Milch, creator of the Luftwaffe, had visited Hatfield Aeroedrome. On 1 July *The Times* described a lunch between Milch and Marshall Trenchard of the RAF. On 17 January 1937 The Times reported that the British delegation had arrived in Berlin. The 'exchange' was not entirely satisfactory from the German point of view. Milch returned to Britain in Oct 1937. Descending from his new Heinkel 111 bomber, he staggered his British hosts by not beating about the bush and asked how their radiolocaton was coming along! It appears he left empty-handed and a furious Hitler later accused Milch of betraying the secret of German radar to the British. Perhaps Hitler meant that by Milch even mentioning radiolocation he was letting the British know that the Germans knew all about radar. This story does not hold, however, since *Electronics (USA)* had published in September 1935 the full details of German 10 cm radar. Did Hitler therefore blame Milch for letting this article be published?

In their anxiety to wrest Britain's radar secrets, the Germans went so far as to send Zeppelins down the east coast of England under the direction of a General Martini, Luftwaffe Signals, their mission being to determine the wavelengths and operative techniques of the Chain Home stations. Interestingly, Baird is known to have experimentally detected British airships in Wales from BBC Daventry, which had powerful transmitters with a range of many hundreds of miles. It is intriguing to surmise that his activities were somehow connected with the behaviour of the German spyships. For their part, the British were polishing their radar techniques in preparation for a war. In 1938, when Neville Chamberlain made his famous flight to Munich to meet Hitler, his plane was tracked out on RAF radar until it vanished off the screen; no point in missing an opportunity for practising what would one day be a matter of life and death!

As the international scene darkened, Baird was still heavily involved with the Air Ministry, even after the ill-fated television contest with Marconi-EMI. A second Air

Ministry file, Air 2/1775, in the Public Record Office and covering 1936 to 1942 contains details of the Baird Company's role in secretly equipping bombers. In the summer of 1936 the Air Ministry approached Captain A.G.D. West, chief engineer of the Baird Company an an ex-radio intelligence officer in the First World War.[55] They wanted a television guidance system to direct bombers to their target from above the clouds; it was hoped that infra-red could be used. West informed them of one problem, the business tie-up with Fernseh AG in Germany, which necessitated exchanges of technical information. The Baird Company had, however, noted in 1936 that the German government had taken control of all television development and that the Germans in Fernseh were taking all they could get and were giving nothing in return. The Baird Company were considering discontinuing the link.

The file also revealed that the Baird Company had a contract to develop a bomber guidance system for the French government and a possible order to do the same for the Russians, both deals were accepted with British government approval. The definition of the Televisor guidance system required would be 800 lines, offset by 5 images per second. The file stressed that by 6 February 1937 the Russians were willing to pay almost any price for infra-red television cameras. The Japanese, too, tried to visit the company, but the file states that they had been told nothing and had not even been allowed on the premises. A Mr Hecht of the Research and Development Instrument Laboratory at the Air Ministry visited the company and found a chaotic situation the result of the pressures of Air Ministry work, the television contest with Marconi-EMI and the recent disastrous fire at the Crystal Palace. This filed information is particularly valuable, as no other indication has ever been located of the Baird Company's involvement in secret contracts for the British government and other foreign powers. It also throws light on Baird's suspicions that the Crystal Palace blaze was no accident, but an act of sabotage: the fire disrupted their secret Air Ministry work. In Germany, Baird's name was synonymous with British television and, in view of Hitler's obsession with the importance of television, the company would have been an obvious prime target.

By late 1938 the Baird Company still had a continental connection and a French Bloch bomber flew to Hendon airport to be equipped with television reconnissance equipment. Similar work was apparently under way with Marconi-EMI, who were trying to install infra-red Iconoscope television cameras in aircraft. The French, however, preferred the Baird system, as it kept a record of the television images on film which could be examined later at leisure. The ability to record had, of course, been one of the major plus points of Baird Television's equipment in the recent contest at Alexandra Palace.

The French bomber eventually took off for home, to the test centre at Villacoublay, accompanied by a party of Baird engineers who stayed and just managed to escape before the fall of France. The fate of the bomber is unknown, though rumours say it either flew to America or was captured by the Germans. The authors were given a photograph of the bomber taken at Hendon by one of the Baird engineers involved, a Mr Raymond Herbert, who was surprised that so much had been uncovered by the authors about the secret project.

One of the last letters in the file mentions a forthcoming demonstration in January 1940 arranged by Baird and Marconi-EMI to display their respective equipment before Sir Henry Tizard and Robert Watson-Watt. This is followed by total silence on the subject until 1942, when the Air Ministry wrote to Baird's company about a request from the US government for details of the French bomber television reconnaissance system.

The Baird Company had been first in the 1930s to install television in aircraft commercially and even then it was possible to visualise military uses for the equipment. On 4 September 1936 a historic flight took place, with Baird television apparatus weighing 420 lb fitted to a KLM aircraft. flying at 4,000 feet and a speed of 170 mph, passengers witnessed Paul Robeson and Charles Laughton broadcasting from the BBC Television Transmitter. As the plane circled over Croydon and headed for the Olympia building, they also watched a Gaumont-British film of the *Queen Mary's* maiden voyage being televised from Alexandra Palace. Reporting on the flight in a letter to the *Radio Times*, Mr Graeme Norwood said that 'the pictures were clear and the sound became louder and more distinct as the 'plane climbed. At 2,000 ft. reception was perfect.' He commented significantly: 'Many Croydon pilots believe that the day will not be far off when television will assist them in bad weather.' A quote attributed to the Dutch pilot said that it would soon be possible to televise from the ground a film of the aerodrome when it was hidden by fog from the pilot's view. Baird was televising to planes; he could equally televise from them, and with his radio waves and infra-red he was blazing a trail for the bombers of the Second World War.

The year of the Bloch bomber, 1938, saw Baird figure in a weird episode bringing strange publicity at a time when the approaching war and his company's secret work would normally have called for reserve, if not absolute secrecy. On 24 February he left London, travelling overland with his wife to join the P. and 0. Iiner *Strathaird* at Marseilles, on his way to give a paper at the International Radio Congress in Australia. In a story headlined: 'Television in Bombers, Pilots to See Towns 100 Miles Away', the *Daily Telegraph* reported that Baird, President of the Baird Television Company, while being interviewed at Victoria station, revealed that in Australia he intended to continue experiments, probably in a test station at Sydney, on a television set for use in bombers.[56] He is quoted as saying: 'I have already carried out experiments in an aeroplane at Crystal Palace with my television set, for use in bombing aircraft.' The set, carried in the cockpit, apparently enabled the crew to view a town 50-100 miles away. Baird added: 'The invention could be used for reconnaisance work and would be invaluable to scouting planes.'

Why the sudden loophole in Britain's clampdown on detection systems? If this interview was unauthorized and was truly given off the cuff, then Baird or anyone working on sensitive govern-ment contracts would at the least be severely reprimanded. But in fact Baird was giving little or nothing away. There was no mention of infra-red, which was to be officially abandoned by the Air Ministry the following month, nor was there any hint of reflected radio waves. It seems that as he left for Australia he was drawing the spotlight onto himself and therefore drawing attention away from much more secret material and activities back in Britain. One would like to think he was followed half way round the world by enemy agents on a wild goose chase. Certainly the radar game was becoming more complex and convoluted. Many ploys were afoot as the war approached, and it is difficult to believe there was no collusion between the British and the Americans on some aspects of their respective detection methods. On 1 and 16August 1935 *The Times* carried two stories of a Commander P. McNeil, US Signal Corps, Fort Monmouth, New Jersey, who was said to be offering infrared searchlight rangefinding equipment to the War Office in London. McNeil, formerly of the US navy, claimed to be able to detect aircraft in fog at 4 miles and ships at 13 miles. A demonstration at Farnborough failed, though he was eventually able to detect aircraft from a range of 200 yards at Croydon. A similar story appeared in America on 3 August 1935,[57] about infra-red searchlights being used by the US Signal Corps at Fort Monmouth to detect ships and aircraft. The equipment described was a carbon copy of Baird's earlier infra-red searchlight and Noctovision systems of 1927-8, but this was only part of the story. An illustrated article, which appeared in 1945,[58] indicated that in 1934-5 the US Signal Corps at Fort Monmouth had been demonstrating 9-10 cm magnetron-powered, continuous wave, RCA-Westinghouse radar to detect ships, trucks and so on. The infra-red searchlight and television system of McNeil's had been used in conjunction with the radar for accuracy checks. And so McNeil, in 1935, was well aware of the existence of US radar, while, like Baird, he was outwardly pursuing and publicizing infra-red. His visit to Britain may well have been another case of highlighting infra-red while on a secret mission which really concerned radar. This opinion is backed up in a 1935 edition of the American magazine *Electronics*, which reported the same Commander McNeil using an infra-red eye for detecting ships from aboard the Furness liner *Queen of Bermuda*, aided by British destroyers. Distant icebergs, hot gas from ships' funnels and aircraft exhausts were all said to have been detected.[59]

In the Naval Research Laboratory at Washington the chief physicist, Alan Hoyt-Taylor, was reported in 1933 to be investigating Watson-Watt's method of detecting the direction of static, that is electrical storms.[60] It is therefore unlikely that Watson-Watt was not well aware of Hoyt-Taylor's work and therefore of his plane-detecting radar patent, which his own 1935 experiment so closely resembled. Watson-Watt acknowledged the existence of Hoyt-Taylor's patent in his autobiography, called it a 'secret' patent, presumably meaning that he himself could not have known about it. The patent was, however, published in November 1934 and was available to all interested parties.

After the war the story persisted that no prewar collusion had taken place between the Allies, although certain facts indicate a good measure of either co-operation or coincidence. Pulsed radar had appeared simultaneously in Britain and America.[61] E. G.Bowen, an early British radar pioneer, noted with surprise the striking resemblance in the final equipment. The first American ship-to-air warning radar was installed on the battleship *New York* in 1938, with a range of 85 miles and operated at 200 megacycles per second, a frequency which turned out to be, not surprisingly, identical with that of a then current British ground-based system; key parts of both apparatus were almost indistinguishable in each case. British ship radar also first appeared in 1938 aboard the battleship *Rodney* and the cruiser *Sheffield*. The Germans appeared with accurate centimetric gun-ranging radar aboard the *Graf Spee* in the summer of that year, although the radar had been fitted in 1936. It now appears that the prewar radar world was neither as straightforward nor as simple as it is usually depicted, but was rather a hotbed of bluff and deceit.Whatever else he was involved in during the war years, Baird never gav.e up his television experiments. His projects before the outbreak of hostilities had been the development of colour television, often allied with three-dimensional images. It was these aspects which he continued to pursue in his bomb-battered laboratory, a former stable, at 3 Crescent Wood Road, Sydenham, where he worked with two assistants, W. Oxbrow and E. G. 0. Anderson. When Anderson was called up, Baird appealed to a tribunal and this vital assistant was allowed to stay with him until the end of the war. The first accounts of Baird's 3D work had appeared briefly in the press in January 1926, and his first public demonstration took place in 1928. He ignored criticism that colour would be too expensive, believing as he did that monochrome pictures were outdated almost before they had started and that the future lay with colour. He demonstrated a colour television cathode ray tube receiver to the Selsdon Television Advisory Committee in 1934 and intermittently showed colour television in London cinemas from 1937 until 1939.

After the liquidation of the Baird Company in August 1940 its assets were taken over by Cinema Television, now Rank Cintel, a company owned by Gaumont-British, now the Rank Organization, who had held the controlling shares.

They retained the services of Captain West as chief engineer. Baird himself worked independently on various forms of 3D colour television, attracting lavish praise from both the technical and lay press. Screen sizes ranged up to 30 by 24 inches, interlaced six times over in 1940, to achieve a 600-line image with 3D or colour, or both. Some of the 3D systems demonstrated did not require special spectator viewing glasses. By August 1944 he had excelled himself with the Telechrome, the world's first multi-electron gun receiver, triple inter laced for 600 lines.[62] A unique aspect was its global shape, allied to a ridged screen, that took beams from the different electron guns, allowed viewers to watch colour 3D television from either side of the tube, so that two sets of people could watch from opposite sides of a room.

Baird was undoubtedly the world leader in electronic colour and electronic 3D colour television. A testimony to the interest he was arousing was the record number of over 600 members who turned up at the Institute of Radio Engineers in London to hear him give a paper on 3D colour television in October 1943.[63] But it seems there were others who were secretly following his 3D colour work more closely: scientists engaged in the development of 3D colour defence radar were aware of his publications and their apparatus generally followed his line of progress.

An article on stereoscopic displays, including 3D and 3D-colour radar, which appeared two years after Baird's death, suggested that, as far as the author was concerned, the first ever 3D radar display emerged in 1942-3 from a Dr Tricker and colleagues at a Royal Radar Establishment extension in Bristol.[64] Three-dimensional radars were required to give information on an object's bearing, range and height, these three different values to be displayed simultaneously on one screen. The units were required for anti-aircraft gun radar control. In a written communication Dr L. C. Jesty, then working on radar tubes with G.E.C. in London, and a known acquaintance and admirer of Baird,[65] corrected the article's claims by saying: 'Historically in the radar field, the use of perspective and also of colour for providing an additional dimension to the display dates back to about 1939. The perspective display was rejected in the experimental stage, as it proved too complicated to decipher. A two-colour model was used on early equipment.' In early experiments on anti-aircraft gun radar, attempts had been made to put range, bearing and aircraft height on the one cathode ray tube. The two-colour model was based on Baird's two-colour 3D television experiments. The Admiralty Signals Establishment took out a series of 3D radar patents which bore a singular resemblance to Baird's previously published 3D colour television systems. A Mr Warburton of Edinburgh confirmed to the authors that at the beginning of the war his Royal Military College of Science instructors stated that the two-colour 3D radar system was directly based on Baird's two-colour 3D television system. Mr Warburton was being trained at the time as an arnament artificer (radar) in REME, working on radar controlled anti-aircraft guns.

The first radar-controlled guns appeared around London in October 1940 and, as will be shown, Baird was seen lecturing on anti-aircraft gun radar control at exactly this period in Porthcawl, Wales. The clues to the birth of 3D radar once again point to Baird, the figure who had seen the birth of both basic radar and television, and who was now taking the lead in 3D colour television.

All Baird's wartime television work was documented by contemporary newspapers and in technical magazines such as *Electronic Engineering* and *Wireless World*, whereas there was not, nor has there been since, any public record of his wartime involvement in radar. This aspect has remained a closed book, even to his family. However, his own diaries, coupled with a number of independent first-hand accounts by people who saw him in some distinctly odd situations during the war years, provide irrefutable evidence of his hidden link with radar.

Mr Ash Ellis, a retired south London antique dealer living in Durban, South Africa, was in the Heavy Anti-Aircraft Section, 52nd Regiment, Royal Artillery in 1940 when he volunteered for special duties. He then found himself signing the Official Secrets Act before being initiated into the mysteries of gun-ranging radar. Mr Ellis was sent to Porthcawl in south Wales, where a miners' home, The Rest, had beeen commandeered for use as a high security lecture centre on radar. Those attending were lodged in hotels in the area. He recalls:

> *We were all treated the same, regardless of rank, being new boys learning a new technique. I attended a class with one of our commanders, General Sir Frederick Alfred Pile, and the*

man who introduced us to our subject was John Logie Baird. I remember he wore a zip-up Churchill-style siren suit. He talked on the theory of radar and explained everything, including the construction and function of cathode ray tubes. From what we gathered, we clearly understood he was the inventor of radar and that is something I have never had occasion to question. After that we saw him only once more, in the middle of the Battle of Britain, when he turned up at our 4.5 inch gun battery at Barking Park near Ilford, accompanied by Lord Nuffield, Honorary Colonel of our regiment. He inspected the equipment and asked how we were managing.

Ash Ellis, like so many others involved in secret matters during the war, kept the story to himself over the years, but hearing that a book on Baird was planned and feeling that the inventor's true services to his country had gone unmarked, he decided to speak. His 1940 colleague, General Pile, was the General Officer, Commander in Chief of Britain's anti-aircraft defences, whose main task, from 1940 on, was the introduction of radar-controlled anti-aircraft guns, particularly around London.

Despite the disastrous fire at the Crystal Palace, Baird apparently did not sever his links with that building, but quietly kept part of one of the remaining two towers as an alternative laboratory. Though his normal television work was publicized as being elsewhere, he nevertheless carried out hitherto unknown secret experiments in the tower. When war came, it looked as though the days of the Crystal Palace tower were numbered. In 1940,the RAF prepared for the Battle of Britain and German bombers blitzed London, the authorities ordered the destruction of non-essential large buildings or constructions in the London area that might act as 'signposts' to enemy planes. However, when a top official of a demolition firm involved in this work was called to the Ministry of National Security, he was astonished to be told that the two towers at the Crystal Palace were to remain; he was informed that no reason for this order could be given. The man was understandably puzzled, as the local people considered the towers a permanent incitement to German bombers and a hazard to their lives and property. Later the order was rescinded. Nearly forty years afterwards this official, Mr Felix Levy, read an article about John Logie Baird in the New Scientist.[66] In a letter to the journal he recalled the strange decision concerning the Palace towers and its aftermath.[67] Some years afterwards he was told by the same officials that the reason for the demand by the Ministry was that J. L. Baird was working on top secret projects, for which one of the towers was used.' And so Baird is seen, once again, operating secretly, this time on something so vital that the government was willing to risk the towers remaining in place, even though a possible landmark to enemy bombers.

His presence in one of the towers was also confirmed by a housewife, who knew nothing of the authors' research into Baird's secret war. Mrs L. D. Griffiths of Lancing, Sussex, answered a general appeal for information on Baird in the national press. This request deliberately made no reference to the war or radar, yet she and others were to volunteer facts that indicated Baird's involvement in radar. Mrs Griffiths recalled: 'I was a young married woman at the time and knew that John Logie Baird worked in the basement of the Crystal Palace North Tower. It was a large brick structure. He often had the lights on and I presumed, knowing just a few of his contemporaries, he still worked on his *scanned scheme radar*.' (Authors' italics.) Mrs Griffiths added that the towers were obviously helping the German bombers. The Penge square mile was one of the most heavily bombed areas in south London, because of the presence of two main railway lines. It was feared that a hit on the towers could catapult the heavy tops as far as Beckenham, with disastrous results.

Apparently a faint knowledge of Baird's prewar radar work had percolated through to Mrs Griffiths via her husband, who was a keen radio ham and had been an early experimenter with radio. She was also able to conjure up a name from Baird's distant days in Hastings, Joseph Denton, who was still assisting Baird sixteen years on. Denton had also been secretary of the Royal Television Society since it was inaugurated in 1927. The Griffiths were friendly with a cousin of Denton's and knew that he lodged with his cousin's mother. Mrs Griffiths remembered that he was known locally simply as 'the scientist' and that he often worked, despite bitter cold, in cellars below the house. She heard later from his relatives that this work was concerned with radar. On Denton's death in 1945 Baird hurried to his old friend's house and swiftly stripped it of all traces of their joint work, an occurrence to be oddly echoed on Baird's own death just over a year later.

Denton, 'Dizzy' to his acquaintances, had posed a

problem for many of Baird's colleagues. They found him a shadowy figure, an odd bird, and no one really knew his role in the Baird set-up. He never appeared to be involved in anything obvious. One former employee said: 'He occupied a small room with a bed at the back of Baird's laboratory. Quite honestly we thought Baird was just being kind to him, by giving him somewhere to live.' It is now obvious that Denton was one of the very few who shared Baird's hidden life. Perhaps Baird was describing himself and Denton when he made up stories for his children on his visits to Bude in Cornwall during the war. He told them of two flies, Izzy and Dizzy, who lived with their mother, Mrs Flossie Flannelfoot, in various hotels and who both suffered from dreadful colds and wartime food.

Baird was eventually bombed out of his house at Sydenham and went to live for several months at Jordans near Beaconsfield in Buckinghamshire, at the home of Mr and Mrs H. E. Newton, until he found a new laboratory. Mr Newton wrote: 'My wife found John was no trouble; he was completely wrapped up in his inventions for radar and television, all very secret.' Mr Newton said that Baird would not be drawn on his work and that he made numerous calls on their telephone to the USA. When attacked by his recurrent bouts of bronchitis, he continued to work from his bed and Mr Newton recalls that two or three times a week an official limousine would arrive from London with pin-striped officials carrying briefcases. They would gather round his bed, listen to instructions and depart, carrying papers and drawings executed personally by Baird. The Newtons found him a very pleasant individual who eventually became a real friend. He had a strong sense of humour but was so preoccupied with his work that they once found him walking in winter through the snow-covered garden in his bedroom slippers.

Baird's secret involvements go as far back as 1932, when the director of a Scottish engineering firm was asked to manufacture small rectangular metal components for Baird, which were delivered to Oban on the west coast of Scotland. Baird was living there very quietly, but seemed to be in charge of a small fleet of trawlers which were working on some sort of secret experiments off the Scottish coast, which also involved the Royal Navy. 'In the light of what happened during the war,' this informant says, 'I have always thought it was something to do with degaussing and exploding magnetic mines.' (In 1939 Britain defeated Hitler's first secret weapon, the magnetic mine, by 'degaussing' metal ships.)

But perhaps the most unexpected sighting of Baird, which will be described in detail later, was in 1943 at the height of the Battle of the Atlantic when he was spotted in khaki drills, back in his old haunt, Trinidad.

In the years since Baird's death, the official British version of the invention of radar has gained credence by constant repetition that Sir Robert Watson-Watt, of Brechin, invented radar at BBC Daventry on 26 February 1935. Appleton hinted at his own prior claim, based on his use of reflected radio waves to measure the height of the upper layers of the atmosphere. The row that subsequently erupted broke friendships and poisoned relations among the radar scientists. A sample of just how venomous the row became occurred in a lecture by Sir Robert at a Radiolocation Convention in March 1946.[68] He made this startling statement: 'I would admit as founder members of the Radiolocation Club, A. P. Rowe, H. E. Wimperis, A. F. Wilkins, E. G. Bowen, Henry Tizard, Philip Cunliffe-Lister (Lord Swinton), A.V.Hill, P. M.S-. Blackett, Robert Watson-Watt, Adolf Hitler and Hermann Goering. I would in the most friendly manner deny admission to Heinrich Hertz, E.V.Appleton, Breit and Tuve and even R. Eckersley.' Hitler and Goering were accepted by Sir Robert but Appleton was not. Baird was not even mentioned. Sir Robert was to steer clear of any mention of his fellow Scot, even in his autobiography, *Three Steps to Victory*, despite a professional connection that had lasted more than twenty years. In the late 1920s and early 1930s, Watson-Watt as secretary of the Department of Scientific and Industrial Research (D.S. I.R.), was deeply involved in the design and construction of cathode ray tubes, used by Baird and others in television and radar. Significantly it was Watson-Watt who was chosen in January 1935 by Lord Seldon's television advisory committee to supervise the 1935-7 television competition between Baird and Marconi EMI

The radar paternity row was still blazing away when Sir Robert's autobiography was published in 1958. He had not forgiven Appleton for saying he had helped Watson-Watt secure his belated £52,000 award from the government for radar and for telling the Awards Commission that Watson-Watt was the only member of the radar team who wanted to patent his inventions. Watson-Watt alluded to the £11,000 in Swedish crowns paid to Appleton for his Nobel Prize and wrote: 'If there be a distinction between ignoble royalties and Nobel crowns let me say I am one of those who despise money - and find it reasonably useful.' So Sir Robert, the tireless organizer who had successfully loosed funds from Whitehall for the building of the Chain Home radar stations, remained prickly on the subject of radar and was given to making sweeping and sometimes insulting statements. The British government, which had elevated him as front man for their cover-up version of radar's inception, were stuck with their own story.

By this time both Watson-Watt and Appleton were able to ignore John Logie Baird, whose very strong case for the birth of radar superseded their own. He was long since dead and was not even being quoted in the radar story. Yet, as early as 1923, he had realized that what was to become known as radiolocation in Britain and radar in America, could be achieved by merely switch- ing his television techniques from light to radio waves. In an article, *Wireless World and Radio Review* of May 1924, he spelled it out: 'It is possible that at some future date, means may be discovered of sending out energy from point A, bringing it to bear on an object at a distant point B, and causing the object to radiate from its surface energy which, penetrating intermediate obstacles, can be brought to focus at A, rendering it visible. *This would be radio vision in a very diferent sense.*' (Authors' italics).[69] One man in a position of authority in the Second World War could have provided answers to many of the questions on Baird and radar. Unfortunately, he died in California in 1981 before the authors could arrange an interview with him, though he did manage to confirm Baird's role in radar. He was Captain Leonard Frank Plugge, radio pioneer, scientist and politician, whose name appeared frequently in Baird's wartime diaries. It seems that Plugge had been associated with Baird from the early 1920s right through the Second World War, and he always spoke of Baird in glowing terms. In his entry for *Who's Who*, which he revised in the year of his death, he said he had worked with Marconi and David Sarnoff of RCA and added: 'With Baird, invented world's first working television using a scanning wheel.' This was a previously unknown connection between the two. After the First World War Plugge had served with the Department of Scientific Research, Air Ministry, and

RADAR PRE-HISTORY

RF Scanning : French "Obstacle Detectors"

AS *Wireless World* readers know, radar did not emerge fully fledged from nothingness during the war; its technique has been built up stage-by-stage from the contributions of many workers, and its history goes back for quite a respectable number of years. The main steps in the direct line of development have already been described in our pages, but as time goes on many other early uses of the radio echo principle will doubtless come to light.

British Patent No. 292,185, applied for by John Logie Baird as long ago as 1926, describes an arrangement that bears on the face of it a surprising resemblance to H2S, one of the most refined and highly developed applications of modern radar. Baird pointed out that wireless waves can be reflected and refracted like visible light waves, and contemplated "a method of viewing an object consisting in projecting upon it electromagnetic waves of short wavelength." Reflections from the object were passed through a scanning device to a receiver. The output of this receiver was to be used for modulating a source of visible light. A spot of light projected from this source would traverse a screen "in synchronism with the exploration of the object." The most obvious difference between Baird's scheme of 1926 and the present-day H2S is that scanning was done on the receiver side, and not by exploring the object with the transmitter beam.

French technicians were early in the radar field, and it would seem that the first "commercial" application of the principle was in the "obstacle detector" installed aboard the *Normandie* in 1935. In a general review of French technical progress, including that made under great difficulties during the German occupation, P. Brenot, of the Société Française Radioélectrique, gives some interesting sidelights on early radar work. In this review, published in *L'Onde Electrique* for September, 1945, there is a short description of an experimental "obstacle location" station installed in 1936 by SFR at the entrance to the port of Havre. The apparatus worked on decimetre waves.

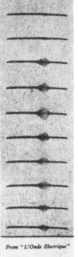

The Sainte Adresse (Havre) experimental obstacle detector. The two parabolic reflectors explored a large sector. The surprisingly modern-looking "display" is also shown. The series of traces indicate echoes from a tug; they grow in amplitude up to the time that the tug cuts the axis of the projector, which was fixed for this test. The trace length represents a total distance of 10km; the measured distance of the tug is here about 4km.

Wireless World 1945, draws attention to the 'surprising' similarity between Bairds patent of 1926 and wartime H2S radar.

would have known of their interest in the use of television in aircraft. As Conservative MP for Chatham and Rochester in the war years he was Private Parliamentary Secretary to the Minister of Aircraft Production, Lord Beaverbrook. When contacted in California during 1980 by Baird's son, Professor Malcolm Baird, he was too ill to give details, but his close friend, Mr Malcolm Peters, wrote that the doughty old pioneer regarded John Logie Baird as the 'top' scientist in the development of radar. The dying Captain Plugge was anxious to set the record straight. (Professor Baird's letter to Plugge had, incidentally, made no mention of any connection between his father and radar.)

There are references in Baird's diaries to renewing 'secret' radar patents, but at some point in his career he almost certainly signed the Official Secrets Act, and so much of his life is a closed book. During his last years, in 1945-6, the 'official' story of radar began to emerge and he seems to have made some cautious and indirect moves himself towards publicizing his now classified research and therefore staking his claim to the invention of radar. An entry in his diary in August 1945 reminds him to 'ring Parr - radar patent'. Parr was editor of *Electronic Engineering*, and the October issue contained this fragment in the correspondence column under the heading 'Radar Anticipated?':

> *The following is an extract from patent GB 292,185 of 21 June 1928 (Television Ltd, and J.L.Baird). . . This invention comprises a method of viewing an object, by projecting upon it electromagnetic waves of short wavelength adjacent to the infra-red radiation in the spectrum, but of longer wavelength than the infra-red rays, exploring the object or the image thereof by a device sensitive to such rays . . . and traversing a spot of light across a screen in synchronism with the exploration of the subject.*[70]

In September, Baird entered more reminders in his diary: 'Get radar from *Engineering* etc., *Illustrated London News*. Contact Maybank.' Maybank was editor of *Wireless World*, and the December issue of that periodical carried a statement that went even further than that in *Electronic Engineering*. In an article headed 'Radar Prehistory', it said:

> *British Patent No. 292,185, applied for as long ago as 1926, describes an arrangement that bears on the face of it, a*

remarkable resemblance to H2S, one of the most refined and highly developed applications of modern radar. Baird pointed out that wireless waves can be reflected and refracted like visible light waves and contemplated a method of viewing an object, consisting of projecting upon it electromagnetic waves of short wavelength.'[71]

H2S was the centimetric radar mapping system carried in British and American bombers in the Second World War, enabling them to fly above cloud level or at night, yet know all about the ground and cities below them. Navigation and the accuracy of bombing were aided by the landmarks which appeared in visual form on a radar television screen in the aircraft.

These two articles, presumably inspired by Baird himself, give some indication of what was going on behind the scenes. The references in the diary to *Engineering* and *Illustrated London News* are presumably to the fact that those two periodicals carried the first articles on radar published after the war. Neither mentioned Baird, who would certainly also have been annoyed at the absence of any reference to his own object detection work in a published lecture on radar given to the Institute of Electrical Engineers by his old friend, Sir Edward Appleton, in April 1945.[72] If claims were already being made under the cloak of officialdom (Appleton was secretary of the DSIR, the body responsible for funding the radar and atomic bomb programmes), then Baird could see the long-term dangers to his own reputation in this field.

At his death, only a few hints remained. Much may still be uncovered, but this chapter has attempted to fill in some of the major gaps.

Secret work apart, however, Baird's normal television experiments in wartime looked like shaping the industry's peacetime future. When the British government set up a committee in February 1944 to advise on what form the country's national television service should take after the war, Baird was the only private witness, though large companies such as GEC, working on wartime radar; Marconi-EMI, also in radar; and Scophony, later Scophony-Baird, involved in secret signalling by television, were also consulted. Many members of the committee, presided over by Lord Hankey, had been on Lord Selsdon's Advisory Committee in the mid-thirties, which had decided against

Baird's equipment in favour of the rival Marconi-EMI system. However, the Hankey Committee were to produce a white paper on Britain's future television system and they largely followed Baird's suggestions. He had recommended the use of the old standard 405 lines until a new system could take over three years later. The new service should aim for 1000-line definition, 3D and colour. He was also in favour of extending the service to America and Europe, for standardizing international television communications and for recognizing Russia as a great potential market for sets and programmes. The Hankey Committee report of 28 March 1945 recommended 405 lines, black and white, though definition should be improved to 1,000 lines as Baird had suggested, and hopefully they would add 3D and colour.

Since Baird was the only person to demonstrate all these elements by that date, it looked as though he was about to play a major role in television after the war. The Hankey Report, incidentally, drew attention to the similarities between radar and television.

A fascinating account of Baird and his television work during the war testified to the quality of both his colour and 3D colour experiments. The *News Chronicle* reported in 1944 on a demonstration of the Baird Telechrome and facsimile television at his London home. It said that the colour was as natural as any colour film the writer had ever seen. Even the grain on a pipe and a bead of perspiration were highlighted. Significantly, when it was suggested by a puzzled reporter that the government might be induced to find him a laboratory in a safe area, Baird merely smiled and replied disarmingly: 'That would be very nice, but I doubt if the government is interested enough to do any such thing. I have been given no tangible evidence of government interest."[73] And so, again, Baird was slamming home the message that he was in no way involved with his country's war. If it had been possible for those present to study what was happening in radar and secret signalling at that juncture, they might have taken his comments with a pinch of salt.

The safety aspect no doubt was uppermost in the minds of the press during the demonstration. Egon Larsen's book, *Inventor's Scrapbook*, said that the journalists had braved doodlebugs all the way from Fleet Street.[74] Larsen noted that Baird was using a new dummy for colour television. Instead of his old standby, Bill, he had Useless Eustace, a coloured papier mache doll, adorned with a picturesque costume which comprised a tailcoat of hunting pink, blue trousers and a shag pipe, all topped by the headdress of an Arab shiek. They found Baird working amid little heaps of broken glass and demolished pieces of furniture, and behind shutters which had been blasted into lopsided angles by Hitler's flying bombs, several of which had landed in the vicinity. Larsen wrote: 'The intrepid Scotsman had made up his mind to stick to it, and he saw it through with the same unflinching determination that had been his characteristic feature a score of years before at Hastings.' When Baird died in 1946, his health undermined by the punishing workload of the war years, the general impression was that he had continued working safely on television. But two newspaper articles contradicted this. An unidentified article, almost certainly from the *Daily Telegraph*, and probably dated about December 1941, stated: 'Many of Baird's experiments and inventions have been invaluable in war, but he won't talk about them. He will not even say if they are being used, although before the war it was freely predicted that at least one startling discovery of his would be of tremendous value to an air force.' But perhaps the most tantalizing reference was an obituary of the inventor published in the *Daily Herald* on 15 June 1946, which said: 'The full story of Baird cannot yet be told. During the war, at Sydenham, he was working, not only on an invention for the government, which is still on the secret list, but also on new research of his own.'[75] The obituary may have been referring to another of Baird's secrets. Perhaps just as important as radar, perhaps even more important as the war progressed, was another facet of this man's fertile mind, the use of television for ultra high-speed secret signalling.

NOTES

1 S. A. Moseley, *John Baird, the Romance and Tragedy of the pioneer of Television*, Odhams, 1952, p. 226.
2 'Britain's Secret Weapon Revealed, Scotsman's Device to Trap Raiders, First Official Disclosure', *Glasgow Herald*, I June 1941, p. 5.
3 News of the industry - Radar Stories Are Released by USA and Great Britain'*Electronics (USA)*, June 1943, p. 274.
4 A Clandestine Business', *Fortune*, No. 4, 6 October 1945.
5 Dulany Terrett, *The United States in World War II - the Technical Services - the Signal Corps: The emergency (to December 1941)*, Office of the Chief of Military History, Department of the Army, Washington, DC, 1956, p. 201.

6   R.B.Colton, 'Radar in the United States Army; Early Developments at the Signal Corps, Fort Monmouth, New Jersey', *Proc. IRE, (USA), 33, November* 1945, pp. 740-53.

7   M.M. Carpentier, 'France and Thomson - CSF Contribution to Radar, Radar conference, Arlington, Virginia, April 1975 (abstracted in *IEEE Trans. Aero-space and Electronic Systems, AES -11, No. 3*, May 1975, p. 419.)

8   A. Price, *Instruments of Darkness*, W. Kimber, 1967, p. 59.

9   J.F.Ramsay, 'Microwave Antenna and Waveguide Techniques before 1900', *Proc. IRE (USA)*, 1958, pp. 405-15.

10   *Wireless World*, 8 November 1935, p. 491 'Feelers for Ships, Microwave Equipment Described', *Wireless World*, 26 June 1936, pp. 623-4.

11   G.Marconi,'RadioTelegraphy',*Proc. IRE(USA)*, 10,1922,p.215.

12   Baird, GB patent No. 292,185, 'Reflected Radio Wave Television System'; application dated 21 December 1926, accepted 21 June 1928.

13   Baird, GB patent No. 297,014, 'Improved Receiver for Reflected Radiowave Television System'; application dated 10 March 1927, accepted 10 September 1928.

14   O. Lodge, 'The work of Hertz', *Proc. Royal Institution*, XIV 1983, 95,pp. 321-49.

15   A Fleming, 'Electrons, Electric Waves and Wireless Telephony', *Wireless World and Radio Review*, 23 December 1922, pp. 396-401.

16   British Royal Navy, provisional secret GB, patent No. 6,433, issued to Salmond and Alder, 'Detection of Ships and Aircraft by Reflected Radio Waves'; applied for in 1928.

17   R.W. Clarke, *Tizard*, Methuen, 1965. References: 'Army Radar' (Chapter of Book) by A.P. Sayer. Recorded in, *Inventions Book of Royal Engineers Board*, January 1931, ch. Army Radar.

18   'News of the Industry - Radar Stories...'

19   'Personalities, Dr A. Hoyt-Taylor,' *Wireless World*, September 1944, p.281.

20   G Briet and M.A. Tuve, 'A Test of the Existence of the Conducting Layer'. *Physics Review*, 28 September 1926, p.554.

21   E.V. Appleton and M.A.F. Barnett, 'First Measurement of the Distance Travelled by Radio Waves', *Proc. Royal Society*, A, 109, 1925, p.261.

22   R. Tiltman, 'Noctovision', *Television*, March 1928, pp.40-41.

23   'Blacklight over London', *Glasgow Herald*, 21 February 1927.

24   Baird, 'Television', letter *Nature*, 29 January 1927, p.161.

25   E. Free, 'In the World's Laboratories, the Possibilities of Television', *Popular Radio (USA)*, March 1927, pp. 267-68.

26   'Ultimatum to PMG, How Televison and Secret Rays Were Preserved for Britain, Inventor's Story', *Sunday News*, 13 February 1927.

27   'The Invisible Searchlight, Seeing in the Dark', *Illustrated London News*, 25 December 1926.

28   'Seeing through Fog, Television Demonstration, an Admiral's View of It', *The Observer*, 24 April 1927.

29   'Daylight Television, A New Baird System', *Popular Wireless*, 4 August 1928.

30   E.V. Appleton, 'Those Ghost Images', *Television*, November 1930, p.357.

31   *Tizard*

32   E.L.C. White, 'A method of Continuous Observation of the Equivalent Height of the Kennelly-Heavyside Layer', *Proc. Cambridge*

Phil. Soc, XXVII, 1930-31, pp. 445-50,
33 E.V. Appleton and G. Builder, 'A Simple Method of Investigating Wireless Echoes of Short Delay', *Nature*, 127, 1931, p. 970.
34 R. Watson-Watt, *Three Steps to Victory*, Odhams, 1957.
35 'France and Thomson CSF'.
36 E.C.S. Megaw, 'The High Powered Pulsed Magnetron', *Journal of the I EE*, 93, IIIA, p. 46. 1946 radiolocation Convention.
37 'Microwaves to Detect Aircraft', *Elecronics (USA)*, September 1935, pp. 18-19.
38 *Three Steps to Victory*
39 'Detection of Ships and Aircraft by Reflected Radio Waves'.
40 *Tizard*
41 S. Desmond, 'When London Was Gassed', *Television*, Nov. 1928, pp.38-46.
42 'News fo the Week - The death Ray Again', *Wireless World*, 21 September 1934.
43 W.P. Jolly, *Marconi*, Constable, 1972, pp. 266-67. D. Marconi, *My Father Marconi*, Muller, 1962
44 G. Marconi, 'The Electron Art - in the News', *Electronics* (USA), October 1935, p. 386.
45 G. Marconi, 'The Electron Art - in the News', *Electronics* (USA), October 1935, p.386.
46 E. Barwell, *The Death Ray Man*, Hutchinson, 1943
47 *Three steps to Victory*
48 R. Nalder, *British Army Signals in the Second World War*, Royal Signals Institute, London, 1953.
49 'TV, German Plea for British Cooperation', *Glasgow Herald*, 10 July 1935 TV, German Plea for British Cooperation', *The Times*, 10 July 1935, p.13g
50 'Television for Air Defence, German Source under Military Control', *The Times*, 10 August 1935, p.10e.
51 'Radio Exhibition in Berlin', *The Times*, 17 August 1935, p.9e.
52 B. Norman, *Here's Looking at You*, BBC Publications, 1984.
53 F.W. Winterbotham, *The Nazi Connection*, Weidenfeld and B. Nicholson, 1978, P.164.
54 L. Fargo, *The Game of the Foxes*, Bantam, 1973, p.103.
55 G Everson, *The Story of Television, The Life of P.T. Farnsworth*, Norton, New York, 1949, reprinted by Arno Press, 1974.
56 'Television in bombers, Pilots to See Towns 100 Miles Away', *Daily Telegraph*, 25 February 1938.
57 'Army's Mystery Ray', *New York American*, 3 August 1935.
58 'Radar in the United States Army".
59 *Electronics* (USA), 17 April 1935, p.139.
60 *Electronics* (USA), May 1933, p.133.
61 E. G. Bowen, *Textbook of Radar*, C.U.P., 3rd edition, 1954 p.3.
62 'Baird Telechrome', *Wireless World*, August 1944, p. 136.
63 'Colour Television', *Journal of the IRE*, X, No. 4, April 1950, p.125.
64 E. Parker and P.R. Wallis, 'Three-dimensional Cathode Ray Tube Displays', *Journal of the IEE*, 95, III, 1948, p.371.
65 L.C. Jesty, letter, *Electronics and Power*, April 1976, p.247.
66 P. Waddell, 'Seeing by Wireless', *New Scientist*, 11 November 1976, pp. 341-43.
67 F.L. Levy, 'Gap in the Record', letter *New Scientist*, 25 November 1975,

p.489.

68 R. Watson-Watt, 'The Evolution of Radiolocation', *Journal of the IEE*, 93, 1946, pp. 374-82.

69 J.L. Baird, 'An Account of some Experiments in Television', *Wireless World and Radio Review*, 7 May 1924, pp. 153-55.

70 'Radar Anticipated', correspondence, *Electronic Engineering*, Oct. 1945, p.742.

71 'Radar Prehistory', *Wireless World*, December 1945, p.357.

72 E.V. Appleton, 'The Scientific Principles of Radiolocation', *Journal of IEE*, 92, April-May 1945, p.340.

73 'Baird Gives Television Colour and Depth', *News Chronicle*, 16 August 1944.

74 E. Larsen, *Inventor's Scrapbook*, Lindsay Drummond, 1947.

75 'Baird Is Dead - Television Brought Life of Broken Dreams', *Daily Herald*, 15 June 1946.

10

The Great Enigma

Though the outbreak of war in 1939 closed down British television, a group of WRNS were destined to spend much of the war gazing into television sets from the unlikely location of a windy clifftop at Beachy Head in Sussex. As Allied and enemy fighters and bombers droned back and forth above them, they watched variety shows, boxing matches and outdoor scenes direct from the heart of occupied Paris, all by courtesy of the Third Reich. With breathtaking naivety, the Germans had started a television service from the Magic City Theatre in Paris, unaware that this provided the British with an electronic eye into the city. Programmes were picked up regularly for intelligence monitoring by aerials specially erected on England's south coast.

The British had discovered the potential pitfalls of wartime television at Brighton on 26 June 1938 when a team from EMI led by television expert George Kelsey picked up high-definition television pictures from France, using special receivers and aerials. They reported finding that British programmes might conversely be received and used by an enemy. This plus the potential of deliberate RAF interference with German bomber guidance systems, by using Alexandra Palace transmitters, were the probable reasons for Britain's decision to black out television for the duration of the war. The Germans had launched their service blissfully ignorant of the surveillance of Kelsey, now a wing commander, and his specially selected intelligence-gathering unit of French and German speaking servicewomen. The information received pinpointed the presence in Paris of individual high ranking German officers and helped gauge morale and living conditions in the city, and so television was used as an instrument of intelligence to spy upon the Nazis. But could it supplement its passive, receptive role by more direct and thrusting moves against the enemy?

JLB, 1940-41 with 600 line television, screen 2'6" x 2".

The answer was in the affirmative in one vitally important area, that of secret signalling. Secret messages by television are almost as old as television itself. The new medium readily lent itself to the ancient art of cyphers as used by spies throughout the centuries. With television, vastly more complex possibilities were opened up for clandestine signalling. By its very nature, the television system transmitted a stupendous amount of information in an extremely short time. It did not take cypher experts long to realize that these information factors could be juggled with and used to 'scramble' codes and cyphers in such a way that they would confuse any unauthorized receiving stations.

Signs of this early awareness emerged in 1926, the very year that Baird gave his first public display of true television pictures. The first known patent for secret signalling by television in the British Index of Patents is No. 264,174, dated 1926, by Dr Karolus of the German Telefunken Company. The patent describes coded information on film, being transmitted by using a Nipkow disc scanner for 30-line images. Prominent combines in other countries were swift to follow. In 1927 C.W.Hansell obtained a television secret signalling patent, GB No. 295, 601, for Marconi, and in the same year a US patent No. 1,751,584, for a similar unit, this time for RCA. The patents involved the use of fibre optics tube bundles; Hansell was regarded as second in the world with fibre optics, after Baird.

Baird did not follow their example by showing an open interest in the subject. He proved reticent on secret signalling, even more so than in the field of detection systems - his silence on signalling equalled that on the use of reflected radio waves in his Noctovisor. But, as with the radio waves, this can be interpreted as a pointer to his involvement; the indications were there. His 1927 American patent on an infra-red Noctovisor mentioned the use of infra-red waves for signalling; and, as noted before, he was seen in army uniform with signallers at Aldershot in 1928 by an eye witness who spoke of experiments in 'cine-tele transmissions'. It is clear that Baird was working at this time on signalling techniques as well as radiolocation. His reported presence at Aldershot coincides with the report in the secret Air Ministry file (2/S24132) that successful secret signalling experiments by television were carried out that very year at Woolwich by the British army.

Though in its infancy, television was the most attractive system available, combining as it did a ready-made channel for conveying cyphered messages with the most secrecy and a potential for vast improvement. Interest in television for this purpose grew during the 1930s, though direct references are few. One is contained in a book on television in 1935 which stated that television was being used for secret code and picture transmissions.[1] And in the same year Baird's old assistant, H. J. Barton-Chapple, observed in another book that transmitting morse by television was far superior to using wireless. Images apparently emerged clearly through atmospheric disturbances, whereas sound was greatly distorted.[2] Barton-Chapple's claim is particularly apt when related to a comment by Sir Colin Gubbins, who controlled Special Operations Executive (SOE) during the Second World War. SOE dispatched agents throughout occupied Europe and Sir Colin claimed that, without high-frequency morse links, S O E would have been groping in the dark.[3]

In June 1928 Baird's friend and associate, Sir Ambrose Fleming, wrote: 'The infra-red invisible rays have only recently been put to practical use by John Logie Baird in his very important Noctovision experiments and for other purposes in secret signalling.'⁴ Again it was this aspect of Baird's work that drew the attention of A. V. Alexander, First Lord of the Admiralty, two years later in July 1930, when he was televised by the Baird Company at the London Coliseum. He talked then of the possibility of such an invention for naval secret signalling, but hoped that it would be used for peace and not for war. ⁵

The use of television signalling in the Second World War has rarely if ever been mentioned. Even today such a claim is met with a certain degree of incredulity. Nations seldom make a point of referring to their secret signalling systems: forty years can pass before even an indication is given of some method previously used and, in such a case, one can rest assured that the system revealed has been rendered defunct by equipment far more efficient and secure. During the Second World War secret signalling by radio was an accepted fact, but for many reasons television had no place in the public imagination. Few people had owned prewar television sets. It seemed a complicated system necessitating transmitting and receiving stations too large for the covert use of signals in and out of occupied Europe, and how could such messages be recorded? In addition television had closed down on the outbreak of war and vanished from the scene. However, television had been experimented with by the armed services of Britain and Germany in the years preceding the war and there is considerable evidence that it was used by both sides in a manner which made the secret cypher duel far more complicated and dangerous than has ever been revealed.

Much has been written about Enigma, the German cyphering machine, which gave rise to the famous British operation codenamed Ultra, for breaking the enemy codes and reading their messages. But the trouble with Enigma, from the German point of view, was that, even using the most sophisticated of their machines, only 80 words a minute in morse could be transmitted by radio. By 1944 the British were to have a television system over 9,000 times faster.

In December 1941 Baird had accepted a consultancy with the Cable and Wireless Company at a salary of £1,000 a year. The company chairman, Sir Edward Wilshaw, explained that this was to help Baird maintain his private television laboratory. The consultancy work concerned the application of television to telegraphy. Baird told his family that the duties were quite nominal, involving just a couple of visits per month, and they, being 250 miles from London, accepted this statement at face value. But Cable and Wireless had been taken over by the British government and now included the Marconi Company, which had a secret television signalling background going back to 1927. It is unlikely that a government agency in time of war would release £1,000 a year (equivalent to almost £20,000 in today's terms) to enable any citizen to maintain private research resources. Baird's speciality at Cable and Wireless was facsimile television, the transmission of printed or filmed material at extremely high speeds, which assumes added significance when considered in connection with an entry in his appointment diary for Thursday 20 November 1941, reading 'Secret signalling!' Other references to signalling would appear in his diaries as the war progressed. In Britain today the Ceefax facsimile television system is descended from Baird's work starting as far back as 1929 when he used tele-cine apparatus for displaying printed material, between regular programmes from Brookmans Park, on his televisor receiver screen.

By 1944 he was recording and replaying typed material on cine film, one cine film frame to one printed page of 500 words, at twenty-five television images or cine frames per second. This meant that in one minute he could transmit 750,000 words, or as a newspaper of the day admiringly observed, the equivalent of five full-length novels.[6] Not only did he have the advantage of an overwhelming amount of coded information on film, but this was made doubly secure by perpetually changing the scanning or the interlacing of the television camera, a system which in modern phraseology can be termed a video scrambler. Alternatively, one could scramble the camera output signals electronically.

This was another example of the intricacy, diversity and scope of Baird's wartime research. Britain has maintained silence on the uses of wartime television, but it could not have afforded to ignore the efforts of the Germans in this field. As the war progressed so did the intensity of the Reich's research into the use of television for military purposes, with achievements which were being matched in Britain mainly by Baird. The Germans, however, were geared for their effort through the efforts of an army of thousands of technicians and workers. As in Britain little, if anything, has been officially revealed about Nazi Germany's military television. But the scale and importance of the work can be discerned in the investigation of even a single firm, Baird's old company, which on the outbreak of war was known as Fernseh Gmbh.

The wartime story of this company, astonishing to say the least, involved major technical innovations, high production and top secrecy. Baird and Loewe had been forced out by the mid-1930s and in 1939 Zeiss-Ikon also withdrew, leaving Bosch, the last of the original partners, as sole proprietors. They had persevered with some of the projects pursued by Baird in Britain, winning a contract to produce television cinema equipment for the German Post Office, which was operating continuously from 1939. Also for the German Post Office they built and installed the main part of a two-way intercommunication system with stations in Hamburg, Berlin, Leipzig and Munich. Though cathode ray tubes were used for reception, mechanical scanning for transmission was adopted, the very compromise which Baird had sought for increased-range efficiency in the mid-thirties but which had been ignored by the B B C in favour of the limitations of the short-range all-electronic system.

As Allied bombers pounded Berlin in 1944 the main Fernseh works were considered so important that they were hastily moved to Obertannwald in Czechoslovakia, in what was then the Sudetenland. A booklet issued in 1979 by the Bosch Company, giving details of fifty years of its achievements in television, carried a section on Fernseh (now Bosch-Fernseh, the video equipment division of Robert Bosch GmbH), by Frithjof Rudert, which covers this dramatic period.[7] Rudert reveals that the name of the company was changed to Farvis as a deliberate camouflage. The new site was a picturesque former spinning mill fitted with laboratories, workshops, design offices and adminis-trative facilities for 800 personnel.

A description of the television apparatus developed as a result of demand from the armed forces proves the most fascinating element in the survey. The disguised Farvis Company were set a series of challenges which meant that almost everything needed to be looked at from a different viewpoint. Problems ranged from the simple task of determining a direction to the sending of maps of the highest resolution. For signals, after extensive field trials, transmitters were built with different wavelengths to suit conditions aboard ships, in hill country and on aircraft. The company also constructed a particularly small camera and a 8 by 9 cm universal receiver, not much larger than a man's fist, the whole unit slightly bigger than a shoebox - incredibly small for the time. A high- power receiver was constructed with a special picture tube in order to display very bright images for observation in daylight. These receivers were housed in airtight containers for use at high altitudes and in the tropics.

The appliances had to conform to some very interesting requirements at a time of all-out war: low bulk, low power demand, high operational reliability even with rough handling, faultless synchronization and extremely simple operation through the use of systematic controls, the very qualities required by troops in the field. From the descriptions it is clear that the German armed forces were using television for purposes other than observation and target finding.

Perhaps the most intriguing item was the development of a rapid-picture system for the transmission of cards, drawings or letters. At the transmission station the picture material was scanned by a CRT flying spot process, just as in Baird's wartime system, and the signals were conveyed to a transmitter. A key signal was switched on 'for just so long as was necessary for a picture to be scanned, and was not easily susceptible to radio direction finding'. Secrecy was obviously the priority, with a burst of signal so rapid it was intended to elude enemy surveillance, recording or direction finding. Secret television signalling could hardly be spelled out more clearly and it would be hard to believe that the Germans did not combine this with their Enigma codes.

So demanding was the schedule that employees worked 60-70 hours a week, with little time for home life in the adjacent small towns of Obertannwald and Morchenstern, which managed to escape Allied bombing throughout the war. However, the whole Farvis episode drew to a dramatic climax in 1945 as the Russians advanced towards the area. A goods train loaded with sections of plant, appliances and some private property was dispatched to Hallein near Salzburg in Austria. After an adventurous journey, a few employees reached a different destination, not Hallein, but Taufkirchen/Vils in Lower Bavaria where there was a minor branch of the Blaupunkt Company, and this was to be the seat of Fernseh for several years. Discreet and skilful negotiations were embarked upon with the United States

Baird in his Sydenham garage heat-treating hand-made cathode ray tubes, 1944.

The inventor and Eddie Anderson, his chief assistant, 1939-46, prepare colour TV experiments with a model at Sydenham, 1944.

occupation forces. Part of the goods train was located and diverted to Taufkirchen with equipment. The small party of Fernseh refugees handed over documents, concerning the secret work at Obertannwald, and were given in return access to impounded goods which enabled them to start production of radio materials. Television engineering was forbidden by the Control Commission.

The transfer of Fernseh television documents could have some bearing on the emergence of a very similar system to Baird's, using a cathode ray tube flying spot transmitter on cine film, which turned up at RCA in the United States in 1949 under the name Ultrafax.[8] The flying spot method had been adopted and developed at Obertannwald.

Fernseh's wartime activities spotlight the emphasis on the application of television by the Germans and reveals the manufacture on a fairly large scale of tough, miniature units for field signalling in secret. The details are particularly valuable in the absence of any detailed Allied description of how they were using television at the time, and one can surmise that their methods were similar. Such facts must add a totally new dimension to the problems that were faced by Allied code interceptors and decrypters, a situation over which a veil has been drawn ever since.

Herr Rudert's facts substantiate a reference in a book published in 1950.[9] citing a British postwar intelligence investigation which found that the enemy used 'devilish ingenuity in the application of television and associated radar'. The intelligence team were apparently shown a laboratory where 200 miniature television tubes had been produced each month. It was also noted that Dr G. Weiss, chief of the German Post Office Laboratory, had revealed in 1946 that Telefunken had developed during the war a secret facsimile television system. The unit was used for the transmission of telegrams, the telegram being scanned and transmitted once only in a twenty-fifth of a second, presumably for security reasons. Another German system, echoing a Baird technique, was a facsimile method as reported in a British technical magazine of 1947.[10] This described a flying spot cathode ray transmitter, which it was claimed had been used for the transmission of maps at the battlefronts.

It is unrealistic to expect that the Allies, with knowledge of the German television offensive, would not utilize such methods themselves, and in fact the system was being developed by the Allies as is revealed by Solomon Sagall. A television pioneer and a contemporary of Baird, Sagall was born in 1902 near Minsk in Russia, and was educated in Germany and at the London School of Economics. He came under the spell of television at an early age and in 1930 founded Scophony Ltd to develop and market an optic-mechanical method of television, the brainchild of a British inventor, George William Walton. In 1940 Sagall moved to America, where he built television equipment for the US Signal Corps,[11] and in the 1980s, as the octogenarian president of Teleglobe Pay-TV Systems Inc., was still pioneering with his pay- television system.

Sagall revealed that during a prewar teabreak at Scophony he had put to his engineers the problem of television for communication between military headquarters and front line commanders, to be used for the transmission of maps and so on, but in such a way that the enemy could not intercept the intelligence. A few days later Dr A. Rosenthal, a member of the Scophony brains trust, came forward with an idea and means of coding and decoding by television.[12] In a letter to the Journal of the Royal Television Society Sagall made the crucial statement: 'Present day Pay-TV scrambling and decoding systems are based on Dr Rosenthal's concept of coding and decoding proposed for use in military operations.'[13] Rosenthal had suggested in 1938 the use of a new kind of cathode ray tube for the long-duration recording of electrical signals. Any signal left a dark trace on the screen which remained for a long time, disappearing only gradually, a quality which rendered the unit unsatisfactory in its basic form for ordinary television. the new tube provided a means of holding a visible record on a screen, to be copied or studied at leisure before being erased. Such a signal could be transmitted in a split second and then discontinued, operating too fast for interception by an enemy, but leaving behind a long- lasting receiver image. In Britain during 1939 Rosenthal applied for a patent for secret signalling by television, GB 530,776. (Interestingly, in 1943 Sagall, in America, was offering his scrambling-television system for sale for use in business security signalling.)

The new tube was called a Skiatron or dark trace tube and a description of the unit appeared in a British technical magazine of 1948, written by a certain G. Wikkenhauser of Scophony Ltd.[14] Like Rosenthal, Wikkenhauser had taken out a provisional British patent for television secret signalling, GB 577,670 (1938), and was one of the individuals who appear in Baird's crammed diary of wartime appointments. Gaumont-British, who had a controlling interest in the prewar Baird Company, were also shareholders in Scophony.

Sir Robert Watson-Watt incorporated the Skiatron tube into the radar system for aircraft tracking and it played a vital part in Allied defences. Baird's old assistant, Ben Clapp, recalls that the Baird Television Company at Lower Sydenham helped to develop the Skiatron and had a Skiatron production line. 27,000 Skiatrons were produced by Bairds company in world war II. Watson-Watt visited the factory several times immediately before the war, and Wikkenhauser indicated other interesting uses for the tube in his article: 'the tube provides immediately a visible record, which can be kept on the screen until erased and examined in detail at leisure. This record can of course be traced on paper or photographed with a simple camera.' It was immeasurably superior to the ordinary fluorescent screen, where great care had to be taken to synchronize the camera shutter to the electrical phenomena. The Skiatron was found to be so effective that direct observation was usually sufficient. Wikkenhauser added that the British Admiralty found the duration of the signal to be of great interest and had the equipment 'developed and used'. Heat and light were applied for cancellation of the traces, thus erasing the previous images. The article revealed that the Germans made tubes of a similar description, with specifications that made the erasure of even a very dark trace possible in 5-10 seconds. A tube of this nature was produced by Telefunken during the war.

Wikkenhauser's information included a detail which bore directly on a wartime achievement of John Logie Baird. He wrote: 'There are other applications which are, of course, essentially the same as those for transient recording which come into the field of facsimile transmission and reception of the instantaneous recording of a single frame television image.' He added that high- definition facsimile images could be transmitted and received immeasurably more quickly with this unit than with other methods used at the time. If the Skiatron receiver tube, with its ability to retain an image for recording and swift erasure afterwards, was combined with Baird's remarkable facsimile transmission

French Marcel Bloch bomber which was equipped with secret television and cine systems by the Baird company and was tested in England and France in 1939.

system, with its vast and speedy word potential, then a formidable instrument for secret signalling was created.

An older and simpler form of recording had, of course, been in existence almost from the birth of television. This was Baird's use of gramophone records, a system which he termed Phonovision. The idea was still to the fore and thriving in 1967 when Westinghouse in America introduced their version, called Phonovid, utilizing an ordinary $33^{1}/_{3}$ rpm gramophone record for high-information packing density: 400 pictures, 200 a side, with accompanying audio, could be recorded on a 12 inch record. When processed through a scan converter, the played-back signal supplied a standard television signal.

Evidence that the Baird Company had the capability of sophisticated television signalling at the start of the war using video recording is reinforced by details of the fascinating equipment they installed in the French Bloch bomber in 1938-9. This system, tested over the countryside west of London and above northern France, was ostensibly for reconnaissance purposes and supplied 400-line images so successfully that pictures from 4,000 feet transmitted to the ground revealed such minute details as the white markings on tennis courts and ripples on water.

Mr Ray Herbert, a member of the Baird team throughout the test flights, says that the transmissions were not isolated events but the results of several years' development work carried out in the highest secrecy. He explains that, since television cameras of the period were relatively crude and difficulties were experienced with poor light, it was agreed to operate Baird's intermediate film process which enabled them to use a 16 mm camera with its superior optical capability.

The plane, therefore, was loaded with a processing tank and equipment in which the film was treated and fixed in sixteen seconds and then run through a cathode ray tube scanner to be converted into TV signals. On the ground the signals were picked up for analysis by a purpose-designed Renault van packed with special equipment which reversed the process in the plane. The television signal was recorded on film. The video recording equipment allowed items of particular interest to be stored and the operator could record a single frame or a series.

The Marcel Bloch 200 twin-engine night bomber usually carried a French pilot, mechanic and three Baird engineers. Reconnaissance was the reason given for the experiments. But it is clear that the system could well be adapted to transmit and accept photographs and messages to and from the ground. The 1936 demonstration aboard a KLM plane over London had shown Baird accepting television signals in the air.

Towards the close of the war, Baird formed a company again. J.L. Baird Ltd, which combined with Scophony after his death, was known as Scophony-Baird. Much of the inventor's wartime apparatus had been stored in the grounds of what was to become Scophony-Baird but, after his death, it mysteriously vanished, never to be seen again. Someone had removed his materials just as Baird himself had urgently gathered in technical items from the home of his assistant, Joseph Denton, when that old friend died in 1945.

Reticence on certain aspects of Baird's wartime work was still being shown in the 1980s by some of his former friends and colleagues. A typical reaction was that of the late Commander J.D. Percy, son of Sir John J. Percy, a director of the original Baird Television Company and a close friend of Baird. J.D. Percy had been chief television engineer of

Scophony-Baird and, when approached by the authors for details of Baird's participation in radar and secret signalling, he refused to comment. Pressed for details by letter, he answered questions on normal television but ignored the other subjects. When Bairds daughter, Diana, came across Commander Percy at a television function in London and inquired about her father's activities in the war, Percy advised her not to dabble, as they were getting into 'murky waters'.

The extent of Baird's involvement in secret war efforts is apparent, however, from his appointments diaries alone. 'Secret signalling' is noted, but on 2 August 1943 there is an even more arresting entry, 'Godfrey (ULTRA)'. In his biography of Baird, Sydney Moseley referred to correspondence in 1939, with Captain J.H. Godfrey, regarding Baird's potential value. That same year Godfrey was appointed Director of Naval Intelligence, his first assistant being Ian Fleming, the future author of the James Bond novels. By 1943 Godfrey was an admiral, a quick-witted and ambitious man who, in his own view, might have become 'C', head of the Secret Service. [15] He was also responsible for the dissemination of Ultra material within the Royal Navy. Godfrey was eventually offered the post of Flag Officer Commanding the Royal Indian Navy by A.V. Alexander, First Lord of the Admiralty, and he went to India early in 1943. It is not known why Baird should name Godfrey at this point, but he was correctly coupling him with Ultra, whose existence was known only to an elite and tiny band.

The First Lord, had of course as far back as 1930 displayed interest in Baird's television as a means of secret signalling. But apparently naval conservatism at this period obstructed the introduction of machine coding, contrary to the wishes of Lord Louis Mountbatten who had pressed for the Royal Navy to follow the examples of the Royal Air Force and the US navy. Surprisingly, although supplied with decrypted Ultra information, Alexander was not told of the Ultra secret, on special orders to Godfrey from Winston Churchill. [16] This attitude can be explained by the tight security net which surrounded Ultra. Alexander was a trusted figure, but he was also a politician who had to report back to the Parliament, and for a time Churchill felt he could not afford to assume loyalty from all those in Parliament not directly involved with him.

The attitude to the Germans at the start of the war was equivocal in certain spheres of higher society, a factor no British Government could ignore. For example, Admiral Sir Barry Domville, Director of British Naval Intelligence from 1927 to 1930, was arrested together with Sir Oswald Mosley leader of Britain's Fascists, and interned from 1940 to 1943. [17] Domville, an ardent admirer of Hitler and a guest at the Nuremberg Rally in 1936, had become chairman of a pro-Nazi organization called the Anglo-GermanLink and was a regular dinner guest of Ambassador Ribbentrop at the German Embassy in London. 'The Link', formed in 1937 to promote friendship with Germany, had thirty-five active branches in Britain and a membership of about 4,400 by 1939 which included some of the most influential people in the land. Prominent members included Frank C. Tiarks, Governor of the Bank of England, the Marquess of Londonderry, (the former Tory Air Minister), Col Frank Yeats-Brown, author of *The Bengal Lancer*, Lord Redesdale, father of the Mitford sisters, and a host of Earls, Lords and captains of industry.

A possibility remains that some of these members may have been placed in 'The Link' as double agents, to encourage Hitler to believe that the wealthy in Britain were pro-Nazi and anti-communist. Domville had a most unexpected secretary, none other than Guy Burgess, who was to defect to Moscow after the war. [18] Burgess's friend and co-Soviet agent, Kim Philby, was also in on the scene and was photographed at an Anglo-German Fellowship dinner on 14 July 1936. [19] The same reference reveals on p.43 that the BBC was started in the early 1920s as a means of quietly raising revenue for British radio manufacturers, in order to develop radio signalling equipment for the British secret service. One of the suggestors for the creation of the BBC was W. Gladstone Murray, who become their chief publicity manager in the 1920s and 1930s and showed great kindness to J.L. Baird. If Murray knew the secret reasons for the creation of the BBC and was involved with the intelligence service then he would have been aware of Baird's similar role, thus explaining their friendship.

In 1941 Baird assumed his only known official post of the war as a consultant with Cable and Wireless, whose chairman, Sir Edward Wilshaw, had long admired his achievements. His brief was the development of high-speed facsimile transmission of cables, photographs etc., a fact which opens another intriguing window into the probable state of high-security communications at the time. Britain has claimed that vital information obtained from Ultra was passed to the Russians without divulging its source. The question then arises, how did such explosive information travel swiftly and securely from London to Moscow? One route was via the famous Second World War Swiss 'Lucy' spy ring, used by British Intelligence to liaise with Moscow, and pretending to receive information directly from spies in Germany. There was also a commercial radio link maintained with Russia throughout the war and operated by none other than Cable and Wireless. In 1944 and 1945, articles by Sir Edward Wilshaw, chairman of the firm, stated that they were transmitting press photographs, drawings and documents 'essential to the prosecution of the war'.[20] Among the locations linked were New York, Cairo, Cape Town, Bombay, Montreal, Berne, Algiers, Stockholm, Melbourne, Sydney - and Moscow. If, as Sir Edward said, the material was essential to the war effort, it would presumably have to be heavily coded to elude a watchful enemy. Should photographs and plans be transmitted by normal radio means, they would have been extremely vulnerable to German interceptors, taking as they did as long as 10 minutes to wire.

Another method was at hand, however - that of John Logie Baird, acting consultant of Cable and Wireless on facsimile television. This could throw light on his diary entries in December 1943 which noted that Russians were visiting his laboratory. On 19 January he named a Russian minister, Sobieloff, and on 23 February he simply noted 'Russian Embassy'. He also referred to the Tass News Agency. It seems he tried to make his visitors feel at home by learning a few Russian words. Fittingly, the first of these was '*Shum*', meaning rush or roar, which can be interpreted as atmospheric crackling or wireless noise.

Another mysterious entry was made in this diary on 10 July 1944, this time concerning America, and also, incidentally, his old firm Fernseh, at that juncture operating secretly at Obertannwald under the name of Farvis. Baird wrote: 'Gee to send (night!) letter USA re Fernseh'. The exclamation mark after 'night' is Baird's own, and the entry seems an obvious reference to the sending of a coded message about his German counterparts, who were engaged in work so similar to his own.

The same wartime diaries bear witness to the extent to which he was pushing himself; he himself is on record as saying that, where his health was concerned, he had been walking on the edge of a precipice. Half way through the war he was admitted to a clinic, and soon after his arrival suffered a heart attack. It was imperative for him to lose weight and he fasted for fifty days, living on a spartan diet of a few ounces of raw carrots plus mustard and cress, which caused him further sickness. He then switched to water alone, eventually sampling a few grapes.

Soon, however, he was back in the fray as though nothing was amiss. His illness does not seem to have deterred him from making a journey overseas to a familiar scene from his past. While make inquiries into Baird's early adventures in Trinidad, the authors uncovered one of the most unexpected wartime sightings of this very secret inventor. In mid-1943 Baird was spotted far from his London haunts in Port of Spain, Trinidad, near the location of his jungle sojurn twenty-three years before. He was seen over a period of some weeks in khaki shirt and knee-length khaki shorts, as worn by officers of the British army, though he displayed no badges or insignia. Light brown socks overlapped at the knee. Mr Vivian Ventour, a radio engineer of Boratria, Trinidad, knowing nothing of the authors' interest in the inventor's wartime activities, answered a letter to a Trinidad newspaper about Baird's soujourn in the West Indies in 1919. His information was startling and did not concern Baird's first visit, but said that he had seen Baird often in the middle of 1943. Mr Ventour wrote: 'He was a stockily built fellow about five feet nine in height. My observation told me that he was sickly, quiet and unassuming.' Baird apparently lived in and operated from a house near a private zoo. Mr Ventour, with his own interest in radio, said that he used to admire the maze of wires and antennae above this house as well as those visible inside the rooms and under the eaves. From the building was emitted a jumble of sounds which varied from music to high-pitched 'di's and da's'.

When further information was requested from Mr Ventour, he suggested that a Brigadier Stokes E. Roberts, whom he had known, should be contacted. He also named a Captain Tudor of the Royal Navy, and thought that 'contacting the War Office for the whereabouts of either gentleman might yield some startling facts about Mr Logie Baird, whom they ought to know, since military intelligence was involved.' Again, there had been no mention to Mr Ventour of any connection between Baird and secret work.

His enigmatic recommendation was followed up by an inquiry to the Ministry of Defence at Stanmore. Middlesex, where the Army Documentation Office said that their lists had been carefully checked but no trace could be found there or at the Army Records Centre, of Bragadier S.E. Roberts. However the Ministry of Defence uncovered a letter from Sir Ogilvie Forbes of the British Embassy, Caracas, in 1946 to the Foreign Secretary, Ernest Bevin, commenting on Stokes Roberts' private tour of Venezuelan military installations. An attached note recorded that Brigadier Stokes Roberts was commander, South Caribbean area, and 'his name and function will be familiar to the Mexico City Embassy'. It is clear that Brigadier Roberts was an intelligence operative. His son, Lt Col. L.E.W. Stokes Roberts, told the authors: 'Shortly after my father's death in 1968 I was approached by the Imperial War Museum on somewhat similar lines regarding his work on intelligence and a thorough search of all his papers revealed nothing on the Second World War. They already had full details on the 1914-18 period. '

The brigadier had liaised closely with American forces during the Second World War and had been awarded the US Legion of Merit, Degree of Officer, by President Truman. Born in 1890, after training at Sandhurst, Roberts had soldiered in India and then fought at Gallipoli and in France, winning the Military Cross. In 1918, while a prisoner at Holzminden, he helped organize a famous tunnel escape. He was chief staff officer to General Carton de Wiart on the ill-fated expedition to Norway in 1940 and the following year took command of the south Caribbean with head-quarters in Trinidad. He was quite a distinguished soldier to have escaped the Army Records - as, of course, had John Logie Baird.

The reason for Baird's presence in the West Indies can only be surmised. The area was a collecting point for transatlantic convoys including many petrol tankers from Texas, and was therefore a hunting ground for U-boats. By mid-1943, when Baird is reported to have turned up, the battle against the submarines was on the verge of being won. The 'Milchcows', or large supply submarines which fuelled and victualled the U-boats, were being sunk thanks to Ultra information which pinpointed their rendezvous locations. New forms of centimetric radar in planes were being used. A new searchlight developed by a Wing Commander Leigh, called the Leigh Light, had been fitted to bombers and operated in conjunction with radar to illuminate and attack submarines at night. Information from a colleague of Wing Commander Leigh suggests that Baird cooperated with Leigh on this project. This and radar could well account for his presence, but again the most likely explanation is the need for coordination of secret signalling in the area.

Secret signalling was meanwhile the preoccupation of one of Baird's closest and most mysterious prewar colleagues, S.G.Morgan, reported alongside him in 1928 with the Royal Signals at Aldershot. Morgan, who in peacetime worked at Lloyd's Bank in London, had experienced a meteoric rise in the ranks of the wartime RAF and was now a key figure in the Allied battles of the Mediterranean theatre. He had joined the RAF on the outbreak of war and by December 1939 was deputy director of signals RAF 'Y' Service.[21] Morgan's brother, a former naval officer, confirmed that Morgan had indeed been associated with Baird for many years and had long been a radio enthusiast. Y Service was a highly secret intelligence arm of the government Code and Cypher School at Bletchley. Before the crytographers could do their work, the signals had first to be intercepted, and that was the task of Y Service. As the Germans had constructed 100,000 Enigmas during the war their task was daunting. But they did more than cope, operating from a stately home, Chicksands Priory, in the Midlands, using a maze of aerials capable of receiving the most distant signals. By 1943 Morgan, known to his friends as Jimmy, had become a wing commander and was the newly designated chief signals intelligence officer of the Mediterranean Air Command. He had been associated with the RAF since 1932 when he was listed as an acting pilot officer, not gazetted. He stayed in the services after the war and held the rank of group captain when he died in the RAF Hospital, Uxbridge, in September 1962. Significantly this close associate of Baird had stepped straight into a secret signalling role at the start of the war, as had many of Baird's prewar assistants.

All the pieces of the jigsaw fit neatly together and point to the wartime use of television, especially for the transmission of high grade coded messages, and Baird's diaries underline the fact. He seldom had a day without some meeting with key figures in the war effort. There were frequent appointments with Appleton and Watson-Watt, with Wikkenhauser of the Skiatron tube, and with Van der Bosch, a leading figure in Dutch electronics. Meetings were held with Sir Frederick Ogilvie, head of the B B C, Admiral Thomson, the Chief Censor, and also Sir John Dalton, who had been involved in First World War signals and was now honorary colonel of the Royal Signals and also the regional controller of Fuel and Power for London and the South-east. Baird also met General Wilkins, a director of Lloyd's Bank, and Admiral Grant, a director of the Marconi Wireless Company. Major Church, a friend and colleague from Baird's days in Germany, is also mentioned. Baird had a meeting with him on 1 November 1941, the same day on which he wrote in his diary: 'Demonstration to Dean, re secret signalling'. He also had many meetings with 'Paris', almost certainly the same 'Paris' who led the army centimetric gun-ranging radar unit, then working under Sir Robert Watson-Watt. One entry comments on the central laboratory manager of Osram Ltd, who is 'doing secret work for the Air Ministry and Admiralty'. On 20 January 1943 he met Sir John Dalton and a General Whittaker, to whom he attributes 'supreme charge, radio-location'. Several meetings with Whittaker followed. On 17 March 1944 he made a memo: 'Submit re-entrant cathode ray tubes, radiolocation apparatus and direction finding apparatus.' And he had frequent appointments with Captain Plugge, Parliamentary Private Secretary to Lord Beaverbrook, Minister for Aircraft Production. On 24 April 1945 Baird wrote the puzzling phrase, 'Move from Palace'. Since he could not be referring to the Crystal Palace Tower, long since demolished, did he mean an honour from Buckingham Palace? On 16 October the same year he referred to 'B. W. and T.' (Boult, Wade and Tennant, his patent agents) and noted: 'Retake out secret patent radar'. The agents appeared again on the 29th of the same month, this time in connection with 'radar depth'. On 24 December he named them once more this time regarding 'radar renewals'. On Christmas Day 1945 he supplied the opportunity for a spectacular gathering of some of the top scientific talents involved in the war. He met Wikkenhauser, Watson-Watt, Appleton and Barton-Chapple, his former assistant who in 1940 had participated in Operation Domino from Alexandra Palace, which had sabotaged the German directional centimetric radio beams for guiding their bombers to selected targets. At the close of the War Scophony were able to offer for sale a commercially available secret signalling TV system or video scrambler. The Rank Organization, formerly Gaumont-British, who had controlled the old Baird Company, were also interested in secret signalling and in 1957 took out a specific patent for signalling by television. In the 1983 Falklands campaign war correspondents saw SAS troops using television apparatus to signal directly from the battlefield to London by Marisat satellite. They were almost certainly witnessing a Baird system that had its active service roots in the Second World War.

Films and stories of that war depict agents laboriously sending messages by radio morse, always in danger of detection by the Gestapo. How much easier and safer it would have been to have sent rapid television signals, to be caught and held on a Skiatron tube. Maps, photographs and complicated plans could have been sent without risking the lives of parachuted agents. High-flying aircraft for relaying television signals would have been the ancestors of the Marisat satellite, a process that had been tested as far back as 1936, when J.L.Baird televised to and from a KLM plane above London. How valuable, too, such a system would have been in maintaining contact with Russia. Daily messages could have been sent that would not be risked by radio and could not wait for the lengthy delay involved in letter dispatch by sea or even air.

That such a system was used is certain. Today video scramblers and high-speed signalling by computer-controlled television systems continue around the world, though they are rarely commented upon. Satellite's have given the system round-the-world range, but the basic formula is still the one worked out by Baird in the early 1920s and later used by his wartime colleagues and their adversaries in Nazi Germany. David Kahn's book *The Codebreakers* notes that in 1973 the National Security Agency of America were using video scramblers for reconnaisance television and for facsimile television.[22] It would appear that the system had been under continouous development since the end of the Second World War.

NOTES

1   M. Scroggie, *Television*, 1935.

2   H.J. Barton-Chapple, *Popular* TV, Pitman, 1935 p. 102.
3.   C. Gubbins, 'Clandestine Radio', *Wireless World*, February 1982, pp. 81-83
4.   A. Fleming, 'Radiation - Visible and Invisible', *Television*, June 1928, pp. 20-21.
5.   A.V. Alexander, 'Television in a Music Hall', *Daily Express*, 29 July 1930.
6.   'Five Novels per Minute', *Daily Telegraph*, 18 July 1944.
7.   Frithjof Rudert, *50 Years of Fernseh, 1929-79*, Robert Bosch GmbH, West Germany.
8.   D.S. Bond and V.J. Duke, 'Ultrafax', *RCA Review*, 1949, pp. 99-115.
9   J. Swift, *Adventures in Vision*, Lehmann, 1950.
10   W.C. Lister, 'the Development of Photo-Telegraphy', *Electronic Engineering*, 19 February 1947, pp. 37-43.
11   S. Sagall, 'Profile", *Broadcasting*, 2 July 1979, p. 105.
12   S Sagall, preparatory notes for a lecture, given to Professor Malcolm Baird by his son Joel Sagall.
13   S. Sagall, letter, *Journal of the Royal Television Society*, 21, No. 3, May - June 1984.
14   G. Wikkenhauser, 'the Skiatron or Dark Trace Tube', *Electronic Engineering*, January 1948, p.20
15   R. Lewin, *Ultra Goes to War*, Hutchinson, 1978
16   P. Beesley, *Very Special Admiral*, Hamish Hamilton, 1980.
17   N. West, *M.I.5.*, Bodley Head, 1981.
18   E. Cookridge, Gehlen, *Spy of the Century*, Hodder and Stoughton, 1971, p. 367.
19   W. Stevenson, *A Man called Intrepid*, the *Secret War 1939-45*, Sphere 1977, (photograph is opposite p. 256).
20   E. Wilshaw, 'World of Wireless - Radio Pictures', *Wireless World*, 1944, † p. 89 'World of Wireless - Pictures by Wireless', *Wireless World*, 1945 p. 380.
21   Aileen Clayton, *The Enemy is Listening*, Hutchinson, 1980.
22   David Kahn, *The Codebreakers*, Sphere, 1973, p 386

11
A Legacy of Triumph

The whirlwind of war ceased. Bombers were grounded, warships mothballed and the intricate network of secret organizations trimmed. For the first time in many years John Logie Baird found time for the contemplation of his personal world, which had vastly changed. The thirties had faded to the crescendo of guns heralding a new and more complex era. Technology had accelerated and whole groups of individuals were now skilled in electronics and were as familiar with cathode ray tubes as they had once been with radio valves. The day of the lone innovator seemed to have passed.

War had taken its toll of Baird and, even as it drew to a close, his colleagues saw that his health was failing. Nevertheless, ever a fighter, his eyes remained fixed firmly on the future and the exhilarating challenges of peacetime. The prospects seemed good. Six years of continual research had given him world leadership technically in all electronic colour and 3D-colour television. He was in an ideal position to assume a major role in guiding the fortunes of postwar television.

With the friend of his schooldays, Jack Buchanan, he floated a new company to promote his postwar project of television in the cinema. This had always been a part of his strategy, the formation of commercial television for which he had petitioned years before, alongside Sagall's Scophony and Marconi-EMI. He also formed a new team of technicians in the expectation that the government would give the go-ahead for a colour service.

But there was a darker aspect to his life at this period. Many familiar faces had departed the scene for ever. Hutchinson was dead, having spent his last years as a contented English farmer. 'Dizzy' Denton, who had shared so many of his secrets, was gone. Baird's brother, John, the lost sheep of the family, had also died in Australia. But perhaps saddest of all was the fate of 'Mephy', Guy Fullerton Robertson, his friend and lifelong confidant from Helensburgh. One blazing hot day during the war, as Baird sat in his garden at 3 Crescent Wood Road, Sydenham, hoping that no air raids would arrive, he was handed a letter. He wrote later:

I could not for the moment realise it. Mephy whom I had just written to and arranged to visit, dead. Suicide! Impossible - why should he commit suicide? Why, without one hint or suggestion, take this irrevocable, final step out of everything? The hopeless finality, the tragic, terrible loss, struck me with brutal force - a terrible loss indeed - and one that could never be replaced. Why did I not go over to Ryde sooner? I could have stopped it. Why did I not write earlier? He never received my last letter. It was delivered the day after his death. Poor Mephy![1]

Ryde, opposite Portsmouth, had been subjected to constant air raid alarms. Mephy could not sleep and his nervous system gave way. One morning he took no breakfast, went to his little studio at Herb Cottage and gassed himself.

These losses depressed Baird, whose physical resources were already low. As his wife noted: 'I knew him better than anyone else did and perhaps saw more than others his moods of depression when he would lie in bed all day long brooding over some reverse.

These fits of depression did not last long and the rebound from them was one full of enthusiasm and vitality. He lived in the present and gave the force of his powerful personality to what he was doing; work, horseplay with Moseley, or relaxed discussion with friends.'

The eight-hour trips from London to his family in Cornwall had become pointlessly arduous and so Margaret rented a house at Bexhill on the Sussex coast; Baird wanted to live by the sea, and it was not too far from London. Thus he returned to the area where his public life had begun, just 6 miles from Hastings.

He commuted to the capital as plans progressed for cinema television. Then, one day in February 1946, he returned from a walk to Bexhill very tired and went straight to bed. During the night he had a stroke. For a time he was bedridden but restless. He would leave the bed and pace around the house. He also developed a longing for fruit, difficult to buy after the war, though Mrs Baird managed to

JLB with the Telechrome, the worlds first all-electronic colour tube from which all today's TV sets are descended.

obtain some from Covent Garden. Every room had a coal fire and an electric heater. The fuel bill was astronomical, but still he felt desperately cold. As the summer arrived he went for short walks. But when Mrs Baird encouragingly said he was much better than he was, he looked at her and replied: 'I am much worse.' Undeterred, in June, he organised from his home a demonstration of his Mark 2 big screen television equipment, televising the Victory Parade at the Classic Cinema, the News Theatre and the Savoy Hotel in London.

A week after the demonstration and the restoration of BBC television, he had a particularly restless night. It was 14 June. Margaret Baird gave him a drink of water. He took her hand and, paraphrasing a poet, said: 'In spite of all thy faults, I love thee still. ' They settled down for the night and she stayed awake until she heard him breathing regularly and quietly. Next morning the room was unnaturally quiet and, before she even looked, she knew he was dead.

Margaret Baird had always found life with Baird exciting and a challenge. It could be exacting but never dull. She was aware that her husband was a great man, though just how great official secrecy did not allow her to know. She decided that he should be buried in Scotland, in his own home town, and he was therefore taken north to rest beside his parents in Helensburgh. He had left no great fortune, just a few thousand pounds, and much of this vanished through the mismanagement of a suspect solicitor who later committed suicide. However, the proud Baird family faced life with the same stoicism and determination that had characterised J. L.B. Margaret Baird returned to South Africa, and was still lecturing in music at a university in her seventies. Diana became a schoolteacher, married, had children and now lives in Scotland. Malcolm, followed in his father's footsteps, studied science and is now a Professor of Chemical Engineering at McMaster University, Hamilton, Ontario, Canada.

This account of Baird's life did not start as an apologia for a forgotten man, but as an inquiry into an accepted story already riddled with contradictions. It did not require special pleading to prove that Baird was a pioneering figure of major status, a giant of the twentieth century. As one new fact led to another, it was impossible to ignore the direction in which the quest for the real Baird was heading. Just as so many dates in his life were incorrect, so were a great many

Press headlines testify to Bairds bewildering range of achievements.

of the basic details. He had not started dabbling in television at Hastings in 1923; television had been a prime interest from the days of his youth. The West Indies investigation showed he was televising some form of picture in 1920. The most persistent argument raised against Baird is his supposed lack of ability and foresight in concentrating on mechanical television during the 1930s. It is generally assumed that the all-electronic system of that time must have been superior. A study of Gemnan achievements of the time, however, shows that a blending of mechanical scanning and cathode ray tube receiver, as used by Baird, could have supplied a clear and reliable television service which would have serviced the whole of Britain instead of the immediate area around London - of which Baird was well aware.

As for electronics, he knew their value and when the time was ripe he moved directly into that sphere, taking the lead with his 1940s research into all-electronic colour and 3D colour television. The war, with its seven-year break in public television, made a true postwar appraisal of his work difficult. It was not long before technical magazines, showing amazing ignorance of his work after 1926, were referring disparagingly to his Meccano-like equipment. They either did not know or chose to turn a blind eye to the impressive advances he made in all electronic television just before his death. They dismissed the angry reactions of veterans who tried to correct these false impressions. It was all too easy to bracket Baird with mechanical television and then point to the present-day superiority of electronics.

The fault was even compounded by those who sought to do justice to his reputation. Exhibitions of Baird's achievements, including one in Helensburgh some years ago, showed how faulty impressions gained credence. Below a Baird televisor were displayed pictures of faces which, it was claimed, had been photographed from an early Baird televisor screen. These puported to show the public what could have been seen on Baird's first screens. The faces were distorted, grotesque, but the wonder was that there were any pictures at all. For the photographs, encountered by the authors before, had been taken originally of images supplied via a Baird Phonovision disc that had lain for almost forty years warping in a damp attic. It was a tribute to Baird's technology that they gave any image at all after so long a period in such conditions.

If achievement and not money is the yardstick of success, then here was no record of failure. Riches would have followed if he had not been decreed an early death at the age of fifty-eight. He was not only a great inventor but one who rendered his country invaluable service in an unstinting and unassuming fashion. The war took his life as surely as it claimed that of the brilliant electronic engineer, A.D.Blumlein of EMI, a radar scientist who died in 1942 while testing H2S radar equipment in an aeroplane. Baird served the Allied cause tirelessly, and when others hurried to stake their claim to glory after the war he took steps to fight them with quiet dignity, never betraying his trust of secrecy.

Perhaps the bulk of the blame for the misunderstandings surrounding Baird must be laid at the feet of those eminent public figures who were only too aware of his talents. Prominent amongst these must be his fellow Scot Sir Robert Watson-Watt. He must have known the truth concerning Baird but never spoke up. While others gleaned rich rewards for their war efforts, Baird's widow and family received not a penny. Sir Robert had been associated with Baird for twenty years and knew his worth, but in his autobiography he committed the sin of omission. He spoke of Baird's German colleague, von Ardenne, of Hoyt-Taylor, Appleton and others, but never once did he hint in his writing of his acquaintanceship with Baird. Watson-Watt had in fact witnessed his detection systems, judged his television in the 1930s and dealt with him during the Second World War. The silence is deafening. In his struggle to secure his claim to be father of radar Sir Robert was not slow to cross swords with many famous scientists, but the name of Baird he prudently avoided.

To be fair, Sir Robert had indeed developed and administered Britain's wartime radar defence in a superlative fashion. It is likely that the 1935 episode concerning radar's supposed inception was foisted upon him by his military and political superiors as a convenient cover for the actual research programme which had started years before. There are signs that this caused considerable conflict within the scientific fraternity which, though muted, occasionally erupted into print. Doubtless this embarassed Sir Robert who, as a public servant, could hardly have changed horses in midstream. An official version had been given and he was stuck with it. The Baird connection did not escape attention in some quarters, however Chambers ' *Dictionary of Scientists* said of Baird in 1951: 'His method of television by infra-red rays led to the development of modern directional devices.' If they had known of his radio wave patents they would have had to amend 'directional devices to 'radar'.

Sir John Reith, too, seemed to have had an odd lapse of memory when he wrote the story of his days at the B B C. He avoided any reference to the man who came to him with television, one of the most important inventions of the century. One would have expected this to be noteworthy, especially since Baird had attended college alongside him in Glasgow. This lapse can perhaps be attributed to temperament. Sir John and Baird had a prickly relationship. The B B C was in its infancy and Baird's arrival with television must have complicated the issue for Reith, who was still in the process of laying the foundations of the most famous broadcasting company in the world. Reith had reason to be wary of Baird, who made no secret of his ambition that television should be a separate commercial service. With sound radio just a few years old, Reith must have regarded this as a threat to his hegemony. If Baird had succeeded with his plan at this early date, the BBC might have developed far differently from the way it did.

The suggestion that Baird, with radar and secret signalling, participated in large-scale clandestine operations which have remained hidden from official histories may seem difficult to accept in the West, where democratic openness is an ideal. But, as revealed before, there is evidence that television was encouraged in pre-War Britain and Germany as a concealed way of boosting the research and manufacture of radar systems. Such a secret policy for British radio was adopted after the First World War. In *A Man Called Intrepid*[2] W. Stevenson revealed how Lord Beaverbrook was one of a small group who, after 1918, produced a case for the formation of the future B B C, on the grounds that it would not only provide a service to millions, but that it would ensure the research and development of radio which would be essential in war for the rapid conveying of messages. Fittingly, one of Beaverbrook's fellow enthusiasts was the former First World War air ace, Gladstone Murray, then aviation correspondent of the *Daily Express* and later BBC publicity director, and one of the friends who did his best to smooth relations between Baird and Reith.

The long arm of coincidence fails to account for the recurring patterns in Baird's story. Captain Plugge, commercial radio entrepreneur, politician and associate of Baird from the mid-1920s through to the Second World War, had attended a lecture on television before the Radio Society of Great Britain in 1924, given by A.A.Campbell-Swinton. At this early date Captain Plugge, commenting on the suggestion whether television could be used for signalling, said:

> *We have learned this evening that television can be summarised by the possibility of sending a great number of signals, of the order of 600 per second, that vary either by position or intensity. I believe it has been the aim of the wireless telegraph companies to be able to send as many signals as they can per second, and it seems to me that in this respect television could be used as a means of transmitting from one station a considerable number of messages in a small period of time.*

The case for secret television signalling could hardly have been put more succinctly. This concept bore fruit as Baird created his facsimile television and the Germans produced their miniature sets at Obertannwald. That Plugge and Baird should have been subsequently so closely associated is therefore hardly surprising.

Even the earliest of Baird's colleagues seem to have hidden depths. Harold Pound, whom he portrayed as a gregarious business friend in his jam-in-thejungle venture of 1919 and later in London, soon afterwards appeared with the call sign 2RH in a list of those licensed to operate experimental radio transmitting stations in the United Kingdom. Baird never revealed that Pound was a radio enthusiast. Also on the list published in 1922 is William Le Queux, the journalist who recorded Baird's experiments in Hastings in 1924 and who had links with the Secret Service dating back to the First World War. The particular aspect of Le Queux's interest in radio is apparent from an article in *Wireless* of 10 September 1925, headed 'The Wireless Spy Menace'.

It may seem strange that Baird's participation in the war effort has never been suspected before. It is only when isolated facts are brought together that this conclusion becomes inescapable. Aileen Clayton, who played a leading role in the Y Service, pointed out long afterwards that secrecy became a way of life. She did not even tell her father about her work. Over 30 years later she still felt a sense of shock when reading that Ultra had been revealed.

Baird's life was packed with intense activity, bewildering in its variety. He was seemingly tireless and seldom found time just to stand and stare. Even when one has found a way through the labyrinth of his efforts to the central core of his activities one has a suspicion that there is still much more to be uncovered. He had immense self-control, great humour and boundless self-confidence. He did not much care how he dressed but was vain enough to be proud of his lion's mane of fair hair, which usually collapsed over his forehead as he worked. In his enthusiasm he could be thoughtless, but in Margaret Baird he had an uncomplaining helpmate who put up with the idiosyncrasies of time, finance and habitation. He loved his children, though the war deprived him of their company, and would take them on long walks on the seashore when he had the chance. He helped them to make a telephone, just as he had in his own childhood, and he used poster paints to teach them elementary optics. Once he travelled all the way from London in order to bring them a stray cat from a bombed-out area.

Most people liked him. His employees nicknamed him 'Personality Joe'. It is clear from their comments years later that he did not mind letting them believe they knew more about a subject than he did. The true extent of his work and his abilities was his own business and he was content with that, although he would act swiftly when he sensed a challenge from a competitor.

He had an open mind and many enthusiasms. He saw no reason, for example, why television could not be used to explore the subject of spiritualism. He enjoyed yoga and would sometimes be found in his room in an almost deathlike trance from which he emerged lively and smiling. A painting at the University of Glasgow shows him with a hand on a glowing cathode ray tube which portrays Prometheus, the prophetic suggestion being that by means of television man may yet see all that was, or will be. It catches the spirit of the man.

His life was so dedicated to action that his personality is often elusive. He appears a will o' the wisp, difficult to pin down. That he won loyalty is obvious since so many of his friends and colleagues - Morgan, Denton, Mephy and many others - remained with him through the years. He could be charming and kind, but it was his courage and tenacity that most people remembered. Margaret Baird found him curiously impervious to air raids. He would seldom go to a shelter and once, as the earth shuddered from an explosion nearby, she asked him, 'Is that a bomb?'

He replied: 'No, go to sleep. It's only the guns.' A fitting tribute came in a memorial issued by the Television Society in London; it was written by J. D. Percy, who said:

> *The indisputable fact remains, however, that the world's first practical transmission by what we now know as sequential scan television was achieved in a Hastings garret, which in 1924 was home to a Scottish gentleman whose great courage was to defeat bodily ailments, disbelief, even hunger- and whose faith in an idea was to cause such a degree of thought to be given to its perfection that even within the span of his own lifetime, moving pictures by wireless were commonplace in thousands of homes.*

The late Dame Rebecca West once wrote about Baird that he was obviously the man who sowed the seed but did not reap the harvest. When questioned about this remark, Dame Rebecca replied: 'It was written on the basis of an afternoon spent with somebody interested in Baird's discovery, who took us to an office studio near Piccadilly. This was in the twenties, I think. Baird was charming to me, but I had the feeling he was not one of the lucky ones of the world. I have always longed to see the transmission again that I saw that day because it made me much better looking than I ever was and how this was done I cannot think.' Dame Rebecca was prophetic. Baird had laboured, and others had received the material rewards. But his life had been a drama; the satisfaction for him was in the living of it. She probably sensed an almost intangible quality in Baird, an element that distanced him from others operating in the same field. He was no consolidator, no boardroom wrangler, though he would wade in and do battle with the best of them. But there was something of the artist in his personality. Several times he had a fortune in his grasp, but his spirit and burning curiosity led him back to the drawing board and the laboratory where the future was in the making.

When Apollo 10 sent live colour pictures of the moon 200,000 miles back through space to the living rooms of the world, the astronauts used a system which had made its first public appearance half a century before in the arcade in Hastings. The arid lunar landscape was recorded by means of a colour field-sequential scanned system camera using a rotating multicolour filter disc. Baird would have appreciated that.

A curious episode from 1984 must finally refute the arguments of those who still believe that Baird was outdated even in his own lifetime. In June 1984, when a reporter from the Glasgow Herald inquired of the Ministry of Defence about the wartime experiments of John Logie Baird, he received an unexpected response: 'No comment. Much of his work is still classified.'

NOTES

I   *Sermons, Soap and Television*, ch. 9, p. 12.
2   W. Stevenson. *A Man Called Intrepid, The Secret War* 1939 5. Sphere, 1976.

Epilogue
Damned Facts

As the world moves towards the millennium, the power of television is such that it has become a weapon of revolution, as in Romania. Prime targets in the internal strife of any nation are the means of communication, mainly the television stations.

This book has shown that television, quite apart from its domestic role, was recognised from the start as an invention which could be crucial in war. It had hardly surfaced before it was channelled into detection systems and secret signalling.

Naturally, governments avoided emphasis of this use, and the public in many countries merely witnessed what appeared to be research on television for the home and perhaps the cinema. However, in the light of its clandestine role, the whole question of what was really happening among the commercial companies developing it before World War II must be looked at from a fresh angle.

Television, radar and secret signalling were combined in many different ways to aid the Allied cause. Radar was combined with television to create a system called TELERAN to convey information between a plane and ground. Television was used for guiding missiles, and with secret signalling in a system known as IFF (Identification, Friend or Foe), which distinguished enemy aircraft from Allied planes. It could also be adapted as straight radar.

Since this book first appeared, a wealth of new material has confirmed the vital role of John Logie Baird in the development of televisions and radar. Early references to his alternative ideas for the new technology abounded in newspapers of the period, but such intriguing titbits vanished as the great game progressed and the nations lined up for war.

It is clear that very little can be taken for granted regarding traditional versions of how radio, television and radar emerged.

As was revealed recently on television, one of the most striking aspects of the time was how certain American industrial giants bought almost the whole of Britain's heavy electrical engineering industry in the 1920s and 30s. One company was specially active. General Electric of America owned British Thomson Houston who made everything from dynamos to power stations. In the late 1920s they bought Metropolitan Vickers and took out 60 per cent of the shares of GEC in Britain. A special arrangement had to be made to prevent those shares from running the company.

Essentially, therefore, American-owned companies dominated the heavy electrical engineering industry of Britain. That same industry would build the vital Chain Home radar stations between 1937 and '39, the first contract going to Metro-Vickers. It is now known the Americans had an ongoing radar programme from 1930, just one year after Baird's radar system was patented in the United States. RCA, the Radio Corporation of America, was one of the major companies involved in the programme and, as it transpires, they were the radio-producing division of GE, USA.

Because of their tremendous ability in radio and the finance available, America came to control television and radar production in the 1930s. However, because of the US Neutrality Act, repealed shortly after the start of World War II, the technology could not be sold openly to Britain. The America First movement, led by figures like Charles Lindbergh, were pressing to keep America out of any conflict involving Britain, France, Germany and Russia. The swap of radar technology with Britain would have been political dynamite for any American administration.

The authors have found, however, that patents owned by General Electric of America surfaced at their British-owned companies. As we revealed, a very unwilling Watson-Watt was ordered by his Air Ministry boss, H.E. Wimperis, to take out radar patents in 1935 and '36, thus forestalling the radar patents of General Electric which appeared in Britain in 1937. This saved the British paying large royalties to the Americans and strengthened claims to a supposedly unaided radar programme.

It is even possible that the United States paid the American companies in Britain to produce the radars. This would have suited the American military establishment who are on record in publications as wanting the British and French navies to control the Atlantic while the USA built a huge navy, starting in 1933, to operate in the Pacific and checkmate Japan.

Those ships required radar urgently, every bit as much as Chain Home stations were needed on the ground in Britain. Significantly the British and US navies simultaneously produced their first-known ship radars in 1937 with identical wavelengths of 6.7 metres, also used by the British TV systems at the Crystal and Alexandra Palaces.

But where had radar started? Readers will recall the spiked disc used by Baird in Hastings as early as 1923. He was experimenting with what is now known to have been a pulsed radar set, and his first radar patent dated from 1926, four years before the American programme was launched. The Americans freely admit in publications that they had nothing in radar before 1930.

With Baird leading the field and generating the necessary pioneering radar technology in the 1920s, why did his television company not have the leading role in the British radar programme? The answer must be that the Baird company did not have sufficient financial and industrial muscle to tackle such a mammoth operation.

That television and radar came from the same stable now seems obvious. In 1986 the British magazine *New Scientist* carried an article by Barry Fox on the similarity between the two. Mr Fox claimed in his piece that a King's Messenger had been dispatched to Baird in the summer of 1936 and the inventor was told that the King wanted his TV transmitter, built for Baird by Metropolitan Vickers (General Electric of USA), and this was passed on to Watson-Watt and became his first successful radar transmitter.

The first successful radar trials in Britain using aircraft, not surprisingly therefore, took place between 30 August and 11 September 1936, using the national TV wavelength of 6.7 metres. Recently the *New Scientist*, continuing the theme, produced a diagram showing how, by simple means, an ordinary television set could be used as radar.

It is therefore quite clear that the systems were easily interchangeable and production facilities were also virtually identical. Thus television served for years as the breeding-ground and cover for radar.

Descriptions of American and German radar were available in the mid-thirties, especially in America, and, presumably, copies of the magazines carrying such accounts were available in British libraries, even the important article on German radar which appeared in the American journal *Electronics* of September 1935.

Surprisingly, to this day, former members of Air Ministry Intelligence who report to MI6, still claim they knew nothing of German radar until the outbreak of war. Their claim is contradicted by these contemporary accounts and by the facts in this book.

They can hardly have been unaware of the rumbustious approach of Erhard Milch, creator of the Luftwaffe, later Generalfeldmarschal, who, as described earlier, arrived in Britain and shocked his hosts by inquiring about British radar. Another publication has been noted that quotes Milch speaking in the ante-room of the Officers' Mess at Fighter Command. 'Now, gentlemen, let us be frank, how are you getting on with your experiments in the detection by radio of aircraft approaching your shores?'

Apparently more than one glass crashed to the floor as Milch persisted: 'Come, gentlemen, there is no need to be so cagey. We've known for some time that you were developing a system of radiolocation. So are we, and we think we are a jump ahead of you.'

Given the British Establishment's passion for secrecy, there were other reasons for the radar black-out. There was never any accountability to the British public for the cost of the radar programme. Parliament was not told of radar, nor, to be fair, were the administrations in other countries about their own developments.

Yet somehow or other, several hundred million pounds were spent on the British radar stations, which, if announced, would have been, to say the least, politically sensitive at a time of mass unemployment and stringent budgets. Also the fact that the radars were ordered by the British from American-controlled companies allowed the circumvention of the American Neutrality Act in total secrecy.

When the time came Britain was to handle her radar with great skill and cunning, learning to use it strategically. German refinements often proved successful in the short term but had built-in drawbacks, such as vulnerability to jamming, that the British managed to exploit while avoiding such pitfalls themselves.

The complexity of the pre-war situation also casts new

light on the early opposition to Baird from the BBC and why there could be other factors at work in the choice of the Marconi-EMI television system for Britain in 1936. Native ingenuity was not allowed to succeed at the expense of a grander master plan.

A look at the early structuring of the BBC provides some fascinating facts. Originally, the British Broadcasting Company, created in late 1922, consisted of six of the biggest radio-producing companies in the country. Their make-up reveals intriguing links which were noted at the time by critics concerned about the strength of American represen-tation.

The companies were Metropolitan Vickers, originally British Westinghouse, a branch of the American Westinghouse Company, and subsequently owned by General Electric USA; British Thomson Houston, also bought by GE of America; British GEC, 60 per cent of whose shares, as we have seen, were owned by GE USA; The Radio Communication Company, specialising in naval radio, which had information and patent swaps with Metro-Vickers; Marconi in Britain whose American firm was forced in 1919 by US Government order to join with GE to form RCA; and Western Electric, also American-owned, part of the American Telephone and Telegraph Company who were linked by patent swaps and trade agreements with G.E., USA in the 1930s.

As previously suggested, Marconi in Britain were exchanging technical information with RCA in America, and this is not surprising when one considers that across the Atlantic both were linked. Baird had frequently complained that American equipment was coming into this country through the back door.

RCA was the radio-producing division of GE in America. Earlier in the book, Gerry Allighan, head of publicity for the British Radio Manufacturers Association, was quoted as claiming in 1932 that the Chief Engineer of the National Broadcasting Company of America, which was essentially RCA, had told him that they were intending to broadcast American programmes through the BBC.

Western Electric in America had a research wing which became known as Bell Laboratories, the very firm which almost broke Baird's company in April 1927 with the unexpected transmission of TV signals 200 miles between Washington and New York, the first admitted public television in the USA.

With the BBC linked to such associates, it is hardly surprising that Baird had a tough struggle to launch his television. The fact that he reached as far as he did is a remarkable testimony to his ability and willpower. Although Reith and Baird were not compatible, a new dimension to their differences can be discerned.

It had been publicly announced that the BBC had been set up to look after the radio interests of its six constitutent companies and by 1926, when it had become a Corporation, the licence fee set by the GPO was used in part for research and development to produce better radios from those six companies. Two of Baird's most consistent opponents were P.P. Eckersley and Noel Ashbridge, both Chief Engineers at the BBC. Each had been with Marconi previous to joining the BBC.

Baird the loner had to raise money privately, and was therefore at another disadvantage. Even as regards sound transmission, he had to go cap-in-hand to the BBC which had a monopoly granted by the GPO.

The rivalry between Baird and Marconi-EMI also takes on new dimensions when one considers the GE factor. In December 1929 RCA bought the Marconiphone Company. Slightly later, RCA also purchased Columbia Graphophone, and merged it with their subsidiary, HMV, to form EMI. RCA held 27 per cent of the EMI shares, and David Sarnoff, President of RCA, became a director, as did Marconi. Whichever way Baird twisted, he was ultimately encountering GE of America, usually in the shape of a subsidiary.

Since television and radar were virtually identical technology the same pattern appears in the evolution of radar.

With such a line-up against him, it is understandable that Baird turned to powerful but unorthodox allies, one of whom was Captain Leonard Plugge, owner of the International Broadcasting Company which comprised Radio Normandie, Radio Luxembourg, Radio Toulouse and Radio Parisienne, among others, from which bases he waged commercial war on the BBC.

Several newspaper accounts of late 1928 and early 1929 indicate that Baird was joining forces with the pirate radio operators and would send in his own TV pictures to Britain should the BBC not back down and grant him a transmitter. This adds credence to the claims in a submission prepared for *Who's Who* just before Captain Plugge's death that he had co-invented television with his friend, John Logie Baird.

As it transpired, the BBC did back down and allowed Baird a transmitter for vision at Brookmans Park, London, and another for sound from the BBC station at Daventry.

Although a maverick commercially, Plugge developed into a considerable establishment figure who, as previously noted, became a Tory MP, and Parliamantary Private Secretary to Lord Beaverbrook when he was wartime Minister of Aircraft Production. Plugge was also involved in radio propaganda, and recent publications reveal that his Radio Luxembourg was used by MI6 to send recorded messages by the British Prime Minister, Neville Chamberlain, direct to the German people.

It is evident from the totally independent reports of Baird's activities and sightings at top-secret centres both before and during the war, that he moved in very high-level intelligence circles. The busy inventor who formed a German company and had links throughout Europe, who would vanish for days before reappearing to puzzled employees, was obviously leading a secret as well as a public life.

When Telephoning with regard to this letter please ask for Extension Number........ 195.*/*   *LH : 67*

TELEGRAMS : Ballooning, South Farnborough.
TELEPHONE : 108 North Camp, 361 Aldershot, &
      103 Farnborough.
  All Stores to be addressed :—   **ROYAL AIRCRAFT ESTABLISHMENT,**
    R.A.E. Siding.
    Farnborough Station.   **SOUTH FARNBOROUGH,**
      Southern Railway
      (L. & S.W. Section)   **SECRET**   **HANTS.**
  All communications to be addressed to
    The Chief Superintendent.
OUR REFERENCE: W.T.3/S.619/7.
YOUR REFERENCE:
                              1st. November, 1929.
                                  6C616

        The Secretary,
        Air Ministry,
          Kingsway, W.C.2.

        For the attention of the Director of Scientific Research.

                  Television.
                  S.24132.

2552.   A visit was made to the Signals Experimental Establishment, Woolwich Common, on Friday October 25th. at which a demonstration was witnessed of the area system of telegraphy developed by that Establishment.

One of Baird's main supporters in the BBC was Major Bill Gladstone Murray, its chief publicity director in the 1920s and 1930s who was tipped to succeed Sir John Reith as Director General. Gladstone Murray, a former air ace and aviation correspondent for the *Daily Express*, quit mysteriously, however,in October, 1936, in circumstances that puzzled BBC staff. He became General Manager of the Canadian Broadcasting Corporation.

CBC was used as a cover to establish the now-famous Camp X connected with Special Operations Executive. This secret camp at Oshawa on Lake Ontario appeared to be an ordinary radio-centre. CBC told townspeople it was erecting radio aerials. Gladstone Murray's great friend, Sir William Stephenson, codenamed Intrepid by Churchill, used his own money to buy the ground in small lots to avoid suspicion. By World War II Gladstone Murray was a leading member of SOE.

It is unlikely that radar would be the reason for Baird moving with such frequency in intelligence circles. His other early preoccupation is almost certainly the key, and that is secret signalling.

We have noted how the late Mr James Heath, of Edinburgh, reported that he had worked with Baird, described as a Reserve officer, on secret singalling at Mons Barracks, Aldershot, in 1928 and '29. One critic of this book attacked this, stating that the authors were fortunate in having a dead witness who could not be cross-examined. In fact Mr Heath's letter was originally sent to a Miss Bannister, of the Public Library in Baird's home town, Helensburgh, and was passed to the authors. Confirmation of Mr Heath's veracity as to the work then under way at Aldershot is in a letter from the secret Air Ministry file, Air 2S24132, released by the Public Records Office, Kew. This describes a visit by the Royal Aircraft Establishment officials to the Army Signals Establishment at Woolwich Common who were using television for secret signalling. One of the telephone numbers for the RAE Farnborough, given on the letterhead, is North Barracks, Aldershot. The letter is dated 1929, one of the years quoted by Mr Heath.

Television was a godsend to secret signalling and was leapt upon by governments and the military in many nations, though details are sparse, and come mainly from Germany.

In a letter to one of the authors, West Germany's leading

radar historian, Fritz Trenkle, said that Germany and Russia commonly used television secret signalling in World War II, mainly on the Eastern Front. The Allies would have been foolish not to have utilised TV, especially as they had been experimenting with it for secret signalling since the 1920s. There is published evidence that at least one British company had its TV signalling equipment examined by the Ministry of War at the outbreak of World War II.

In the 1920s, the Marconi Company of Great Britain used their beam radio system, referred to earlier in the book, to send facsimile information from Australia to Britain. Cine film shot in Australia was scanned and sent by radio to Britain where the same film was rebuilt on fresh film and viewed just hours after transmission from Australia.

The film in these experiments only ran for a few seconds, but the principle had been proved, that large amounts of facsimile information could be sent by radio, using cine film at transmitter and receiver. There was a drawback, however. Messages were at the mercy of the weather. Atmospheric conditions varied greatly between Britain and Australia, throwing up all forms of problem from sunbursts to lightning storms, all of which disrupt radio waves, and sometimes messages might not arrive. Such a system was also a poor security risk, as the radio waves could be intercepted and recorded by an enemy. From these recordings it would be possible for the interceptor to decode at leisure.

A much safer method is to transmit the information via underwater cables, but even here a technical problem appears. The metal of the cable prevents large amounts of technical data being transmitted quickly through the cable. High carrier frequencies cannot be used to carry that information. Operators have to reduce the carrier frequency down to the values of that used in telephony. The cables, after all, were designed for conventional telephone conversations and telegraphy.

Normal television with its 25 images a second requires high carrier frequencies, much greater than those for telephony. Were television images capable, therefore, of being carried safely thousands of miles by underwater cables? The surprising answer is, yes. In the 1960s a series of articles indicated clearly that a special cine-television system had been used to send TV 3000 miles over the trans-Atlantic cable. The system used pre-recorded data on cine film at the transmitter, and then recorded that data on cine film at the receiver. 200-line images were used, one image every eight seconds, in other words slow-scan, low-frequency, a technique commonly used today.

Interestingly, 200 lines were John Logie Baird's television standard in the 1930s. Baird's system was ready and in full working order well before the war and, with no adaptation, could have sent TV images many thousands of miles across the routes of underwater cables in World War II. Many of Baird's colleagues interviewed noted his preoccupation with sending images over vast distances. It should be remembered too that Baird's only officially-known appointment during the war was consultant to Cable and Wireless in matters concerning television applied to telegraphy.

Cable and Wireless had a worldwide network of radio stations and underwater cables. The Axis powers did not manage to interfere with these cables in the war, the cables only coming to the surface at a few well-guarded spots. Cable and Wireless are on record in World War II as stating that they wanted television to speed up their telegraphy. Their role was a vital one in the prosecution of the war, securely sending millions of telegrams, drawings, letters and documents all over the world.

Some of these cables passed through a spot familiar to Baird: Trinidad, scene of his early adventures and where he was spotted in 1943. The existence of those cables could explain his presence in the Caribbean at this crucial stage of the war. He was possibly checking on their efficiency.

The cables were guarded by the British and American navies, and one can understand the importance of Baird to the British Director of Naval Intelligence, Rear Admiral J.H. Godfrey, who, as noted earlier, was approached regarding Baird by Sydney Moseley at the start of the war.

A series of patents have recently been discovered on the subject of slow-scan TV using cine film and sometimes the memory cathode tubes described earlier. Some of these patents were issued before, and others just after, the war, and interestingly all the companies and personnel involved were acquainted with Baird. It appears that Baird was not acting on his own but was part of a group effort. However, as TV consultant to Cable and Wireless during the war, his role must have been primary.

One recalls those tantalising entries in his wartime

diaries, one of them mentioning the sending of a night letter to the USA. It is intriguing to note that the technology was at hand for Churchill and Roosevelt to communicate by vision and sound via the underwater cables, their conversation and images recorded on cine film or memory tubes. It is just possible that locked in vaults in Whitehall and Washington are some remarkable historic recordings of those two great leaders.

After the war it was claimed in Germany that the Nazis had managed to intercept coded radio messages between Churchill and Roosevelt. Knowing the Allied superiority in the field of collecting enemy messages and decoding them, such a glaring slip-up would be curious.

It is possible that such messages were carrying misleading information and were designed to be captured and code-cracked. The only documented way whereby Roosevelt and Churchill spoke to each other was by telephone using gramophone records of specially-created sounds to scramble their conversation. An exactly similar record was required on both sides of the Atlantic to unscramble the radioed telephone talk. How good, secure and easily-used such a system was is debatable. Conversely, a TV link by cable would have been totally secure with the Germans unaware that messages were being transmitted.

In August 1988 British Telecom honoured Baird's centenary by unveiling a special plaque in Glasgow's Central hotel, the scene of his record-breaking transmission from London to Glasgow in 1927. This was a fitting gesture, as BT along with the Post Office are the successors of the GPO who were amongst Baird's firmest supporters. After the Glasgow ceremony a BT official revealed to the authors that Baird had been a regular visitor to the GPO Research Station at Dollis Hill, London, during the war. It is now known that Dollis Hill supplied much of the coding and decoding equipment for nearby Bletchley Park, which handled the Ultra secret, breaking the German Enigma codes. Not far from Dollis Hill is Whaddon Hall, the private radio station of MI6 during the war. From Whaddon Hall MI6 radio transmitted Ultra information to all concerned. The authors have found that Baird was also a visitor to the Hall. It could be that Whaddon Hall was experimenting with very fast and secure television signalling.

Another Baird link with the Ultra secret is the connection the authors have found that he had with a Polish group in

Special Operations Executive. This team were based at Stanmore, part of the Bletchley Park Group, and were led by a very old friend and admirer of the inventor. Recently it was revealed that this group were believed to have been working on TV secret signalling.

Radio security for the Ultra Secret group was headed from 1938 by Richard Gambier Parry, who originally worked under Gladstone Murray at the BBC. Parry is on record as an anti-Baird type who was angered by the inventor's clashes with the BBC. It is possible that Parry was alarmed that details emerging from such crossing of swords would reveal too many aspects of the secret side of the BBC. It is not surprising that during the war so many BBC personnel were switched to intelligence and radar.

Even Electra House, HQ of Cable and Wireless, had its secret side. Built at the Victoria Embankment, London, just before the war, it was bomb-and gas-proof. In fact Electra House was part of the Bletchley Park group. All suspicious cables were sent to Bletchley for possible decoding. The building also housed sections of the intelligence services and their black radio section which specialised in sending highly-misleading information into Axis countries. They also struck out at the enemy more directly. A U-boat listening to German radio would suddenly be told that it would be sunk on that trip. Luftwaffe pilots would receive wrong directions in perfect German, and arguments would break out in the aircraft between their own controllers and the imposters in Britain. The British transmitter for these messages was at Woburn Abbey.

The authors have letters written from a woman who was a young girl in the '30s and who says that her father, A.G. Harding, worked at a hospital in the village of Bryanston near Blandford, Dorset, used by the military following World War I. This, she says, was a secret signalling centre patrolled by armed guards in plain clothes. All she ever learned was that 'our men in Germany' were being contacted. She recalls John Logie Baird as a regular visitor and, intriguingly, she remembers one particular visit when she claims Baird was accompanied by Marconi and the Duke of York, the future King George VI. She says the Prince of Wales was also a visitor.

Today the old metallic cables of Cable and Wireless are being replaced by fibre-optic cables. Information is sent along light beams which are easily capable of simultaneously carrying conventional TV station signals, telephone, facsimile and telegraphy link-ups. Baird's invention of fibre optics has been thoroughly researched by Dr Peter Waddell, and the details were published in the bound proceedings of the Seventh International Conference, Fibre Optics and Electronics, Olympia, London, in April 1989 (SPIE, 'Fibre Optics '89', 1120, pages 128-136). So much interest was created by the revelation that Baird had developed and used fibre optics as early as the '20s that a special lecture had to be arranged at Olympia open to all sessions on that day. Since then, there have been no dissenting voices to the evidence produced.

A whole new dimension to secret signalling before and during World War II gradually emerged as Baird's life was researched. It became obvious that the signalling battle between the Allied and Axis powers was not nearly so clear-cut as related in books published since 1973, when the Enigma Codes and the Ultra secret received their first public airing. It is now evident that both sides were using signalling systems vastly more secure than the Enigma typewriter. Many books since 1973 have suggested that the Allied powers had cracked the Enigma codes in the 1930s. Certainly, as described earlier, British cryptologists were buying and examining the Enigma from 1926, a published fact. When a British secret typewriter named Typex was introduced to the British Army and RAF in 1935, it was described as 'more secure' than the Enigma. How could the British have made this comparison unless they had thoroughly examined Enigma, spotted flaws in the system and exploited these to crack codes from the Enigma machines being used by the Germans?

If this is so, then Appeasement was a fake. Appeasement implied not knowing Hitler's next move. In fact, it now appears that the future Allies were aware of most of these plans, allowing him to make increasingly reckless moves, hastening the outbreak of war and Hitler's eventual defeat. If this sounds odd behaviour, then one must consider the doomsday scenario that might have followed if the war had been delayed. Had not war been declared in 1939, Hitler could well have grown invincible with the first jet aircraft, long-range rockets, superior tanks and anti-tank weapons and, most frightening of all, the atom bomb. It should be remembered that it was the Germans who in 1938 first announced nuclear fission. Hitler expected war in 1938 at

Munich and was surprised when he was given everything he asked for. He then expected war would not come until 1942, when his industry would be fully geared up for a global struggle. It must therefore have been a nasty shock when France and Britain declared war on him in September 1939. That he knocked out the French, who were meant to be the main land opposition with their many army divisions, was a severe initial blow to the Allies, and caused the war to be a much more close-run thing than was possibly anticipated.

Much new material has surfaced, enough for a new book. This epilogue has simply tried to connect the varied strands that emerge from a close study of John Logie Baird. The eventual answers were dramatic. Baird must now be reassessed. There was much of the Celt in his make-up. He battled and achieved, but showed scant respect for rewards. Perhaps he felt there was a certain vulgarity in too much success. Today, however, he must be recognised as a man of genius and destiny who helped shape not only his own age but the decades to come.

Index

Index